Current Topics in
Developmental Biology

Volume 25

Current Topics in Developmental Biology

Volume 25

Edited by

Hans R. Bode
Developmental Biology Center
Department of Developmental and Cell Biology
University of California, Irvine
Irvine, California

Academic Press, Inc.
Harcourt Brace Jovanovich, Publishers
San Diego   New York   Boston   London   Sydney   Tokyo   Toronto

Academic Press, Inc.
San Diego, California 92101

United Kingdom Edition published by
Academic Press Limited
24–28 Oval Road, London NW1 7DX

Library of Congress Catalog Number: 66-28604

International Standard Book Number: 0-12-153125-2

PRINTED IN THE UNITED STATES OF AMERICA
91 92 93 94   9 8 7 6 5 4 3 2 1

Contents

1

How Do Sperm Activate Eggs?
Richard Nuccitelli

2

Dorsal–Ventral Pattern Formation in the *Drosophila* Embryo: The Role of Zygotically Active Genes
Edwin L. Ferguson and Kathryn V. Anderson

3

Inducing Factors and the Mechanism of Body Pattern Formation in Vertebrate Embryos
Jonathan Cooke

4

Patterning of Body Segments of the Zebrafish Embryo
Charles B. Kimmel, Thomas F. Schilling, and Kohei Hatta

5

Proteoglycans in Development
Paul F. Goetinck

6

Sequential Segregation and Fate of Developmentally Restricted Intermediate Cell Populations in the Neural Crest Lineage

James A. Weston

7

Development of Mouse Hematopoietic Lineages

Shelly Heimfeld and Irving L. Weissman

8

Control of Cell Lineage and Cell Fate during Nematode Development

Paul W. Sternberg

Contributors

Numbers in parentheses indicate the pages on which the authors' contributions begin.

Kathryn V. Anderson Division of Genetics, Department of Molecular and Cell Biology, Life Science Addition, University of California, Berkeley, Berkeley, California 94720 (17)

Jonathan Cooke Laboratory of Embryogenesis, National Institute for Medical Research, Mill Hill, London NW7 1AA, England (45)

Edwin L. Ferguson Division of Genetics, Department of Molecular and Cell Biology, Life Science Addition, University of California, Berkeley, Berkeley, California 94720 (17)

Paul F. Goetinck La Jolla Cancer Research Foundation, La Jolla, California 92037 (111)

Kohei Hatta Institute of Neuroscience, University of Oregon, Eugene, Oregon 97403 (77)

Shelly Heimfeld Department of Pathology and the Howard Hughes Medical Institute, Stanford Medical Center, Stanford, California 94305 (155)

Charles B. Kimmel Institute of Neuroscience, University of Oregon, Eugene, Oregon 97403 (77)

Richard Nuccitelli Department of Zoology, University of California, Davis, Davis, California 95616 (1)

Thomas F. Schilling Institute of Neuroscience, University of Oregon, Eugene, Oregon 97403 (77)

Paul W. Sternberg Howard Hughes Medical Institute, Division of Biology, California Institute of Technology, Pasadena, California 91125 (177)

Irving L. Weissman Department of Pathology and the Howard Hughes Medical Institute, Stanford Medical Center, Stanford, California 94305 (155)

James A. Weston Institute of Neuroscience, University of Oregon, Eugene, Oregon 97403 (133)

Preface

The field of developmental biology consists of a number of areas such as pattern formation, morphogenesis, and differentiation, to name three that are clearly related to one another, in that all are processes that lead to the development of a functioning organism from a fertilized egg. Though they are clearly interrelated, the study of these areas has proceeded quite independently. Until recently people studying, for example, patterning events in early embryogenesis need not have been greatly concerned with what others were learning about the events and mechanisms of differentiation that occurred late in development. This is changing. The pace of uncovering the molecules involved in various developmental processes is ever-increasing. This has led to the exciting and quite profound discovery that the same ligands, receptors, second messenger systems, and classes of transcription factors are used again and again at different stages of development, in different tissues and organs, and in very disparate organisms. In turn, this has increased communication and cross-fertilization in the several subdisciplines of developmental biology.

This same impulse has also led to change of emphasis in this series. In its early years CTDB had eclectic volumes dealing with a variety of topics. In more recent years volumes have been topical. This made sense as information was growing exponentially, and reviews of distinct areas were of value. Now it is, once again, probably more useful to approach the field as a whole as strands of knowledge increasingly overlap from one area to another, and common themes emerge. At the same time one can see how far understanding in different developmental processes has progressed.

Starting with this volume, CTDB will once again be eclectic in content. Both themes of currently different levels of understanding, and of common molecular bases are evident in the ensuing chapters.

Understanding of the several developmental processes varies. In some, such as the issue of metamerism in vertebrates (Kimmel *et al.*), the principles, or rules, are being defined at the tissue and cell level. In many tissues and organs, there is an overall understanding of the cell types making up the tissue or organ, and a reasonable idea as to the behaviors and interactions of these cells. More precise definitions of cell types, their cell lineage relationships, and behaviors provide a more complete understanding. Chapters on the neural crest (Weston) and blood tissue (Heimfeld and Weissman) illustrate this point. In cases where such precision has been reached, a molecular, and where feasible a genetic, analysis is underway. The contributions on dorsal-ventral patterning in *Drosophila* (Anderson) and vulval development in *C. elegans* (Sternberg) are examples.

At the same time similar molecular themes appear in different chapters. The roles of growth factors in early amphibian induction events (Cooke), in hemopoiesis (Heimfeld and Weissman) and postulated in neural crest development (Weston) as well as receptors for known and unknown growth factors in early patterning events in *Drosophila* (Anderson), and *C. elegans* (Sternberg) are described. The roles of second messenger systems are discussed in egg activation (Nuccitelli) and *C. elegans* (Sternberg), and those of homeobox-containing genes in zebrafish (Kimmel) and *Drosophila* (Anderson). In addition to these well-studied classes of molecules, there are other classes not as well understood that most likely also play crucial roles in development. Proteoglycans (Goetinck) are an example. With the continuing elucidation of their structure and function, their roles and their relationships to other classes of molecules will become clear.

The volumes in this series serve another purpose worth emphasizing. Reviews of the large amount of data and evidence currently being generated are important to bring order to information within any particular subdiscipline of a field. Of equal, if not more, importance are attempts to put all this information into a picture that describes how a particular developmental process works. Because the information is incomplete such an exercise is more or less speculative, and quite often will be provocative. Yet, it is clearly of heuristic value, and authors of reviews in this series are encouraged "to paint the picture" if they wish. The chapters by Kimmel *et al.* and Weston are examples in which an author has described their view of a process.

1

How Do Sperm Activate Eggs?

Richard Nuccitelli
Department of Zoology
University of California, Davis
Davis, California 95616

This question of how sperm activate eggs has occupied many developmental biologists over the years and has recently received much attention, stimulated by new information on signal transduction mechanisms in other cell types. With the elucidation of the role of the inositol cycle and protein kinases in cellular responses, such as intracellular calcium ion concentration ($[Ca^{2+}]_i$) and intracellular pH (pH_i) changes, following the binding of various ligands such as growth factors and hormones (Berridge, 1987; Hanks *et al.*, 1989), it was natural to ask whether the activation of eggs by sperm binding utilized similar mechanisms. The answer to this question remains unclear, as discussed below, because, while key components of the inositol cycle are present and activatable in unfertilized eggs, we are still not certain that the sperm actually uses them as major components of the normal activation pathway.

Over the past decade we have learned that a transient $[Ca^{2+}]_i$ increase and a permanent pH_i increase accompany egg activation in many species, and treatments that activate eggs usually generate these ionic changes. These recent discoveries were anticipated by the observations of many of the embryologists working in this field 90 years ago, such as Morgan (1899), Hertwig (1896), Loeb

(1899, 1913), and Guyer (1907), who found that development could be initiated in unfertilized eggs by artificial means which usually required Ca^{2+} influx or an imposed cytoplasmic alkalinization. These early investigators spent years working out the conditions that would lead to egg activation in the absence of sperm; however, today researchers in this area are much more interested to learn exactly how the sperm itself activates the egg.

I. Recent History

A. Intracellular pH Changes

Research over the past 15 years has uncovered a great deal of information regarding the steps involved in the mechanism of egg activation. The first to be discovered was the pH_i increase in the sea urchin egg (for reviews see Busa and Nuccitelli, 1984; Epel, 1990). This was initially measured in egg homogenates (Johnson et al., 1976; Lopo and Vacquier, 1977) and then more reliably in living eggs with pH-sensitive microelectrodes (Shen and Steinhardt, 1978). A permanent pH_i increase from 6.8 to 7.3 occurs within 5 minutes of fertilization in Lytechnius pictus eggs. Nearly identical results have been obtained by measuring the distribution of weak acids across the plasma membrane (Johnson and Epel, 1981), and ^{31}P-NMR reveals a pH_i increase of similar magnitude (i.e., 7.1–7.5) after fertilization of Strongylocentrotus purpuratus eggs (Winkler et al., 1982). Similar increases in pH_i have been observed in the activated eggs of other invertebrates, including those of Clypeaster (Hamaguchi, 1982) and crab (Herve et al., 1989; Goudeau et al., 1989), and have been inferred from acid release from the eggs of the mollusks Spisula (Ichio and Rebhun, 1988) and Barnea (Dube and Guerrier, 1982) and from those of the echiuran worm, Urechis caupo (Paul, 1975).

However, while this pH_i increase seems to be common in activating invertebrate eggs, there certainly are exceptions. Eggs of the sea star Pisaster do not alkalinize after fertilization, nor do they release significant amounts of acid (Johnson and Epel, 1982). Other studies which have failed to detect acid release upon activation include two other starfish species (Peaucellier and Doree, 1981), the mussel Mytilus, and the limpet Acmaea (Paul, 1975). Direct measurements of pH_i in eggs of the ascidian Ciona intestinalis failed to detect any change in pH_i during the first 7 minutes following activation (Russo et al., 1989).

Surprisingly little has been done on the study of pH_i in vertebrate eggs. The only studies I know of are from my own laboratory, where we have measured a 0.24 U alkalinization in the egg of the frog Xenopus laevis as determined by both pH microelectrodes and ^{31}P-NMR (Webb and Nuccitelli, 1981; Nuccitelli et al., 1981). Although the physiological role of this pH_i change is uncertain, the occurrence of substantial permanent pH_i changes in organisms as distantly related as sea urchins and frogs certainly suggests that these changes may play a significant role in egg activation.

B. Intracellular Ca^{2+} Changes

In contrast to the variability of pH_i changes following egg activation, the transient increase in $[Ca^{2+}]_i$ appears to be universal and has been found in all eggs investigated in both invertebrates and vertebrates (reviewed by L. F. Jaffe, 1985). These observations have a long rich history beginning at the turn of the century, when so many embryologists were studying artificial parthenogenesis. Prick activation required external calcium, so it was assumed that this ion played a key role in activation. More recent studies with calcium/proton ionophores, voltage-induced membrane pores, and Ca^{2+} microinjection have confirmed these early indicators that an imposed increase in $[Ca^{2+}]_i$ is a universal activator of both invertebrate and vertebrate eggs (Chambers et al., 1974; Steinhardt et al., 1974; Rossignol et al., 1983; Cross, 1981; Gilkey, 1983). These observations have been extensively reviewed by Whitaker and Steinhardt (1982, 1985) and by Jaffe (1983, 1985), so I do not go into further detail here.

The other two tests of the importance of a $[Ca^{2+}]_i$ increase for egg activation are to determine whether such an increase occurs naturally following fertilization, and to determine whether blocking the natural increase blocks activation. The $[Ca^{2+}]_i$ increase has passed both of these tests. The sperm or activating stimulus generates a wave of increased free $[Ca^{2+}]_i$ beginning at the point of interaction with the egg in all activating eggs investigated, including echinoderms, tunicates, fish, frogs, and mammals (Table I). Therefore, this transient $[Ca^{2+}]_i$ increase appears to be an important universal step in egg activation. Furthermore, if this natural $[Ca^{2+}]_i$ increase is blocked by microinjecting Ca^{2+} chelators into the egg prior to activation, egg activation is also blocked in the two groups tested: sea urchins (Zucker et al., 1978; Hamaguchi and Hiramoto, 1981;

Table I Measured Waves of Increased Free $[Ca^{2+}]_i$ Accompanying Egg Activation

Group	Species	Method	Reference
Echinoderms	A. punctulata	Aequorin	Eisen et al. (1984)
	Lytechinus variegatus	Aequorin	Swann and Whitaker (1986)
	Lytechinus pictus	fura-2	Hafner et al. (1988)
	Arbacia forbesi	Aequorin	Eisen et al. (1984)
	Scaphechinus mirabilis	Aequorin	Yoshimoto et al. (1986)
	Clypeaster japonicus	Aequorin	Yoshimoto et al. (1986), Hamaguchi and Hamaguchi (1990)
Tunicate	Phallusia mammillata	Aequorin	Speksnijder et al. (1990)
Fish	Oryzias latipes	Aequorin	Gilkey et al. (1978), Yoshimoto et al. (1986), Hiramoto et al. (1989), Iwamatsu et al. (1988b)
Frog	Xenopus laevis	Ca^{2+} electrodes	Busa and Nuccitelli (1985)
	X. laevis	Aequorin	Kubota et al. (1987)
Mammal	Golden hamster	Aequorin	Miyazaki et al. (1986)

Swann and Whitaker, 1986; Turner et al., 1986) and frogs (Kline, 1988). Therefore, there is no doubt that the transient increase in free $[Ca^{2+}]_i$ levels is a universal and necessary component in the mechanism of egg activation. However, what is not so clear is how the sperm triggers this universal response in the fertilized egg.

II. Recent Evidence for Involvement of the Inositol Cycle and G Proteins in Egg Activation

A. Phosphatidylinositol Turnover during Egg Activation

Six years ago the answer to how sperm trigger egg activation appeared to be at hand when L. A. Jaffe and colleagues detected an increase in the amount of both phosphatidylinositol bisphosphate (PIP_2) and phosphatidylinositol monophosphate (PIP) in the plasma membrane by 20 seconds after fertilization in sea urchin eggs (Turner et al., 1984). They speculated that the egg might be generating $Ins(1,4,5)P_3$ upon fertilization to release Ca^{2+} from intracellular stores, because this sugar had been identified as a product of the hydrolysis of PIP_2. A few months later Whitaker and Irvine (1984) showed that the microinjection of small amounts of inositol trisphosphate [$Ins(1,4,5)P_3$] activated sea urchin eggs. Subsequently, $Ins(1,4,5)P_3$ has been found to activate eggs from a wide range of both invertebrate and vertebrate species at physiological concentrations in the 10–1000 nM range (Table II), and the intracellular target appears to be the endoplasmic reticulum, based on studies of stratified eggs of both sea urchins and frogs (Eisen and Reynolds, 1985; Nuccitelli et al., 1989; Han and Nuccitelli, 1990) and microsome preparations in sea urchin eggs (Clapper and Lee, 1986).

Further evidence for the stimulation of PIP_2 turnover and $Ins(1,4,5)P_3$ and diacylglycerol (DAG) production in sea urchin eggs has appeared (Kamel et al., 1985; Ciapa and Whitaker, 1986). These observations suggest that inositol lipid hydrolysis occurs naturally during egg activation; however, the direct evidence for endogenous $Ins(1,4,5)P_3$ release is underwhelming. The only two published investigations in which sea urchin eggs were labeled with [^{3}H]inositol before fertilization and $Ins(1,4,5)P_3$ production was measured following fertilization yielded somewhat different results. In the first, eggs were labeled by exposing them to [^{3}H]inositol (125 μCi/ml) for 4 hours. Thereafter, 1-minute time points were taken and the $Ins(1,4,5)P_3$ levels increased 660% by 10 minutes following fertilization (Kamel et al., 1985). In the second, eggs were labeled for 18 hours, and a 40% increase in $Ins(1,4,5)P_3$ was detected within 10 seconds after fertilization. However, by 1 minute there was a reduction, followed by a second rise, which increased only to 70% above prefertilization levels (Ciapa and Whitaker, 1986), rather than 660%.

Another approach that supported the involvement of PIP_2 hydrolysis was a study of isolated egg cortices measured in vitro (Whitaker and Aitchison, 1985).

Table II Species Whose Eggs Have Been Found to be Activated by Ins(1,4,5)P$_3$ Microinjection

Group	Species	Volume of Cytoplasm (nl)	[Ins(1,4,5)P$_3$] Required	Reference
Mollusca	*Spisula solidissima*	0.087	2×10^{-21} mol/20 pM	Bloom *et al.* (1988)
Echinoderms	*Lytechinus pictus*	0.53	5×10^{-18} mol/10 nM	Whitaker and Irvine (1984)
			1.3×10^{-18} mol/2.5 μM[a]	Crossley *et al.* (1988), Swann and Whitaker (1986)
	Lytechinus variegatus	0.53	1.4×10^{-17} mol/28 nM	Turner *et al.* (1986)
	Strongylocentrotus purpuratus	0.22	7×10^{-18} mol/32 nM	Slack *et al.* (1986)
	Asterina miniata	4.2	4×10^{-17} mol/10 nM	Chiba *et al.* (1990), Picard *et al.* (1985)
Tunicate	*Ciona intestinalis*	1.15	?	Dale (1988
Fish	*Oryzias latipes*	30	5×10^{-16} mol/20 nM	Nuccitelli (1987)
Frogs	*Xenopus laevis*	910	7×10^{-16} mol/0.8 nM[b]	Busa *et al.* (1985)
	Discoglossus pictus	2100	4×10^{-15} mol/1.9 nM[c]	Nuccitelli *et al.*(1988)
Mammals	Golden hamster	0.1	4×10^{-19} mol/2 nM	Miyazaki (1988)
	Hamster	0.1	3.5×10^{-17} mol/350 nM	Cran *et al.* (1988)
	Sheep	0.53	2.2×10^{-16} mol/420 nM	Cran *et al.* (1988)

[a]This concentration of 2.5 μM is based on that in the injection pipette and was found to be optimal for activation.
[b]If one uses a more reasonable target volume of a sphere 100 μm in diameter, centered on the injection pipette, the threshold concentration becomes 1.3 μM.
[c]If one uses a more reasonable target volume of a sphere 100 μm in diameter, centered on the injection pipette, the threshold concentration becomes 7.6 μM.

In this preparation a Ca^{2+}-dependent PIP_2 hydrolysis was measured and blocked by neomycin. This established that micromolar Ca^{2+} levels could trigger PIP_2 hydrolysis in these cortices and provided support for the notion that the wave of Ca^{2+} release could be propagated by a wave of $Ins(1,4,5)P_3$ release. This hypothesis was again put forth by Swann and Whitaker (1986) in whole-egg studies, in which they pointed out that injecting pure Ca^{2+} without a buffer does not activate the sea urchin egg as it does some others (e.g., that of the frog) and concluded that $Ins(1,4,5)P_3$ diffuses through the egg much more readily than does Ca^{2+}. Therefore, they felt that $Ins(1,4,5)P_3$-induced Ca^{2+} release is more likely to account for the progressive release of calcium at fertilization than is Ca^{2+}-induced Ca^{2+} release. However, injection of pure Ca^{2+} solutions, rather than buffered solutions, is problematic, since cells have a strong Ca^{2+}-buffering capacity and sometimes form vesicles around the injection pipette. Therefore, a negative result when using an unbuffered Ca^{2+} injection solution is not conclusive.

An indirect indicator of PIP_2 turnover following fertilization is the decrease in PIP kinase activity that has been measured in sea urchin eggs (Oberdorf et al., 1989). This decrease does not occur when cortical granule exocytosis is blocked by high hydrostatic pressure, so this decrease in activity is related to cortical granule exocytosis. Oberdorf et al. localized PIP kinase activity to the cortical region of the unfertilized egg, while the PI kinase activity was found in both cortical and noncortical membranes.

There are few observations on the involvement of inositol lipid hydrolysis in activating eggs of any other species. Doree's laboratory reported that the PIP_2 level falls in frog eggs following activation (Peuch et al., 1985), and my laboratory has confirmed this (unpublished observations). However, we have been unable to detect $Ins(1,4,5)P_3$ levels in activating frog eggs labeled with $[^3H]$inositol.

B. Involvement of G Proteins in Egg Activation

Yet another line of evidence that suggests the involvement of inositol lipid hydrolysis in egg activation is the activating ability of agents that stimulate or activate GTP-binding proteins (G proteins). This has been reviewed by L. A. Jaffe (1989, 1990), so I mention this only briefly here. Many receptors for neurotransmitters, hormones, and light act to relay the signal reception event by means of a G protein, which, in turn, stimulates phospholipase C to hydrolyze PIP_2 (Gilman, 1987). The first evidence that a G protein might be involved in the egg activation mechanism was the observation that sea urchin eggs could be activated when microinjected with the metabolically stable guanine nucleotide analog GTP-γ-S (Turner et al., 1986). This stable form resists hydrolysis, so it both activates the G protein and lengthens the duration of the activated state. Subsequently, both frog and hamster eggs have been shown to be activated by GTP-γ-S injection (Kline et al., 1990; Miyazaki, 1988). In all of these eggs, prior injection of the calcium chelator EGTA blocks the ability of GTP-γ-S to stimulate the cortical reaction, so the G protein appears to stimulate the activation pathway prior to the Ca^{2+} release step. A second indicator that G proteins are present is that microinjection of cholera toxin, which is known to specifically modify some G proteins to activate them, activated sea urchin eggs (Turner et al., 1987), again in a Ca^{2+}-dependent manner.

The third line of evidence suggesting that egg activation might involve G proteins was the discovery that frog and starfish eggs could be activated by the extracellular application of neurotransmitters known to act by way of G proteins, if the receptors for those transmitters were expressed in the egg plasma membrane by introducing the appropriate mRNA into the egg (Kline et al., 1988; Shilling et al., 1990). These observations left no doubt that a G protein was present in the eggs of these two species and that its stimulation could activate the egg. However, the presence of this pathway in the egg does not necessarily mean that the sperm itself utilizes it to activate the egg. Indeed, at least three direct tests of this hypothesis have failed to provide conclusive evidence to support it.

One test for the involvement of G proteins in normal fertilization is to determine whether an inhibitor of G protein activity blocks sperm-induced activation. While microinjection of the inhibitor GDP-β-S blocks sperm-induced cortical vesicle exocytosis (Turner et al., 1986), it was originally reported that $Ins(1,4,5)P_3$ injection could bypass this block. However, more recent work has shown that, depending on the timing of the injections, GDP-β-S can block the $Ins(1,4,5)P_3$ response; these results are not consistent with a simple action of GDP-β-S on an egg G protein (Kline et al., 1990). Moreover, the presence of 3 mM GDP-β-S does not block the wave of increased free Ca^{2+} in the sea urchin egg even when cortical granule exocytosis is blocked (Whitaker et al., 1989; Crossley et al., 1991). As with most negative results, a firm conclusion cannot be drawn from this inability of GDP-β-S to block the Ca^{2+} wave. It could be that the amount of GDP-β-S required to interfere with sperm-induced cortical granule exocytosis is less than that required to block the Ca^{2+} wave. In fact I discuss below that, at least in the frog egg, the Ca^{2+} wave is not required for cortical granule exocytosis and can be uncoupled from exocytosis.

While many of the data addressing these questions have been collected with sea urchin eggs, a few other systems have also been studied. In contrast to the sea urchin egg, the hamster egg Ca^{2+} response following fertilization is blocked by GDP-β-S microinjection (Miyazaki, 1988), suggesting that G proteins may be an integral link in the activation mechanism in that egg.

A second test of the involvement of G proteins was reported by Whitaker and colleagues (Whitaker and Crossley, 1990; Crossley et al., 1991). When PIP_2 is hydrolyzed, $Ins(1,4,5)P_3$ and DAG are formed. Whitaker wanted to monitor the DAG arm of the pathway under conditions in which the natural Ca^{2+} increase was blocked. They presented data from sea urchin eggs in which intracellular $[Ca^{2+}]$ increases were prevented by injection with the calcium chelator BAPTA, and DAG production was monitored by measuring the change in pH_i generated by the Na/H antiporter that is known to be stimulated by protein kinase C (PKC), which is, in turn, stimulated by DAG (Swann and Whitaker, 1985; Shen and Burgart, 1986). Whitaker's group found that under these conditions of BAPTA loading, sperm can fertilize the egg, but no pH_i increase occurs, whereas GTP-γ-S injection does stimulate a partial pH_i increase. They argued that this implies that, while there is a G protein present in the egg, the sperm are not using it in the natural activation pathway. However, one could also argue that the sperm-induced stimulation of the G protein requires a Ca^{2+} rise or is directly blocked by BAPTA. Thus, the involvement of G proteins in sperm–egg activation is still uncertain. G proteins are certainly present in the egg and readily capable of triggering egg activation in sea urchins, frogs, and hamsters, but we have no direct evidence to date that the sperm uses them at fertilization.

The third test of the involvement of G proteins is an elegant set of experiments by Rakow and Shen (1990) and Crossley $et\ al.$ (1991). They compared the Ca^{2+}-releasing ability of sperm, injected Ins(1,4,5)P_3, and GTP-γ-S in sea urchin eggs loaded with heparin, which is known to compete with Ins(1,4,5)P_3 for binding to its receptor. They found that heparin dramatically reduces both Ins(1,4,5)P_3- and GTP-γ-S-induced Ca^{2+} release, but has no effect on the amplitude of sperm-induced Ca^{2+} release. Thus, they showed that the activation of G proteins triggers an Ins(1,4,5)P_3-sensitive Ca^{2+} release, but that the sperm does not release this store via the Ins(1,4,5)P_3 receptor. This is the best evidence to date that the sperm activates the wave of increased free $[Ca^{2+}]_i$ without relying exclusively on Ins(1,4,5)P_3 production. However, it should be noted that heparin prolonged the latent period from 20 to 85 seconds (Crossley $et\ al.$, 1991). This result suggests that Ins(1,4,5)P_3 production may indeed be one component of the sperm-induced response, though not absolutely required for Ca^{2+} release.

C. Involvement of DAG and Protein Kinase C in Egg Activation

There is also evidence supporting the involvement of the other product of PIP_2 hydrolysis, DAG, in the egg activation pathway. I have already mentioned that DAG has been shown to stimulate the pH_i increase in sea urchin eggs without a $[Ca^{2+}]_i$ increase (Swann and Whitaker, 1985; Shen and Burgart, 1986). More recent studies implicate DAG in the cortical reaction as well.

The phorbol ester, phorbol 12-myristate 13-acetate (PMA), mimics DAG action, binding to the regulatory site of PKC to stimulate its activity. Thus, by applying either DAG or PMA, one can stimulate PKC without stimulating the hydrolysis of PIP_2. The response of the egg to PMA addition is quite different in the sea urchin than in the frog and the mouse. The sea urchin egg responds by shifting most of its cortical granules away from the plasma membrane deeper into the cytoplasm (Ciapa $et\ al.$, 1988), and $[Ca^{2+}]_i$ levels are unperturbed. In contrast, the eggs of the mouse and the frog, $X.\ laevis$, respond to PMA levels as low as 160 and 25 nM, respectively, by undergoing cortical granule exocytosis

(Cuthbertson and Cobbold, 1985; Colonna *et al.*, 1989; Bement and Capco, 1989), and in the frog egg cortical contraction and cleavage furrow initiation are also observed. The main difference between the PMA responses of these two species is the $[Ca^{2+}]_i$ level. As in the sea urchin, $[Ca^{2+}]_i$ levels do not increase, but actually decrease a bit in frog eggs upon PMA addition, and the same response occurs in the presence of the calcium chelator BAPTA (Bement and Capco, 1990). We have imaged the whole *Xenopus* egg loaded with the Ca^{2+}-sensitive probe fura-2 and have confirmed that $[Ca^{2+}]_i$ levels do not increase during the PMA-stimulated cortical reaction (Larabell and Nuccitelli, 1991). In contrast to this, the mouse egg responds to PMA addition (324 n*M*) with sustained oscillations in $[Ca^{2+}]_i$ that are quite similar to those observed in the fertilized egg.

The second line of evidence suggesting that PKC may be involved in cortical granule exocytosis downstream of the Ca^{2+} wave is based on the ability of PKC inhibitors to partially suppress cortical granule release. Sphingosine and H-7 both reduced the amount of cortical granule exocytosis in response to both A23187 and PMA treatment by 50–80% (Bement and Capco, 1990). This suggests that PKC activity is required for normal exocytosis and that inhibiting this activity can reduce the degree of exocytosis, although a fertilization envelope is still formed (Larabell Nuccitelli, 1991). Therefore, in frog and mouse eggs the normal series of activation events indeed may involve the activation of PKC via the hydrolysis of PIP_2 or possibly another lipid (e.g., phosphatidylcholine).

It should be noted here that the PKC-induced pH_i increase observed in sea urchin eggs can also be stimulated via the Ca^{2+}–calmodulin pathway. A recent paper by Shen (1989) presented evidence that the cytoplasmic alkalinization is calmodulin dependent. The Ca^{2+}–calmodulin antagonist W-7 was found to block both the fertilization- and PMA-induced increases in pH_i more reliably than the PKC antagonists K252a, H-7, or retinoic acid, and Shen concluded that the activation of the Na/H antiporter can occur by a PKC-independent pathway.

III. Current Thoughts and Hypotheses on Egg Activation Mechanisms

A. Hypothesis 1: Sperm–Egg Fusion Triggers PIP_2 Hydrolysis via a G Protein to Trigger the Ca^{2+} Wave

While the current evidence in support of fertilization-triggered PIP_2 hydrolysis consists of only a few papers, a change in PIP_2 levels has been detected in both sea urchin and frog eggs, and the expected increase in phosphoinositol sugars has been measured in sea urchin eggs. Admittedly, the lack of data from more than two species and the difference among those data reported in sea urchins make for a weak case thus far. Of the other two requirements to prove the hypothesis, only one has been demonstrated: (1) the ability of Ins(1,4,5)P$_3$, GTP-γ-S, cholera toxin, and G protein-related receptors to activate a variety of eggs and the ability of phorbol esters to trigger the cortical reaction in frog eggs do support the hypothesis, in that imposed changes in known components of the inositol cascade do activate eggs; (2) blocking the cascade should prevent activation; however the GDP-β-S injections did not give conclusive results and there is thus far no effective way to block Ins(1,4,5)P$_3$ or DAG production in cells to test this arm of the hypothesis.

The other data that lead some investigators to seek alternative hypotheses are the failure of sperm to activate the pH$_i$ increase in BAPTA-loaded eggs, as described in Section II,B; the fact that the sperm-activated Ca^{2+} response is independent of intracellular heparin, whereas Ins(1,4,5)P$_3$-activated Ca^{2+} release is not; and the presence of a "latent period" (discussed in Section III,C) between sperm–egg fusion and the initiation of the Ca^{2+} wave in some eggs.

B. Hypothesis 2: Sperm–Egg Fusion Stimulates a Tyrosine Kinase That Activates the Egg via Protein Phosphorylation

The two main signal transduction mechanisms used by most growth factors are the stimulation of PIP$_2$ hydrolysis and the stimulation of protein kinases (e.g., tyrosine kinase). It is therefore reasonable to investigate the possibility that sperm–egg fusion stimulates a protein kinase. Kinsey and colleagues have detected a high-molecular-weight cortex protein that is phosphorylated within 1 minute of fertilization in sea urchin eggs (Peaucellier et al., 1988). Within 15 minutes this protein is largely dephosphorylated or otherwise degraded. Kinsey and co-workers more recently found that this phosphorylation exhibits a steep pH dependence, with the physiological change in pH from 6.8 to 7.4 doubling the specific activity of the kinase (Jiang et al., 1989). Thus, the normal pH$_i$ increase that occurs in the egg may be involved in stimulating this phosphorylation. However, since the normal pH$_i$ increase follows the [Ca^{2+}]$_i$ increase, it is not clear whether this kinase activity is directly involved in the stimulation of the [Ca^{2+}]$_i$ increase at activation.

C. Hypothesis 3: A Diffusible Activator Passes from the Sperm to the Egg

Since most eggs can be parthenogenetically activated, there is no absolute requirement for sperm in the egg activation machinery. However, clearly the sperm must interact with this machinery to trigger activation. Hypotheses 1 and 2 would have the sperm mimic a hormone or growth factor by binding to a sperm receptor, stimulating a protein kinase or the hydrolysis of PIP$_2$. However, two observations have led to a third hypothesis in which the sperm releases a diffusible activator into the egg, which stimulates the egg activation machinery.

The first observation hinges on the timing of activation. In many animal species the period between sperm–egg fusion and the initiation of the Ca^{2+} increase (the so-called "latent period") is longer than one would expect based on simple G protein activation times. Examples of typical latent periods are provided in Table III; they tend to run from about 10 to 40 seconds. Such times are of sufficient duration for small molecules to diffuse from the sperm into the egg, assuming that the main body of the sperm is in direct contact with the egg; a long acrosomal process could greatly increase the time required for diffusion to occur.

The second observation came from Chambers and colleagues, who have found that sperm can fuse transiently with the egg for many seconds without activating it (Chambers, 1989). This observation was a result of capacitance measurements not yet published, so it is somewhat preliminary. However, it has led some investigators to question why a G protein would not be activated during this period of many seconds, whereas one can easily see that the delivery of a diffusible molecule from the sperm would be cut off.

These observations have led both Chambers (personal communication) and Whitaker et al. (1989) to suggest that perhaps the latent period reflects the time required for a molecule to diffuse from the sperm into the egg. This idea also receives support by the observation made some years ago by Dale et al. (1985) that an extract made from sperm will activate sea urchin eggs when microinjected into the egg. In addition, Swann has found that microinjecting a factor from hamster sperm into hamster eggs induces the repetitive Ca^{2+} pulses characteristic of fertilization in this egg (Swann, 1990), and a fraction prepared from

Table III   Species in Which a Latent Period between the Time of Sperm–Egg Fusion and the Initiation of a $[Ca^{2+}]_i$ Increase Has Been Observed

Group	Species	Latent Period (seconds)	Reference
Echinoderms	P. miliaris	19–23	Allen and Griffin (1958)
	Strongylocentrotus purpuratus	30–45	L. A. Jaffe et al. (1978)
	Lytechinus pictus	7–40	Shen and Steinhardt (1984), Crossley et al. (1991)
	L. variegatus	12	Lynn et al. (1988)
Fish	Oryzias latipes	5–8	Nuccitelli (1980), Iwamatsu et al. (1988a), Iwamatsu (1989)
Frogs	Rana pipiens	10	Jaffe and Schlichter (1985)
	Xenopus laevis	30–60	Busa and Nuccitelli (1985), Kubota et al. (1987)
Mammal	Golden hamster	10–30	Miyazaki (1988)

rabbit sperm has been found to activate both rabbit and mouse eggs following injection into the cytoplasm (Stice and Robl, 1990).

It will be interesting to learn whether such diffusible factors interact with the inositol cascade or trigger Ca^{2+} release from the endoplasmic reticulum in an $Ins(1,4,5)P_3$-independent manner. One candidate for this factor is cyclic ADP-ribose which is a good calcium-releasing agent (Clapper et al., 1987; Lee et al., 1989).

D. Hypothesis 4: Sperm–Egg Fusion Introduces Sufficient Ca^{2+} into the Egg to Trigger a Wave of Ca^{2+}-Induced Ca^{2+} Release

This hypothesis is similar to hypothesis 3, with the diffusible substance being Ca^{2+}; however, it does not necessarily require the involvement of PIP_2 hydrolysis and $Ins(1,4,5)P_3$ production, because the wave of Ca^{2+} release could be self-propagating. L. F. Jaffe (1980, 1983) has been the main proponent of this mechanism and most recently argues that the sperm could introduce sufficient Ca^{2+} into the egg through ion channels in the inner acrosomal membrane of the fused sperm. Data in support of this idea include the known Ca^{2+} influx into the sperm following the acrosome reaction (Schackmann and Shapiro, 1981) and the latent period between Ca^{2+} injection and egg activation reported in some species (Iwamatsu and Ito, 1986). However, this idea is not supported by the demonstration that sea urchin eggs can be fertilized in Ca^{2+}-free sea water (Chambers and Angeloni, 1981; Schmidt et al., 1982). One possible criticism of these experiments is that they required preactivated sperm, which normally have increased levels of Ca^{2+}, so one could argue that they have sufficient Ca^{2+} to act as a Ca^{2+} source themselves.

Another line of reasoning that tends to cast doubt on a sperm receptor-mediated transduction and tends to support a Ca^{2+}-induced Ca^{2+} release mechanism is that deuterostome eggs cannot be activated by contact with sperm-specific binding molecules such as bindin. If there were a sperm receptor in the plasma membrane that communicated sperm binding by stimulating inositol lipid turnover or protein kinase activity, one might expect this receptor to be stimulated by some sperm surface molecule. In contrast, eggs of protostomes (e.g., as Urechis) can be activated by acrosomal proteins from the sperm (Gould and Stephano, 1987), but the $[Ca^{2+}]_i$ increase in these eggs is known to come from influx through the plasma membrane, rather than release from intracellular stores. L. F. Jaffe (1983) has proposed that this difference between deuterostomes and protostomes can be attributed to differences in their Ca^{2+} response to sperm. Specifically, deuterostomes exhibit a propagated release of Ca^{2+} from intracellular stores, whereas protostomes exhibit a synchronous increase due to influx from the external medium. Thus, in cases in which Ca^{2+} influx is required for activation, sperm proteins stimulate such influx when contacting the egg. In eggs in which the Ca^{2+} comes mainly from intracellular stores, Jaffe proposes that the sperm introduces sufficient Ca^{2+} to stimulate a wave of Ca^{2+}-induced Ca^{2+} release from these stores.

E. So How Does the Sperm Activate the Egg?

In the end we will probably learn that some combination of the above mechanisms is at work to generate the activation process. Ca^{2+}-induced Ca^{2+} release is a good candidate where sources of PIP_2 are scarce, far from the plasma membrane. However, near the membrane it would be surprising if PIP_2 hydrolysis were not involved, since the critical enzyme here, phospholipase C, is stimulated by elevated Ca^{2+} levels in the physiological range (Melin *et al.*, 1986; Bennett and Crooke, 1987; Rebecchi and Rosen, 1987; Rhee *et al.*, 1989). Similarly, the ability of intermediates in the inositol cascade (e.g., G proteins and $Ins(1,4,5)P_3$) to activate eggs, along with the presence of measured endogenous turnover of PIP_2 during fertilization, suggests that this cascade is also involved. However, it is not clear how this cascade would generate the latent period. One possibility is that the sperm–G protein interaction is slow. Since the bound sperm only interacts with receptors in a restricted region of the surface of the egg and cannot exhibit the lateral mobility of a receptor such as that of acetylcholine, G proteins would have to be activated by diffusing to the sperm and then must diffuse away to activate the phospholipase C. Thus, it may well take some time for this process to release sufficient $Ins(1,4,5)P_3$ to activate the Ca^{2+} wave. We have found in the *Xenopus* egg that there is a small amount of Ca^{2+} release for every pulse of $Ins(1,4,5)P_3$ injected, and the wave of increased free Ca^{2+} is not triggered until a threshold Ca^{2+} level is exceeded (Busa *et al.*, 1985). If this were the case, the initial slow increase in $[Ca^{2+}]_i$ observed during the latent period (Whitaker *et al.*, 1989) should be independent of extracellular Ca^{2+}. A careful study of the dependence, if any, of the duration of the latent period on extracellular Ca^{2+} levels should help to distinguish between hypotheses 1 and 3 (Section III,A and C).

Many other experiments must be done to determine which of these mechanisms are normally utilized during activation. We must find ways to completely shut down the inositol cascade to determine whether Ca^{2+}-induced Ca^{2+} release is sufficient to activate. This could be accomplished by the introduction of either function-blocking antibodies to phospholipase C or PIP_2, or sufficient $Ins(1,4,5)P_3$-binding proteins to soak up all of the $Ins(1,4,5)P_3$ produced before it can release Ca^{2+}. This latter experiment, like the heparin injection experiments, would reduce the Ca^{2+}-releasing ability of $Ins(1,4,5)P_3$, but would not block the other arm of the inositol pathway: DAG production.

Once we determine how the sperm triggers the Ca^{2+} wave, we must address the next step in activation. How does the Ca^{2+} wave initiate the cell cycle and protein synthesis? The recent advances in our understanding of cell cycle controls would suggest that Ca^{2+}-stimulated phosphatases and kinases will be important players in this next step. But what are their target proteins? Many question remain to be answered, but the pace is quickening and by the end of this century we may finally understand how the various parthenogenetic treatments discovered by embryologists at the beginning of this century actually work to activate development.

References

Allen, R. D., and Griffin, J. L. (1958). *Exp. Cell Res.* **15**, 163–173.
Bement, W. M., and Capco, D. G. (1989). *J. Cell Biol.* **108**, 885–892.
Bement, W. M., and Capco, D. G. (1990). *Cell Regul.* **1**, 315–326.
Bennett, C. F., and Crooke, S. T. (1987). *J. Biol. Chem.* **262**, 13789–13797.
Berridge, M. J. (1987). *Annu. Rev. Biochem.* **56**, 159–193.
Bloom, T. L., Szuts, E. Z. and Eckberg, W. R. (1988). *Dev. Biol.* **129**, 532–540.
Busa, W. B., and Nuccitelli, R. (1984). *Am. J. Physiol.* **246**, R409–R438.
Busa, W. B., and Nuccitelli, R. (1985). *J. Cell Biol.* **100**, 1325–1329.
Busa, W. B., Ferguson, J. E., Joseph, S. K., Williamson, J. R., and Nuccitelli, R. (1985). *J. Cell Biol.* **101**, 677–682.
Chambers, E. L. (1989). *In* "Mechanisms of Egg Activation" (R. Nuccitelli, G. N. Cherr, and W. H. Clark, Jr., eds.), pp. 1–18. Plenum, New York.
Chambers, E. L., and Angeloni, S. V. (1981). *J. Cell Biol.* **91**, 181a.
Chambers, E. L., Pressman, B. C., and Rose, B. (1974). *Biochem. Biophys. Res. Commun.* **60**, 126–132.
Chiba, K., Kado, R. T., and Jaffe, L. A. (1990). *Dev. Biol.* **140**, 300–306.
Ciapa, B., and Whitaker, M. (1986). *FEBS Lett.* **195**, 347–351.
Ciapa, B., Crossley, I., and De Renzis, G. (1988). *Dev. Biol.* **128**, 142–149.
Clapper, D. L., and Lee, H. C. (1986). *J. Biol. Chem.* **260**, 13947–13950.
Clapper, D. L., Walseth, T. F., Dargie, P. J., and Lee, H. C. (1987). *J. Biol. Chem.* **262**, 9561–9568.
Colonna, R., Tatone, C., Malgaroli, A., Eusebi, F., and Mangia, F. (1989). *Gamete Res.* **24**, 171–183.
Cran, D. G., Moor, R. M., and Irvine, R. F. (1988). *J. Cell Sci.* **91**, 139–144.
Cross, N. L. (1981). *Dev. Biol.* **85**, 380–384.
Crossley, I., Swann, K., Chambers, E., and Whitaker, M. (1988). *Biochem. J.* **252**, 257–262.
Crossley, I., Whalley, R., and Whitaker, M. J. (1991). *Cell. Regul.* **2**, 121–133.
Cuthbertson, K. S. R., and Cobbold, P. H. (1985). *Nature (London)* **316**, 541–542.
Dale, B. (1988). *Exp. Cell Res.* **177**, 205–211.
Dale, B., DeFelice, L. J., and Ehrenstein, G. (1985). *Exp. Cell Res.* **41**, 1068–1070.
Dube, F., and Guerrier, P. (1982). *Dev. Growth Differ.* **24**, 163–172.
Eisen, A., and Reynolds, G. T. (1985). *J. Cell Biol.* **100**, 1522–1527.
Eisen, A., Kiehart, D. P., Wieland, S. J., and Reynolds, G. T. (1984). *J. Cell Biol.* **99**, 1647–1654.
Epel, D. (1990). *Cell Differ. Dev.* **29**, 1–12.
Gilkey, J. C. (1983). *J. Cell Biol.* **97**, 669–678.
Gilkey, J. C., Jaffe, L. F., Ridgway, E. B., and Reynolds, G. T. (1978). *J. Cell Biol.* **76**, 448–466.
Gilman, A. G. (1987). *Annu. Rev. Biochem.* **56**, 615–649.

Goudeau, M., Herve, M., and Goudeau, H. (1989). *Biochim. Biophys. Acta* **1014,** 14–25.
Gould, M., and Stephano, J. L. (1987). *Science* **235,** 1654–1656.
Guyer, M. (1907). *Science* **25,** 910–911.
Hafner, M., Petzelt, C., Nobiling, R., Pawley, J. B., Kramp, D., and Schatten, G. (1988). *Cell Motil. Cytoskeleton* **9,** 271–277.
Hamaguchi, M. S. (1982). *Dev. Growth Differ.* **24,** 443–452.
Hamaguchi, Y., and Hiramoto, Y. (1981). *Exp. Cell Res.* **134,** 171–179.
Hamaguchi, Y., and Hamaguchi, M. S. (1990). *Cell. Struct. Funct.* **15,** 159–162.
Han, J.-K., and Nuccitelli, R. (1990). *J. Cell Biol.* **110,** 1103–1110.
Hanks, S. K., Quinn, A. M., and Hunter, T. (1989). *Science* **241,** 42–51.
Hertwig, R. (1896). *Festschr. Carl Gegenbaur* **2,** 23.
Herve, M., Goudeau, M., Neumann, J. M., Debouzy, J. C., and Goudeau, H. (1989). *Eur. Biophys. J.* **17,** 191–200.
Hiramoto, Y., Yoshimoto, Y., and Iwamatsu, T. (1989). *Acta Histochem. Cytochem.* **22,** 153–156.
Ichio, I., and Rebhun, L. I. (1988). *Cell Motil. Cytoskeleton* **10,** 344.
Iwamatsu, T. (1989). *Dev. Growth Differ.* **31,** 39–44.
Iwamatsu, T., and Ito, S. (1986). *Dev. Growth Differ.* **28,** 303–310.
Iwamatsu, T., Yoshimoto, Y., and Hiramoto, Y. (1988a). *Dev. Biol.* **129,** 191–197.
Iwamatsu, T., Yoshimoto, Y., and Hiramoto, Y. (1988b). *Dev. Biol.* **125,** 451–457.
Jaffe, L. A. (1989). *In* "Mechanisms of Egg Activation" (R. Nuccitelli, G. N. Cherr, and W. H. Clark, Jr., eds.), pp. 152–155. Plenum, New York.
Jaffe, L. F. (1980). *Ann. N.Y. Acad. Sci.* **339,** 86–101.
Jaffe, L. F. (1983). *Dev. Biol.* **99,** 265–276.
Jaffe, L. F. (1985). *In* "Biology of Fertilization" (C. B. Metz and A. Monroy, eds.), pp. 127–165. Academic Press, Orlando, Florida.
Jaffe, L. A., and Schlichter, L. C. (1985). *J. Physiol. (London)* **358,** 299–319.
Jaffe, L. A., Hagiwara, S., and Kado, R. T. (1978). *Dev. Biol.* **67,** 243–248.
Jiang, W., Veno, P. A., Peaucellier, G., and Kinsey, W. H. (1989). *J. Cell Biol.* **109,** 127a.
Johnson, C. H., and Epel, D. (1981). *J. Cell Biol.* **89,** 284–291.
Johnson, C. H., and Epel, D. (1982). *Dev. Biol.* **92,** 461–469.
Johnson, J. D., Epel, D., and Paul, M. (1976). *Nature (London)* **262,** 661–664.
Kamel, L. C., Bailey, J., Schoenbaum, L., and Kinsey, W. (1985). *Lipids* **20,** 350–356.
Kline, D. (1988). *Dev. Biol.* **126,** 346–361.
Kline, D., Simoncini, L., Mandel, G., Maue, R. A., Kado, R. T., and Jaffe, L. A. (1988). *Science* **241,** 464–467.
Kline, D., Kado, R. T., Kopf, G. S., and Jaffe, L. A. (1990). *NATO Adv. Study Inst. Ser.,* **H45,** pp. 529–541. Springer-Verlag, Berlin.
Kubota, H. Y., Yoshimoto, Y., Yoneda, M., and Hiramoto, Y. (1987). *Dev. Biol.* **119,** 129–136.
Larabell, C., and Nuccitelli, R. (1991). *Dev. Biol.,* Submitted.
Lee, H. C., Walseth, T. F., Bratt, G. T., Haynes, R. N., and Clapper, D. L. (1989). *J. Biol. Chem.* **264,** 1608–1615.
Loeb, J. (1899). *Am. J. Physiol.* **3,** 135.
Loeb, J. (1913). "Artificial Parthenogenesis and Fertilization." Univ. of Chicago Press, Chicago.
Lopo, A., and Vacquier, V. D. (1977). *Nature (London)* **269,** 590–592.
Lynn, J. W., McCulloh, D. H., and Chambers, E. L. (1988). *Dev. Biol.* **128,** 305–323.
Melin, P.-M., Sundler, R., and Jergil, B. (1986). *FEBS Lett.* **198,** 85–88.
Miyazaki, S. (1988). *J. Cell Biol.* **106,** 345–353.
Miyazaki, S. I., Hashimoto, N., Yoshimoto, Y., Kishimoto, T., Igusa, Y., and Hiramoto, Y. (1986). *Dev. Biol.* **118,** 259–267.
Morgan, R. H. (1899). *Wilhelm Roux's Arch. Dev. Biol.* **9,** 489.
Nuccitelli, R. (1980). *Dev. Biol.* **76,** 483–498.

Nuccitelli, R. (1987). *Dev. Biol.* **122**, 522–534.

Nuccitelli, R., Webb, D. J., Lagier, S. T., and Matson, G. B. (1981). *Proc. Natl. Acad. Sci. U.S.A* **78**, 4421–4425.

Nuccitelli, R., Kline, D., Busa, W. B., Talevi, R., and Campanella, C. (1988). *Dev. Biol.* **130**, 120–132.

Nuccitelli, R., Ferguson, J., and Han, J.-K. (1989). *In* "Mechanisms of Egg Activation" (R. Nuccitelli, G. N. Cherr, and W. H. Clark, Jr., eds.), pp. 215–230. Plenum, New York.

Oberdorf, J., Vilar-Rojas, C., and Epel, D. (1989). *Dev. Biol.* **131**, 236–242.

Paul, M. (1975). *Dev. Biol.* **43**, 299–312.

Peaucellier, G., and Doree, M. (1981). *Dev. Growth Differ.* **23**, 287–296.

Peaucellier, G., Veno, P. A., and Kinsey, W. H. (1988). *J. Biol. Chem.* **263**, 13806–13811.

Peuch, C. J., Picard, A., and Doree, M. (1985). *FEBS Lett.* **187**, 61–64.

Picard, A., Giraud, F., LeBouffant, F., Sladeczek, F., LePeuch, C., and Doree, M. (1985). *FEBS Lett.* **182**, 446–450.

Rakow, T. L., and Shen, S. S. (1990). *Proc. Natl. Acad. Sci. U.S.A.* **87**, 9285–9289.

Rebecchi, M. J., and Rosen, O. M. (1987). *J. Biol. Chem.* **262**, 12526–12532.

Rhee, S. G., Suh, P.-G., Ryu, S.-H., and Lee, S. Y. (1989). *Science* **244**, 546–550.

Rossignol, D. P., Decker, G. L., Lennarz, W. J., Tsong, T. Y., and Teissie, J. (1983). *Biochim. Biophys. Acta* **763**, 346–355.

Russo, P., Pecorella, M. A., DeSantis, A., and Dale, B. (1989). *J. Exp. Zool.* **250**, 329–332.

Schackmann, R. W., and Shapiro, B. M. (1981). *Dev. Biol.* **81**, 145–154.

Schmidt, T., Patton, C., and Epel, D. (1982). *Dev. Biol.* **90**, 284–290.

Shen, S. S. (1989). *Biochem. Biophys. Res. Commun.* **161**, 1100–1108.

Shen, S. S., and Burgart, L. J. (1986). *J. Cell. Physiol.* **127**, 330–340.

Shen, S. S., and Steinhardt, R. A. (1978). *Nature (London)* **272**, 253–254.

Shen, S. S., and Steinhardt, R. A. (1984). *Proc. Natl. Acad. Sci. U.S.A.* **81**, 1436–1439.

Shilling, F., Mandel, G., and Jaffe, L. A. (1990). *Cell Regul.* **1**, 465–469.

Slack, B. E., Bell, J. E., and Benos, D. J. (1986). *Am. J. Physiol.* **250**, C340–C344.

Speksnijder, J. E., Sardet, C., and Jaffe, L. F. (1990). *J. Cell Biol.* **110**, 1589–1598.

Steinhardt, R., Epel, D., Carroll, E. J., and Yanagimachi, R. (1974). *Nature (London)* **252**, 41–43.

Stice, S. L., and Robl, J. M. (1990). *Mol. Reprod. Dev.* **25**, 272–280.

Swann, K. (1990). *Development* **110**, 1295–1302.

Swann, K., and Whitaker, M. J. (1985). *Nature (London)* **314**, 274–277.

Swann, K., and Whitaker, M. (1986). *J. Cell Biol.* **103**, 2333–2342.

Turner, P. R., Sheetz, M. P., and Jaffe, L. A. (1984). *Nature (London)* **310**, 414–415.

Turner, P. R., Jaffe, L. A., and Fein, A. (1986). *J. Cell Biol.* **102**, 70–76.

Turner, P. R., Jaffe, L. A., and Primakoff, P. (1987). *Dev. Biol.* **120**, 577–583.

Webb, D. J., and Nuccitelli, R. (1981). *J. Cell Biol.* **91**, 562–567.

Whitaker, M., and Aitchison, M. (1985). *FEBS Lett.* **182**, 119–124.

Whitaker, M., and Crossley, I. (1990). *In* "Nato ASI Series," vol. H45, pp. 433–443. Springer-Verlag, Berlin.

Whitaker, M., and Irvine, R. F. (1984). *Nature (London)* **312**, 636–639.

Whitaker, M. J., and Steinhardt, R. A. (1985). *Q. Rev. Biophys.* **15**, 593–666.

Whitaker, M. J., and Steinhardt, R. A. (1985). *In* "Biology of Fertilization" (C. B. Metz and A. Monroy, eds.), pp. 167–221. Academic Press, Orlando, Florida.

Whitaker, M., Swann, K., and Crossley, I. (1989). *In* "Mechanisms of Egg Activation" (R. Nuccitelli, G. N. Cherr, and W. H. Clark, Jr., eds.), pp. 157–172. Plenum, New York.

Winkler, M. M., Matson, G. B., Hershey, J. W. B., and Bradbury, E. M. (1982). *Exp. Cell Res.* **139**, 217–222.

Yoshimoto, Y., Iwamatsu, T., Hirano, K. I., and Hiramoto, Y. (1986). *Dev. Growth. Differ.* **28**, 583–596.

Zucker, R. S., Steinhardt, R. A., and Winkler, M. M. (1978). *Dev. Biol.* **65**, 285–295.

2

Dorsal–Ventral Pattern Formation in the *Drosophila* Embryo: The Role of Zygotically Active Genes

Edwin L. Ferguson and Kathryn V. Anderson
Division of Genetics
Department of Molecular and Cell Biology
Life Science Addition
University of California, Berkeley
Berkeley, California 94720

I. Introduction

A combination of powerful genetic and molecular tools has made possible enormous strides in our understanding of the mechanisms that generate pattern and fix cell fate in the *Drosophila* embryo. Gradients of authentic morphogens have been visualized, the mechanisms that generate these gradients are partially understood, and targets for the morphogens have been identified. One important aspect of embryogenesis is that several different pattern-forming processes operate during early development. The application of the same basic genetic and molecular tools is making it possible to elucidate the logical framework and the molecular mechanisms that generate pattern in each of these different processes.

This chapter describes the zygotically active genes that specify the dorsal–ventral pattern of the *Drosophila* embryo. These genes respond to a gradient of maternal positional information that defines their realms of activity, and they, in turn, fix these domains and may direct subsequent patterning within these regions. Since these genes respond to and interpret maternal positional information, they are, in a sense, the dorsal–ventral counterparts of the anterior–posterior segmentation genes. However, the rules that control the action of the dorsal–ventral genes are very different from the rules that govern segmentation. As

Current Topics in Developmental Biology, Vol. 25

could be expected, transcription factors and growth factor-like molecules are important in both axes, but, by studying dorsal–ventral patterning, we are discovering new ways in which these kinds of molecules can control development.

Most of the zygotically expressed genes known to be required for dorsal–ventral patterning in the embryo were defined in the saturation mutagenesis experiments carried out by Nüsslein-Volhard, Wieschaus, Jürgens, and Kluding (Nüsslein-Volhard et al., 1984; Jürgens et al., 1984; Wieschaus et al., 1984). From the cuticular phenotypes of differentiated mutant embryos, these workers identified genes that are required to allow the normal development of specific regions of the dorsal–ventral pattern. The most interesting of these mutants, which provide the core of this chapter, are those whose phenotypes are visible early in development and appear to change the fates of defined regions of the embryo. The analysis of the mutant phenotypes and the molecular characterization of the regulation and activity of the zygotically required dorsal–ventral patterning genes have provided important insights into the relationships between cell position and differentiated fate.

A great deal more must be learned before we can describe the mechanisms that zygotically expressed gene products use to specify the dorsal–ventral pattern. For the purposes of this chapter, however, we adopt a particular perspective about early zygotic dorsal–ventral pattern formation based on the phenotypes of known mutants. In this view three primary dorsal–ventral embryonic fields are defined in response to the maternal morphogen gradient. To establish these three fields, zygotically active dorsal–ventral patterning genes are transcribed locally in response to defined thresholds of maternal morphogen, and, in addition, the activities of their gene products are also essential in defining the extents of the three fields. The establishment of a ventral domain that gives rise to the mesoderm requires two known zygotically expressed genes. A dorsal domain that gives rise to the dorsal epidermis and the amnioserosa is specified by seven genes. No zygotic genes are known that are necessary to define the ventrolateral domain that gives rise to the ventral nerve cord and the ventral epidermis. The ventrolateral domain may therefore represent a ground state, with its boundaries indirectly specified by inhibition from the ventral and dorsal domains.

Although these three domains are initially defined in response to a single maternal morphogen, the fixing of each of these regions and subsequent patterning within each region differ fundamentally in mechanism from patterning in the other two regions. By studying each of these domains, we have the opportunity to understand three different patterning systems and how the three are integrated to generate the pattern in the whole animal.

II. Dorsal–Ventral Pattern: Fate Map, Mitotic Domains, Morphogenesis, and Regulative Capacity

The dorsal–ventral pattern of embryonic development becomes apparent during the first extended asynchronous cell cycle in the embryo, the 14th cycle after fertilization, which coincides with the onset of the morphogenetic movements of gastrulation. Gastrulation begins with the invagination of a strip of cells along the ventral midline in the ventral furrow to create the presumptive mesoderm. At the time that the ventral furrow forms, lateral cells fold in to create the cephalic furrow, which marks the line between the future head and the thorax of the embryo. Ventral furrow invagination lasts for only about 10 minutes and is immediately followed by other morphogenetic movements, including germ band extension, in which the mesoderm and the overlying ectodermal cells on the ventral side of the embryo extend, pushing the cells at the posterior end of the embryo up along the dorsal side.

Shortly after the beginning of gastrulation, groups of adjacent cells enter mitosis together in spatial patterns that are highly reproducible from embryo to embryo. Foe (1989) mapped these mitotic domains and found that groups of cells derived from defined anterior–posterior and dorsal–ventral positions in the cellular blastoderm always enter mitosis at a characteristic time. In the central (anterior–posterior) region of the embryo, which will give rise to the thorax and the abdomen of the larva, the mitotic domain pattern defines seven discrete regions around the dorsal–ventral circumference (Fig. 1).

Each dorsal–ventral mitotic domain is correlated with the future differentiated cell type derived from that region. Mitotic domain 10 corresponds to the extreme ventral cells that invaginate in the ventral furrow and give rise to mesoderm. The next lateral mitotic domain (domain 14) comes from the single-cell-wide strip that flanks the ventral furrow cells and corresponds to the mesectoderm, which generates the specialized glia and neurons of the midline. Domain M (and subregion 25) is the next most lateral one- to two-cell-wide strip and contributes to the ventral epidermis and the ventral nerve cord. The next most lateral is domain N (and subregions 16, 17, and 21), which also contributes to both the ventral epidemis and the ventral nerve cord. Moving dorsally, domain 11 gives rise to the dorsal epidermis. Domain 19 is a single-cell-wide domain at the dorsal margin of the dorsal epidermis. The most dorsal cells of the embryo do not divide and give rise to the extraembryonic amnioserosa. This general correlation between cell type and dorsal–ventral position does not always hold in detail. For example, most cells of domain 11 give rise to the dorsal epidermis, but a small number of these cells give rise to cells of the peripheral nervous system.

Although cells behave in a region-specific manner beginning at the time of gastrulation, individual cells in dorsal parts of the embryo retain considerable regulative capacity for several hours after gastrulation (Technau and Campos-Ortega, 1986; Technau et al., 1988). In transplantation experiments single labeled cells that were transplanted immediately after gastrulation from a ventral to a dorsal position gave rise to clones of cells with epidermal and central nervous system (CNS) morphology, as they would in their normal position. In contrast, dorsal cells, which do not give rise to CNS cells *in situ*, do generate progeny with CNS morphology when transplanted to ventral positions, acquiring the behavior of the host region into which they were transplanted. In heterochronic transplants

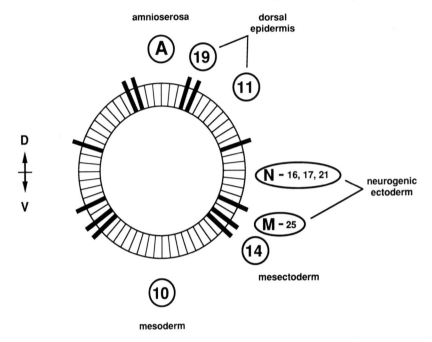

Fig. 1 The dorsal–ventral (D and V, respectively) mitotic domain map, adapted from the data of Foe (1989). The 14th nuclear division after fertilization is the first asynchronous cell cycle. In cycle 14 cells divide in clusters that reflect their dorsal–ventral position in the blastoderm embryo. In the region of the embryo that gives rise to the thorax and the abdomen of the larva, there are seven distinct cycle 14 mitotic domains. The midventral cells that give rise to the mesoderm form mitotic domain 10 and divide 75 minutes after the beginning of cellularization of the blastoderm, which is 25 minutes after the beginning of gastrulation. Cells of mitotic domain 14, the presumptive mesecto-derm, divide 35 minutes after the beginning of gastrulation. Cells of domains M and N, the future neurogenic ectoderm, divide over a broader period, from 50 to 130 minutes after gastrulation begins. Within domains M and N smaller segmentally repeated clusters of cells in domains 16, 17, 21, and 25 divide synchronously. Domain 11 cells divide 30 minutes after the onset of gastrulation, and cells of domain 19, which form the dorsal margin of the epidermis, divide 50 minutes after gastrulation. The dorsal-most cells of the blastoderm (A) never divide after cellularization.

cells taken from dorsal positions 3 hours after gastrulation and transplanted into ventral sites of newly gastrulated embryos also gave rise to CNS cells. By this time, the dorsal epidermal cells have undergone three postblastoderm mitoses, engaged in extensive morphogenetic movements, and expressed a large number of genes in a region-specific manner (see below). Thus, while dorsal cells have initiated the steps necessary for dorsal differentiation, single dorsal cells are not irreversibly programmed and are still sensitive to external cues. The acquisition of the ability to differentiate as a CNS cell when transplanted into ventral regions could reflect either a loss of repression of CNS differentiation normally exerted dorsally or a positive ventral neurogenic signal. In either case the state of dorsal determination must be responsive to local extracellular signals.

III. Maternal Gradient of Positional Information: *dorsal* Protein

The dorsal–ventral pattern of the embryo is built on a framework of maternal information. Twelve maternal effect genes are known to be required for generation of the embryonic dorsal–ventral pattern: 11 dorsal group genes and *cactus* (Anderson and Nüsslein-Volhard, 1986; Schüpbach and Wieschaus, 1989). In the absence of the activity of any one of the dorsal group genes, cells at all embryonic positions differentiate dorsal epidermis and all lateral and ventral pattern elements, including the ventral nerve cord, ventral epidermis, and mesoderm, fail to develop. Partial loss of activity of a dorsal group gene causes the preferential loss of the most ventral pattern elements, with corresponding expansion of the remaining lateral and dorsal structures (Nüsslein-Volhard, 1979). The requirement for a greater amount of these gene products to produce ventral, rather than lateral, structures was the initial indication that dorsal–ventral patterning depended on a gradient of maternal morphogen. Loss of maternal activity of the *cactus* gene has an opposing phenotype: No cells differentiate dorsal epidermis and the number of cells giving rise to lateral and ventral pattern elements increases (Schüpbach and Wieschaus, 1989; Roth *et al.*, 1989). Analysis of double-mutant phenotypes suggested a pathway of action of the maternal genes in which the product of the *dorsal* gene is the final step in the maternal pathway (Anderson *et al.*, 1985; Roth *et al.*, 1989).

The genetic prediction that the output of the maternal pathway is the ventral-to-dorsal gradient of activity of the *dorsal* gene product has been confirmed by the molecular analysis of the *dorsal* gene. The *dorsal* protein is found in the nuclei of the syncytial blastoderm embryo in a ventral-to-dorsal gradient (Steward *et al.*, 1988): *dorsal* protein is most concentrated in ventrally positioned nuclei, decreases in concentration in lateral nuclei, and is not detectable in dorsal nuclei. Although the *dorsal* protein is present in a nuclear gradient, the *dorsal* mRNA is uniformly distributed in the embryo and is translated throughout the embryo. The nuclear gradient of *dorsal* protein is generated by a gradient of nuclear translocation: The *dorsal* protein is present at all positions in the wild-type embryo, ventrally in the nuclei and dorsally in the cytoplasm (Roth *et al.*, 1989; Rushlow *et al.*, 1989; Steward, 1989). The nuclear translocation of *dorsal* protein depends on all other dorsal group genes. In embryos that lack maternal activity of any other dorsal group gene, *dorsal* protein is present and is exclusively cytoplasmic. In the absence of maternal *cactus* activity, nuclei at all dorsal–ventral positions contain *dorsal* protein.

The *dorsal* protein is similar to the protein encoded by the avian oncogene *rel*

(Steward, 1987), which is believed to act as a transcriptional activator (Gelinas and Temin, 1988). Expression of the *dorsal* protein in *Drosophila* tissue culture cells leads to the activation of transcription of several target promoters in a sequence-independent manner (Rushlow *et al.*, 1989). The nuclear location of the active *dorsal* protein, the ability of *dorsal* to activate transcription, and the requirement for *dorsal* for local transcription of certain zygotic genes (see below), make it likely that *dorsal* acts directly to regulate the transcription of target zygotic genes, leading to the expression of these genes in specific dorsal–ventral domains of the embryo (Fig. 2).

Region-specific transcription in response to the *dorsal* gradient requires that defined threshold concentrations of *dorsal* exist, above which a target gene is activated or repressed. It is not possible to deduce directly the number of different threshold concentrations of *dorsal* or the number of target genes that are significant to the embryo, either by inspecting the morphology of the differentiated larva or by assessing what genes depend on *dorsal* for localized expression, since there is considerable refinement of the initial pattern based on the interactions among the zygotically expressed genes that are the direct targets of *dorsal*.

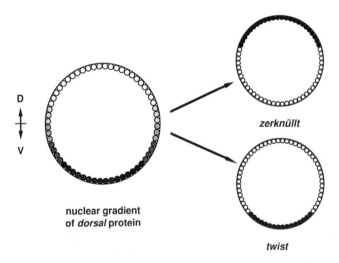

Fig. 2 The nuclear gradient of the dorsal protein leads to transcription of zygotic genes in discrete dorsal–ventral domains at the syncytial blastoderm stage. The *dorsal* protein is present in a nuclear concentration gradient, with its highest levels in ventral nuclei, decreasing gradually in more lateral and dorsal nuclei. Threshold levels from this smooth gradient define the region of transcription of target zygotic genes. The high concentrations of *dorsal* protein in ventral nuclei lead to the transcription of the *twist* gene in those nuclei that lie in the ventral-most 25% of the embryo. The high and intermediate concentrations of *dorsal* protein in ventral and lateral nuclei repress transcription of the *zerknüllt* gene, allowing its transcription in the nuclei in the dorsal-most 40% of the embryo.

Roth *et al.* (1989) have argued that at least four regions are directly defined by threshold concentrations of *dorsal*: extreme ventral (mesoderm), ventrolateral (neurogenic ectoderm), dorsolateral (dorsolateral ectoderm), and dorsal (dorsal ectoderm). Their argument is based on the observation that maternal effect mutants exist which give rise to radially symmetric embryos in which cells at all dorsal–ventral positions give rise to a single cell type with one of these four identities. Thus, the generation of these four cellular identities cannot depend on the interactions among zygotic genes expressed in distinct dorsal–ventral regions. The four regions (equivalent to three threshold concentrations of *dorsal*) represent the minimum number of regions directly defined by *dorsal*, although it is possible that there are additional significant threshold concentrations of *dorsal*.

Not all dorsal–ventral positions can be directly defined by *dorsal* concentration. Most obviously, the final dorsal–ventral pattern of the larva is too detailed to be specified directly by *dorsal* concentrations. However, even the first dorsal–ventral subdivisions that can be seen in the cycle 14 mitotic domains are not all directly defined by *dorsal*. For example, the complete absence of *dorsal* activity leads to dorsal epidermal development rather than the production of the dorsal-most pattern element, the amnioserosa, by cells at all dorsal–ventral positions, indicating that the development of the amnioserosa must rely on interactions among zygotically active genes.

In the subsequent sections we discuss the three major domains that, as defined by mutant phenotypes, reflect the realms of activity of the zygotic pattern genes. The ventral domain appears to be activated by high concentrations of *dorsal*. The dorsal domain is specified by low concentrations of *dorsal*. The ventrolateral domain appears to be only indirectly defined by *dorsal*, and instead may be negatively defined by repression from both ventral and dorsal domains.

IV. Ventral Domain: Mesoderm

The first morphogenetic event of *Drosophila* development is the invagination of a strip 50–60 cells long in the anterior–posterior axis and 16 cells wide on the ventral midline in the ventral furrow (Foe, 1989). In the course of 10 minutes, these cells constrict apically, buckle in, and invaginate as a tube of cells. All mesodermal derivatives, including somatic and visceral musculature, fat body, and gonads, derive from the invaginated cells.

In the screens to identify zygotic lethal mutations with visible effects on the larval cuticle pattern, two genes, *twist* and *snail*, were identified where mutants have cuticle phenotypes with the same twisted body and head defects produced by weak maternal effect alleles of dorsal group mutants (Fig. 3) (Nüsslein-Volhard *et al.*, 1984). Like weak dorsal group mutants, *twist* and *snail* mutant

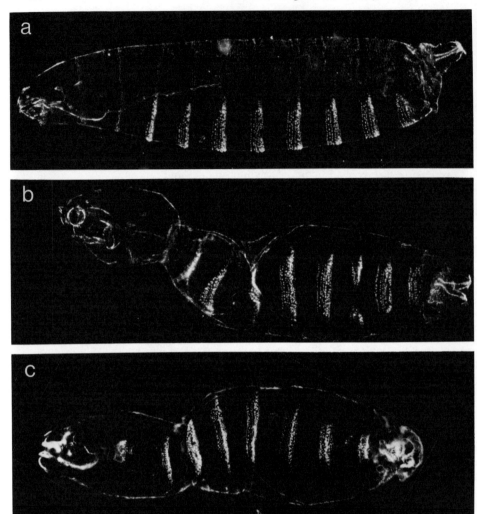

Fig. 3 The similarity of the cuticular phenotypes of weak dorsalizing maternal effect mutants and the zygotic mutant *twist*. (a) The cuticular pattern of a first instar wild-type *Drosophila* larva. Anterior is to the left; dorsal, up. In the thorax and the abdomen the hallmarks of the dorsal–ventral cuticular pattern are the bands of ventral denticles, which derive from the ventrolateral and lateral regions of the blastoderm, and the fine dorsal hairs, which derive from dorsal and dorsolateral regions of the blastoderm. (b) A weakly dorsalized embryo produced by a female of the genotype ea^3/ea^1. This embryo, like those produced by very weak alleles at any of the dorsal group loci, has most of the cuticular pattern elements of the wild-type dorsal–ventral pattern, including ventral denticle bands of essentially normal width. This weakly dorsalizing phenotype is characterized by its head defects and the twist in the thoracic region. (c) An embryo homozygous for $twist^{IIH07}$, showing the same cuticular defects seen in the weakly dorsalized maternal effect mutant in (b).

embryos fail to make a ventral furrow at gastrulation and subsequently lack the mesodermal derivatives made by the cells that normally invaginate in the ventral furrow.

The failure of *twist* and *snail* mutant embryos to make a ventral furrow is the earliest visible pattern defect in any zygotic lethal mutation, and is a dramatic demonstration of the importance of early zygotic transcription. The requirement for *twist* and *snail* activity is purely zygotic: The embryonic phenotype of *twist* or *snail* mutant embryos from females that lack *twist* or *snail* activity in the germ line is identical to that of embryos from heterozygous mothers (Frohnhöfer, 1982). The temperature-sensitive period of a weak *twist* allele for survival to adult stages is 2–4 hours after egg-laying, suggesting that the only time in the life cycle that *twist* activity is required is at the late blastoderm and early gastrula stages (Thisse *et al.*, 1987a).

Because the mutant phenotypes of *twist* and *snail* are similar to those of weak dorsal group mutants, it seemed likely that these genes are components of a common pathway. The *twist* and *snail* genes also interact genetically with the *dorsal* gene. The *dorsal* gene is dosage sensitive: Females heterozygous for *dorsal* deficiencies in defined genetic backgrounds produce weakly dorsalized embryos at high temperatures (Nüsslein-Volhard, 1979). While *twist* and *snail* are recessive mutations, embryos produced by mothers that have only one wild-type copy of *dorsal* and are also heterozygous for *twist* and *snail* die as weakly dorsalized embryos, even at low temperatures (Simpson, 1983).

Analysis of the expression of the *twist* gene showed that the *twist* transcript becomes detectable before cellularization of the blastoderm, when it is confined to the ventral quarter of the embryo (Thisse *et al.*, 1987b). Transcription of *twist* depends on the activity of maternal dorsal group genes, including *dorsal* (Thisse *et al.*, 1987b). Because *dorsal* acts at the end of the maternal pathway and *dorsal* nuclear protein is at maximal levels in ventral nuclei when *twist* transcript becomes detectable, it seems likely that a high concentration of nuclear *dorsal* protein directly activates the transcription of *twist*. In genetic terms, *twist* is downstream of *dorsal* on the pathway that allows mesodermal differentiation, and the dependence of *twist* transcription on high concentrations of *dorsal* is sufficient to explain the genetic interaction seen between *twist* and *dorsal*.

The *twist* protein is nuclear, and is first detectable in embryos at the beginning of cellularization, when it is seen in a strip of nuclei on the ventral side of the embryo, wrapping up around both the anterior and posterior poles of the embryo (Thisse *et al.*, 1988). The *twist* protein is present in all of the cells that invaginate in the ventral furrow, as well as in a single-cell-wide strip on each side of the furrow, the mesectoderm cells. The ventral furrow extends only from 15–80% of the egg length, but *twist* protein is found in the ventral cells both anterior and posterior to this region, in the endodermal cells that give rise to the anterior and posterior midguts. After gastrulation, *twist* expression becomes restricted to those cells that require *twist* activity: *twist* protein persists in all mesodermal cells, but is no longer found in endodermal cells (Thisse *et al.*, 1988).

From the sequences of the genes, both *twist* and *snail* are likely to act by controlling the transcription of other genes. The *snail* gene encodes a protein with a tandem array of five zinc fingers, typical of those found in several proteins shown to be sequence-specific nucleic acid-binding proteins (Boulay *et al.*, 1987). The *twist* gene is a member of the helix–loop–helix class of DNA-binding transcriptional regulators (Thisse *et al.*, 1988; Murre *et al.*, 1989).

Timing suggests that if *twist* and *snail* indeed act as transcription factors, the genes they regulate encode products that act directly in the process of morphogenesis. Because *twist* protein is first detectable at the beginning of cellularization, there is only 30–40 minutes to accumulate and translate sufficient amounts of target gene products that regulate ventral furrow formation. Because of this short lag time, it seems likely that the targets of *twist* and *snail* do not encode structural proteins necessary for the cell shape changes of furrow formation, but instead encode less abundant proteins that regulate cytoskeletal or cell surface function. The genes for integrin subunit PS2α and xanthine dehydrogenase (*rosy*) are both transcribed in the presumptive ventral furrow cells at a time that makes them possible targets for *twist* and *snail* (Bogaert *et al.*, 1987; Doyle *et al.*, 1989), but mutants that block the activity of either gene have no effect on ventral furrow formation (Leptin *et al.*, 1989; Schalet *et al.*, 1964). Since *twist* and *snail* appear to be the only two genes in the *Drosophila* genome for which loss of zygotic activity blocks ventral furrow formation (Wieschaus and Sweeton, 1988; Merrill *et al.*, 1988), genetics has failed to identify the target genes regulated by *twist* and *snail*. The absence of mutations in these genes suggests that the target genes are redundant or are expressed both maternally and zygotically.

In addition to promoting mesodermal development, *twist* and *snail* also repress the developmental program followed by more lateral cells. In *twist* or *snail* mutant embryos, the cells that normally contribute to the ventral furrow do not die, but are apparently reprogrammed to follow a more lateral developmental pathway. In *snail* mutant embryos, for example, the ventral cells transcribe the *single-minded* gene (Nambu *et al.*, 1990), which is normally expressed only in the cells immediately lateral to the ventral furrow. Thus, the ventral cells in *snail* embryos behave, at least in this respect, like more lateral cells.

The nature and control of patterning within the mesoderm are not understood. In addition to forming fat body, gonads, and both visceral and somatic muscle, the mesoderm generates a somatic musculature with a detailed dorsal–ventral pattern. Although individual cells are committed to differentiate as mesoderm at the time of ventral furrow formation, transplantation experiments showed that they are not committed to differentiating particular mesodermal derivatives (Beer *et al.*, 1987). For example, single ventral furrow cells can give rise to progeny that contribute to both somatic and visceral mesoderm. It is likely that, after invagination, mesodermal cells respond to dorsal–ventral positional information from the ectoderm in deciding specific fates, since ventral furrow cells placed in dorsal regions in the recipient embryo were more likely to make visceral muscles than those placed at ventral sites. Experimental evidence in other insects also indicates that, although the differentiation of the ectoderm is independent of the mesoderm, the decision between visceral and somatic muscle development is based on instruction from the overlying ectoderm (Bock, 1941).

V. Dorsal Regions: Amnioserosa and Dorsal Epidermis

The dorsal region of the embryo gives rise to two tissue types: amnioserosa and dorsal epidermis. The dorsal-most embryonic cells do not divide after the 13th cycle and subsequently give rise to the amnioserosa, which is necessary for proper germ-band extension, but does not directly contribute to the larval cuticle. The dorsolateral cells of the embryo, corresponding to mitotic domains 11 and 19, form the dorsal epidermis, which is characterized in cuticle preparations by a lawn of fine hairs. Seven zygotic genes have been identified that are necessary for the specification of pattern in the dorsal region of the embryo. The cuticular phenotypes of loss-of-function mutants in six of these genes, *decapentaplegic* (*dpp*), *screw*, *tolloid*, *shrew*, *twisted gastrulation*, and *zerknüllt* (*zen*), provide direct evidence of their involvement in this process. In embryos homozygous for a mutation in any of these six genes, a characteristic subset of dorsal structures is replaced by pattern elements located more ventrally, resulting in a partial "ventralization" of the embryonic cuticle (Fig. 4). The involvement of the seventh gene, *short gastrulation* (*sog*), was deduced not from its cuticular phenotype, but rather from its effects on gastrulation and on its molecular and genetic interactions with other genes.

Of the six genes necessary for the production of dorsal structures, loss-of-function mutations in the *dpp* locus have the most severe effect on the embryonic pattern. The *dpp* gene product is required for the production of all structures derived from both the amnioserosa and the dorsal epidermal anlagen (Irish and Gelbart, 1987). In the absence of *dpp* activity, the cells that would normally generate these anlagen give rise to structures characteristic of the more ventral neurogenic ectoderm. This transformation is most easily observed in the abdominal region of embryos that lack *dpp* activity, in which the fine dorsal hairs characteristic of the wild-type dorsal epidermis are replaced by bands of ventral denticles that encircle the embryo. *dpp* null embryos also lack all dorsal and dorsolaterally derived cuticular specializations of the head and the tail.

Embryos lacking any of the remaining five genes have weaker phenotypes than embryos carrying null alleles of *dpp*. Two of the genes, *tolloid* and *screw*, are required for the production of both the amnioserosa and the dorsal-most structures of the dorsal epidermis anlage, but are not needed for the production of the more lateral derivatives of this region (Jürgens *et al.*, 1984; Tearle and Nüsslein-Volhard, 1987). Embryos mutant for either gene retain some of the dorsal hairs

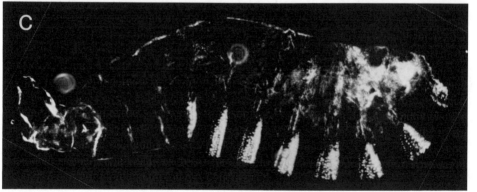

characteristic of the dorsal epidermal tissue, but have widened ventral denticle bands, indicating expansion of the ventral epidermal anlage. The other three genes, *zen*, *twisted gastrulation*, and *shrew*, are required only for the amnioserosa and the dorsal-most regions of the head (Wakimoto *et al.*, 1984; Zusman and Wieschaus, 1985; E. L. Ferguson, unpublished observations).

Partial loss-of-function mutants of *dpp*, *screw*, or *tolloid* can be ordered in an allelic series in which weak alleles delete only the amnioserosa, moderate alleles delete the dorsal-most structures of the dorsal epidermis as well as the amnioserosa, while stronger alleles delete additional dorsolateral structures. These results suggest that the products of these genes are components of a process that is more active in the dorsal-most regions of the embryo than in the dorsolateral regions. For example, these genes could be necessary for the production of a morphogen gradient within this region, where higher concentrations of the morphogen specify more dorsal structures. The progressive loss of dorsal structures is correlated with a dorsalward shift in the border between the neurogenic ectoderm and the dorsal epidermis, suggesting that the same process that specifies pattern within the dorsal epidermis also sets the border between the two domains.

The abnormalities resulting from mutations in any of the six genes are apparent by 30 minutes after the beginning of gastrulation. Mutations in these genes do not perturb the formation of the ventral furrow, but mutations in *dpp*, *screw*, and *tolloid* cause the cephalic furrow to begin dorsally, rather than laterally, indicating that dorsal cells are behaving like cells in more lateral positions. The subsequent events of germ-band extension are abnormal in mutants lacking any of the six genes. In wild-type embryos the cells on the dorsal surface, which form the amnioserosa, become squamous and are pushed laterally by the expanding germ band. In mutant embryos, the dorsal-most cells remain cuboidal and fail to move laterally, blocking the extension of the germ band, which ultimately moves underneath the abnormal dorsal cells into the interior of the embryo. Much later, head involution is blocked and head structures remain external.

Embryos defective in *sog* have abnormalities in gastrulation similar to those in *zen* or *twisted gastrulation* embryos in that the dorsal-most cells remain cuboidal, resulting in the blockage of germ-band extension (Zusman *et al.*, 1988). However, some amnioserosa-like cells are present in *sog* embryos during later em-

Fig. 4 The cuticle phenotypes of zygotic ventralizing mutations. Null alleles of *decapentaplegic* (*dpp*), *tolloid*, and *zerknüllt* (*zen*) all delete dorsal pattern elements, but differ in the severity of their phenotypes. (a) The most extreme phenotype is that of embryos that lack *dpp* activity [genotype: $dpp^{48}/Df(2L)DTD\ 2$]. These embryos lack all dorsal epidermis, while the ventral epidermis, seen as the ventral denticle bands in the cuticle, encircles the embryo. (b) Embryos that lack *tolloid* activity [$tld^{B6}/Df(3R)slo^3$] have reduced dorsal epidermis and slightly expanded ventral denticle belts. (c) Embryos that lack *zen* (zen^{W36}/zen^{W36}) have the normal dorsal–ventral set of cuticular structures, but have the posterior end pulled into the gut, as a consequence of the absence of the amnioserosa, and fail to undergo head involution.

bryogenesis, suggesting that *sog* mutations do not block the differentiation of all amnioserosa cells. Although *sog* affects the behavior of dorsally derived cells, mosaic studies indicate that it is likely to be transcribed in more ventrally positioned cells. In contrast to *twisted gastrulation*, which is required in the most dorsal cells to generate a wild-type pattern (Zusman and Wieschaus, 1985), mosaic embryos in which the *sog* gene is eliminated in ventral cells are less likely to survive than mosaic embryos lacking *sog* in dorsal cells (Zusman *et al.*, 1988).

Unlike the other six genes, which were first characterized on the basis of their embryonic mutant phenotypes, the *dpp* locus was initially identified by mutations that affected the morphology of the adult fly (Spencer *et al.*, 1982). These mutations cause pattern deficiencies and duplications in the epidermal derivatives of some or all imaginal disks. A few alleles isolated because they failed to complement adult phenotypes proved to cause embryonic lethality as homozygotes (Spencer *et al.*, 1982). Further genetic analysis of the *dpp* locus revealed that the loss of *dpp* activity results in a haplolethal phenotype: Embryos heterozygous for a deficiency of the *dpp* region lack the dorsal-most structures and fail to hatch (Irish and Gelbart, 1987). The *dpp* locus is the only known pattern locus which displays a haplolethal phenotype.

The available data suggest that the other genes may be required exclusively at the cellular blastoderm stage. X-Ray-induced mitotic recombination clones or gynandromorphs were used to create genetic mosaics in which imaginal disk cells lacked a wild-type copy of the *zen*, *twisted gastrulation*, or *sog* genes. For all three genes clones of mutant cells were fully viable in the adult, indicating that there is no requirement for the gene product during imaginal disk development (Wakimoto *et al.*, 1984; Zusman and Wieschaus, 1985; Zusman *et al.*, 1988). Genetic mosaics have also been used to obtain clones of germ-line cells mutant for *tolloid*, *twisted gastrulation*, or *sog*. In each case, lack of gene function during oogenesis was not lethal to the germ cells and had no effect on the mutant phenotypes of the progeny, indicating that none of these genes is required during germ cell development (Zusman and Wieschaus, 1985; Zusman *et al.*, 1988; Shimell *et al.*, 1991). Similar experiments with *dpp* also showed that this gene is not required in the maternal germ line (Irish and Gelbart, 1987). In addition, the temperature-sensitive periods for survival to adult stages of *zen* and *tolloid* alleles are 2–4 hours after fertilization, suggesting that the action of these genes is specific to early embryogenesis (Wakimoto *et al.*, 1984; Shimell *et al.*, 1991).

The pattern of expression of the three genes that have been cloned, *zen*, *dpp*, and *tolloid*, has provided evidence that the transcription of these genes is initially controlled by the maternal gradient of the *dorsal* gene product. All three transcripts are initially expressed over the dorsal-most 40% of the circumference of the embryo, as well as over the poles of the embryo, suggesting that they respond to common regulatory signals (Doyle *et al.*, 1986; Rushlow *et al.*, 1987a; St. Johnston and Gelbart, 1987; Shimell *et al.*, 1991). Transcripts of *zen* are seen at the beginning of the syncytial blastoderm stage, when the *dorsal* gradient first appears, making *zen* one of the first detectable products of zygotic transcription (Doyle *et al.*, 1986). Transcripts of *dpp* can be detected slightly later in the syncytial blastoderm stage, at the end of nuclear cycle 11 (St. Johnston and Gelbart, 1987).

For *zen* this early pattern of expression has been shown to be under the control of the maternal gradient of the *dorsal* product (Rushlow *et al.*, 1987b). In syncytial blastoderm embryos produced by mothers mutant for the *dorsal* gene, *zen* protein is expressed at all dorsal–ventral positions. Dissection of the upstream control region of the *zen* gene identified a distal region of the *zen* promoter that contains sequences that are required to prevent *zen* expression in ventral regions of early embryos (Doyle *et al.*, 1989) (Fig. 5). Since this element can mediate ventral repression of a heterologous promoter, it has the properties of a silencer sequence. Recently, Ip *et al.* (1991) have shown that the *dorsal* protein can bind to specific sites within this sequence. It seems likely that *zen* transcription is activated at the beginning of the syncytial blastoderm stage by a global regulator and that the nuclear *dorsal* gene product selectively represses the expression of the *zen* transcript in the ventral regions of the embryo.

Within the dorsal 40% of the embryonic circumference, the *dpp*, *tolloid*, and *zen* genes are uniformly transcribed, suggesting that the gradient of *dorsal* protein defines the dorsal–ventral extent of the expression of the zygotic genes required for dorsal development, but does not affect the level of transcription in the regions in which they are expressed. Therefore it is likely that patterning within the dorsal region of the embryo is specified by interactions among zygotic genes.

Because it has the strongest mutant phenotype of the zygotic ventralizing genes, *dpp* must play an important role in patterning the dorsal regions of the embryo. The sequence of the *dpp* gene indicates that it is a member of the transforming growth factor β (TGF-β) family of proteins (Padgett *et al.*, 1987). All members of this family of proteins are translated as larger precursors that are secreted and cleaved to release the carboxy-terminal approximately 100-amino-acid domain of the molecule, which is then active as a dimer. TGF-β family members are involved in the control of a variety of processes such as cell migration, growth, differentiation, and regulation of the extracellular matrix (Roberts and Sporn, 1988; Roberts *et al.*, 1990). Recently, one member of the TGF-β family, activin A, has been shown to be a potent inducer of mesoderm in *Xenopus* embryos (Smith *et al.*, 1990; van den Eijnden-van Raaij *et al.*, 1990). Of all the TGF-β family members, the *dpp* protein shares the most extensive homology to BMP-2A, one of three bone morphogenesis proteins (BMPs) that were isolated based on their ability to induce ectopic bone formation in rats after subcutaneous implantation (Wozney *et al.*, 1988). The carboxy-terminal domain of the BMP-2A protein is 75% identical to that of *dpp* (Wozney *et al.*, 1988), arguing that BMP-2A is the mammalian homolog of *dpp*.

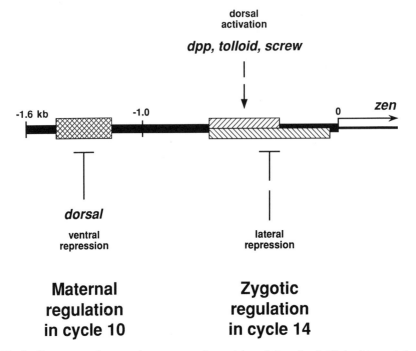

Fig. 5 Upstream regulatory regions necessary for spatial regulation of *zerknüllt* (*zen*) transcription (Doyle *et al.*, 1989). DNA (1.6 kb) upstream of the start site of *zen* transcription contains the cis sites for correct spatial regulation of *zen* transcription at the syncytial and cellular blastoderm stages. The *dorsal*-dependent repression of *zen* transcription in syncytial blastoderm embryos requires sequences −1.4 to −1.2 kb upstream of the start site of *zen* transcription. Correct expression at cycle 14 requires a more proximal region: 660 bp of 5′-flanking sequence is sufficient to drive transcription in the normal nuclei in the dorsal-most 10% of the cellular blastoderm embryo. The activities of *decapentaplegic* (*dpp*), *tolloid*, and *screw* are required for cycle 14 expression. Deletion of the region from −300 to −42 bp allows transcription at cycle 14, but in a broad dorsal and lateral domain instead of the normal dorsal-most 10% of the embryo.

Genetic observations, such as the failure of certain recessive *tolloid* and *dpp* alleles to complement one another, suggested that the products of the *tolloid* and *dpp* genes could physically interact (Ferguson and Anderson, 1991). This hypothesis is further supported by the sequence of the *tolloid* gene (Shimell *et al.*, 1991), which encodes a secreted protein of approximately 120 kDa composed of multiple structural domains. The N-terminal region of the protein is similar to a zinc-binding metalloprotease. The C-terminal region of the protein is composed of multiple copies of two classes of repeating units, EGF-like repeats and repeats of a 120 amino acid domain which is also found in the C1r and C1s components of the human complement cascade.

The first two-thirds of the *tolloid* protein is 41% identical to another protein isolated in the bone morphogenesis assay, BMP-1 (Shimell *et al.*, 1991), the only BMP that is not a TGF-β family member. BMP-1 was identified because the protein copurified with the other BMP proteins, BMP-2A and BMP-3 (Wang *et al.*, 1988), suggesting that the BMPs form a physical complex. Thus, two very different processes, mammalian bone morphogenesis and embryonic dorsal–ventral pattern formation in *Drosophila*, employ very similar molecules, indicating that the underlying molecular interactions have been conserved during evolution and adapted for use in different developmental pathways.

Gene dosage experiments showed that doubling the number of copies of the wild type *dpp* gene completely suppresses weak alleles and partially suppresses null alleles of *tolloid* (Ferguson and Anderson, 1991). Thus, an increase in the dose of *dpp* can bypass the requirements for the *tolloid* gene product, indicating that *tolloid* acts upstream of *dpp* to potentiate *dpp* activity. Similar experiments have indicated that an increase in *dpp* gene dosage can suppress strong, probably null, alleles of the *shrew* gene, arguing that *shrew*, like *tolloid*, functions upstream of *dpp*.

In contrast to *dpp* and *tolloid*, the *zen* gene encodes a homeobox-containing protein (Doyle *et al.*, 1986), suggesting that it is likely to function by controlling the expression of other genes. Transfection studies in *Drosophila* tissue culture cells indicate that the *zen* protein can act as a transcription factor, since it activates transcription of a reporter gene with an upstream sequence containing a homeobox binding site (Han *et al.*, 1989).

Molecular experiments have shown that *zen* most likely acts downstream of the *dpp* gene. At the cellular blastoderm stage (cycle 14), the *zen* transcript becomes restricted to the dorsal-most 10% of the egg circumference (Doyle *et al.*, 1986). This later transcription of *zen* is both positively and negatively regulated by the products of other zygotic genes (Fig. 5). The *dpp*, *tolloid*, and *screw* genes, as well as *zen* itself, are required for the later expression of *zen* in the dorsal regions; in mutants in any of these genes, *zen* transcripts disappear by cycle 14 (Doyle *et al.*, 1989; Rushlow and Levine, 1990). These results suggest that the cycle 14 expression of *zen* is downstream of other zygotic pattern genes, and thus *zen* could be more directly involved in the activation of genes required for the differentiation of the amnioserosa cells. The dorsal activation of *zen* is mediated through a defined sequence upstream of the *zen* transcript (Doyle *et al.*, 1989), suggesting that *dpp*, *tolloid*, and *screw* indirectly control a transcriptional activator, conceivably the *zen* protein itself, that binds at this site.

An additional element upstream of the *zen* promoter is necessary for the repression of *zen* in dorsolateral cells at cycle 14. In the absence of this element, *zen* continues to be expressed in the dorsal 40% of the egg circumference during cycle 14. A similar pattern of *zen* expression is observed in mutants defective in the *sog* gene (Rushlow and Levine, 1990), directly implicating the *sog* gene in the early events of patterning within the dorsal epidermis.

The paradoxical observations that the *sog* gene is only required in the ventral-most epidermal cells for embryonic viability, but that the most obvious aspect of the *sog* mutant phenotype is caused by defects in the dorsal-most embryonic cells were partially reconciled by the construction of *sog* mutant embryos containing four copies of the wild-type *dpp* gene (Ferguson and Anderson, 1991). While a doubling of the *dpp* gene dosage does not affect the phenotype of *sog*⁺ embryos, in *sog* mutant embryos with four copies of *dpp*, the dorsal epidermal region of the embryo is expanded. Thus, one of the roles of the *sog* gene must be to negatively regulate the activity of *dpp* in the ventral regions of the embryo.

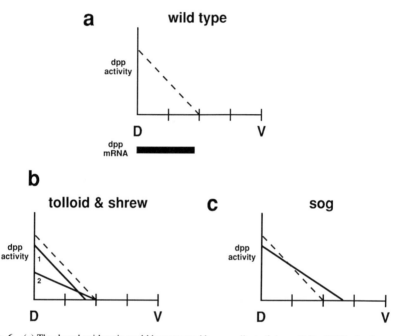

Fig. 6 (a) The dorsal epidermis could be patterned by a gradient of *dpp* activity. While the *dpp* gene is transcribed uniformly in the dorsal 40% of the embryonic circumference, the phenotypes caused by partial loss-of-function mutations in *dpp* indicate that *dpp* is required at higher levels in the dorsal regions of the embryo than in the dorsolateral regions. We postulate that the differential requirement for *dpp* activity reflects a gradient of *dpp* activity and that region-specific post-translational interactions between the *dpp* protein and the products of other zygotic ventralizing genes, including the *tolloid*, *shrew*, and *sog* genes, are necessary for the formation of the proper gradient. (b) The *tolloid* and *shrew* genes act by potentiating *dpp* activity in the dorsal regions of the embryo (see text). In the absence of either of these genes *dpp* activity is reduced in the dorsal epidermis. At the present time we can not distinguish whether *tolloid* and *shrew* genes activate *dpp* uniformly throughout the dorsal epidermis (line 1) or are asymmetrically active within the dorsal epidermis, possibly functioning in the formation of the *dpp* gradient (line 2). (c) Mutations in the *sog* gene result in a redistribution of *dpp* activity within the dorsal–ventral circumference of the embryo. In *sog* mutants, *dpp* activity is reduced in the dorsal regions of the embryo, while *dpp* activity is elevated in the ventral regions of the embryo. Thus, *sog* is currently the best candidate for a gene directly involved in the formation of a gradient of *dpp* activity.

The nonautonomous action of the *sog* gene on the dorsal epidermal cells is likely to be mediated through its effects on *dpp* activity. The dorsal aspect of the *sog* mutant phenotype, loss of amnioserosa cells resulting in failure of germ band extension, is caused by a decrease of *dpp* activity in these cells, since a doubling of the *dpp* gene dosage in a *sog* mutant suppresses this dorsal defect (Ferguson and Anderson, 1991). Thus, wild type *sog* gene activity increases *dpp* activity dorsally while decreasing *dpp* activity ventrally. These results suggest that *sog* may redistribute *dpp* activity over the dorsal–ventral circumference to form a gradient of *dpp* activity.

We suggest that this gradient of *dpp* activity plays a central role in organizing the pattern of the dorsal 40% of the embryo (Fig. 6). The *dpp* allelic series indicates a graded requirement for *dpp*; we believe that this requirement reflects a gradient of *dpp* activity, such that the highest levels of *dpp* activity specify the most dorsal structures. The gradient of *dpp* activity is not generated by transcriptional regulation of *dpp*, but by region-specific interactions among the secreted protein products of other zygotically expressed pattern genes. The products of the *tolloid* and *shrew* loci activate *dpp* in the dorsal regions of the embryo, while the *sog* gene product redistributes *dpp* activity. These interactions, and perhaps others, generate a gradient of *dpp* activity that dictates patterning in the dorsal epidermis and amnioserosa.

It is unclear what genes are involved in the later differentiation of the dorsal regions of the embryo. It is possible that *dpp* also acts later. At germ-band extension, the *dpp* transcript is present in two dorsal–ventral stripes that roughly correspond to cells at the border of the amnioserosa and the dorsal epidermis and cells at the border of the dorsal epidermis and the neurogenic ectoderm, suggesting that *dpp* could also be involved in demarcating the borders between these different regions (St. Johnston and Gelbart, 1987). Other less well-characterized genes, such as *slater* and *schnurri* (Nüsslein-Volhard *et al.*, 1984), appear to be required for differentiation of the dorsal epidermis and could be downstream targets of the initial patterning genes.

VI. Ventrolateral Regions: Neurogenic Ectoderm

The ventrolateral region of the cellular blastoderm makes up the neurogenic ectoderm, which gives rise to both the neuroblasts of the ventral nerve cord and the ventral epidermis. The precursors of these two cell types are intermingled in the neurogenic ectoderm. The neuroblasts separate individually from the epithelium and move into the interior of the embryo, while the cells remaining at the surface give rise to the epidermis. Neuroblast delamination occurs over a period of 3 hours after gastrulation, with neuroblasts arising in three dorsal–ventral regions within the neurogenic ectoderm (Hartenstein and Campos-Ortega, 1984). The cells at the ventral margin of the neurogenic ectoderm, which give rise to midline structures of the CNS, are specialized from early in development and may play a role in patterning the adjacent neurogenic ectoderm.

The size of the neurogenic ectoderm is, directly or indirectly, under the control of the maternal *dorsal* gradient (Campos-Ortega, 1983). No zygotic mutants have been identified that fail to make neurogenic ectoderm, so if *dorsal* activates specific genes that promote the development of the neurogenic ectoderm, these target genes have not been identified. However, it seems more likely that the neurogenic ectoderm is not directly defined by transcriptional regulation by *dorsal*. Instead, if *snail* and *twist* block neurogenic development in ventral cells and *dpp* represses neurogenic development dorsally, the neurogenic ectoderm would represent a default state of determination where neither *twist/snail* nor *dpp* products are active (Fig. 7).

The most obvious patterning event within the neurogenic ectoderm is the segregation of neuroblasts and epidermal cells. Two sets of genes are known to be involved in this process, the genes of the Achaete–scute complex, which respond to axial positional information, and the neurogenic genes, which are involved in local cell–cell interactions that do not directly involve dorsal–ventral positional information.

The best understood aspect of the partitioning of epidermal and neural cell fates is a local lateral inhibition process in which a neuroblast inhibits its neighbors from also entering a neurogenic pathway, leading the neighbors to follow an epidermal pathway (Knust and Campos-Ortega, 1989). This lateral inhibition requires the products of the neurogenic genes, including *Notch*, *Delta*, *Enhancer of split*, *big brain*, *mastermind*, and *neuralized*. In the absence of any one of these gene products, all cells in the neurogenic ectoderm follow a neural pathway of development (Lehmann *et al.*, 1983).

Despite their involvement in local cell–cell interactions rather than any obvious role in dorsal–ventral patterning, several of the neurogenic genes are transcribed in a dorsal–ventrally asymmetric pattern early in development. Zygotic transcripts of *Delta* and *big brain* are found at the cellular blastoderm stage throughout the ventral and dorsal ectodermal regions, but are excluded from the presumptive mesoderm (Vässin *et al.*, 1987; Kopczynski and Muskavitch, 1989; Rao *et al.*, 1990). Within the ectoderm the *Delta* transcript accumulates in a ventral-to-dorsal gradient, while four of the *Enhancer of split* transcripts are found at cellular blastoderm in the two or three cells immediately flanking the presumptive ventral furrow (Knust *et al.*, 1987). The ventral enrichment of *Delta* and *Enhancer of split* transcripts is paradoxical, since these genes are required to promote epidermal, rather than neural, fates, while ventral cells are more likely to become neuroblasts (Hartenstein and Campos-Ortega, 1984).

In addition to the neurogenic genes, which are required for epidermal development, genes of the Achaete–scute complex apparently act within the neurogenic ectoderm to promote neural development (Cabrera *et al.*, 1987). Within each segment neuroblasts arise at stereotyped anterior–posterior and dorsal–ventral

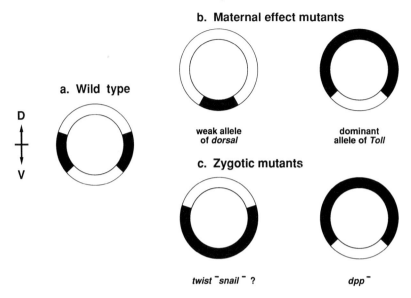

Fig. 7 The region giving rise to neurogenic ectoderm could be defined by either maternally active or zygotically active genes. (a) In the wild-type cellular blastoderm embryo, the cells lying at lateral positions are those that give rise to the neurogenic ectoderm (shaded). (b) Maternal effect mutations that shift the overall dorsal–ventral fate map cause cells at different positions in the blastoderm to give rise to neurogenic ectoderm (Campos-Ortega, 1983). Females homozygous for a weakly dorsalizing maternal effect mutant (dl^2) produce embryos that lack the most ventral pattern elements, and cells that sit in ventral positions give rise to neurogenic ectoderm. Females carrying a dominant ventralizing allele of *Toll* produce embryos that lack dorsal structures, and the neurogenic ectoderm is expanded in the fate map. Thus, it is possible that intermediate levels of maternal dorsal protein specify the boundaries of the neurogenic ectoderm. (c) Zygotic mutants can also change the boundaries of the neurogenic ectoderm. In embryos that lack *decapentaplegic* (*dpp*) activity the neurogenic ectoderm is expanded to encompass the dorsal side of the embryo (Irish and Gelbart, 1987). The ventral cells in embryos that lack *twist* and *snail* gene activities do not invaginate in the ventral furrow and do not give rise to mesoderm. Although the fate of those cells in the mutant embryos is not clear, they may be incorporated into the neurogenic ectoderm. If this were true, it would be possible to define the neurogenic ectoderm as those cells in which neither *twist* and *snail* nor *dpp* is expressed.

positions (Hartenstein and Campos-Ortega, 1984). During the period of neurogenesis, Achaete–scute transcripts are present in a complex anterior–posterior and dorsal–ventral pattern that generally correlates with the position of segregating neuroblasts (Cabrera *et al.*, 1987; Romani *et al.*, 1987). It has been proposed that the Achaete–scute products promote neurogenesis in a cluster of cells, and that, within a cluster, the pattern is refined to generate single neuroblasts by the action of the neurogenic genes (Cabrera *et al.*, 1987). In this model, transcription of the Achaete–scute genes would respond to some, as yet unidentified, dorsal–ventral as well as anterior–posterior positional cues.

The cells at the ventral margin of the neurogenic ectoderm, mitotic domain 14 (the mesectoderm) and mitotic domain M, form the ventral midline after the invagination of the mesoderm. These cells are specialized early in development, with respect to both their cellular behavior and the genes the cells express and require. Mutants lacking any of four zygotically active genes, *single-minded*, *spitz*, *Star*, and *rhomboid*, lack midline derivatives in both the nervous system and the ventral epidermis (Mayer and Nüsslein-Volhard, 1988). In the CNS the loss of midline structures is seen as decreases in the left-to-right spacing of the longitudinal connectives and of identified neuroblasts that express the *even-skipped* antigen. In the epidermis the paired Keilin's organs and the ventral black sensory dots are more closely spaced (left to right) than in wild-type embryos, indicating that the same kind of loss of midventral structures, with corresponding juxtaposition of left and right regions, takes place in the epidermis as in the CNS (Mayer and Nüsslein-Volhard, 1988). The parallel effects of these genes in the CNS and the epidermis suggest that they are required before neuroblasts delaminate from the neurogenic ectoderm.

Of this set *single-minded* mutations cause the largest deletions in the midline of both the CNS and the epidermis. In the CNS the left and right halves of the ventral nerve cord are immediately adjacent to one another, and the normal commissures are completely absent (hence, "*single-minded*") (Thomas *et al.*, 1988).

single-minded is expressed specifically in the mesectodermal cells from early in embryogenesis (Thomas *et al.*, 1988). The gene is first transcribed at the end of the cellular blastoderm stage in a single-cell-wide strip on each side of the embryo immediately flanking the presumptive mesoderm. When the ventral furrow closes, *single-minded* transcripts are found in a two-cell-wide strip. The cells then interdigitate to form a single-cell-wide strip that now occupies the ventral midline, the mesectodermal cells. When the germ band extends, the mesectodermal cells divide once and then come to have an unusual morphology, where the nuclei lie between the mesodermal and ectodermal layers, but the cells retain narrow projections to the surface of the ectoderm. Later, the mesectodermal cells give rise to a defined set of neurons, glia, and other nonneuronal CNS cells (Thomas *et al.*, 1988), and possibly to some epidermal cells (Mayer and Nüsslein-Volhard, 1988). The *single-minded* protein continues to be found in all of the mesectodermal cells until they differentiate, when it becomes restricted to the midline glial cells (Crews *et al.*, 1988).

In *single-minded* mutant embryos, the mesectodermal cells go through the normal postblastoderm mitosis and assume their normal morphology at the extended germ-band stage (Nambu *et al.*, 1990). The first abnormalities in *single-minded* mutant mesectodermal cells are seen when they begin differentiation into neurons and glia. Thus, although *single-minded* is expressed early in development, it is not necessary for the early behavior and morphogenesis of the mesectodermal cells. These results leave open the question of what genes control the early behavior and morphology of the mesectodermal cells.

Mutations in *spitz*, *Star*, or *rhomboid* cause a less extreme narrowing of the epidermis and the CNS (Mayer and Nüsslein-Volhard, 1988). In addition, the Keilin's organs, which derive from ventrolateral cells, are absent or abnormal in these three mutants, which suggests that *spitz*, *Star*, and *rhomboid* might be required in cells just lateral to those that require *single-minded* (Mayer and Nüsslein-Volhard, 1988). Like *single-minded*, *rhomboid* is expressed at the cellular blastoderm stage, where it is first seen bilaterally in a ventrolateral domain, seven or eight cells per side, corresponding to the ventral part of the neurogenic ectoderm (Bier *et al.*, 1990). Immediately thereafter, a strip of dorsal nuclei also begins accumulating *rhomboid* RNA. By the beginning of gastrulation, the ventrolateral *rhomboid* RNA has sharpened in distribution and is limited to the presumptive mesectoderm, the same cells that express *single-minded*. Expression of *rhomboid* persists in the mesectodermal cells until they differentiate.

Since *rhomboid* mutants seem to affect more lateral regions than *single-minded*, it was surprising to find that both genes are primarily transcribed in the mesectoderm. Later in embryogenesis, *rhomboid* is transcribed in a complex pattern, including in cells that could be the precursors of the Keilin's organs (Bier *et al.*, 1990). It is therefore possible that the cuticular defects in *rhomboid* mutants have a complex origin: The decrease in the left-to-right spacing of Keilin's organs and ventral black dots could be due to an early defect in the mesectodermal cells, while the abnormal Keilin's organs could be due to a later effect of *rhomboid*.

How can genes active in the mesectoderm affect the left-to-right spacing of pattern elements in both the CNS and the epidermis? If the mesectoderm contributes to both cell types (Mayer and Nüsslein-Volhard, 1988), then the answer is straightforward. If, however, mesectodermal cells contribute only to the CNS (Thomas *et al.*, 1988; Nambu *et al.*, 1990), then expression of *single-minded* and *rhomboid* in the mesectoderm is required for patterning in the adjacent ectoderm. The sequences of the *rhomboid* gene suggests that it encodes a membrane protein with several membrane-spanning domains (Bier *et al.*, 1990). This result makes it tempting to propose that *rhomboid* is involved in integrating the activity of the mesectoderm cells with the neighboring cells of the neurogenic ectoderm. Future studies on these genes should clarify whether the mesectodermal cells play a role in patterning in the neurogenic ectoderm.

VII. Questions for the Future

The analysis of mutant phenotypes and protein products of zygotically expressed genes required for dorsal–ventral pattern formation has made it clear that by studying patterning within each of the three primary subdivisions of the dorsal–ventral circumference, we can learn about a variety of fundamental problems in developmental biology. In the ventral, presumptive mesodermal, domain the target genes regulated by *twist* and *snail* should include direct regulators of early morphogenetic movements. Studies on the targets of *twist* and *snail* may provide a unique entry point into the regulation of morphogenesis. The data suggest that patterning in the dorsal part of the embryo relies on the extracellular activity of the *dpp* gene product. Studies on how the activity of *dpp* is controlled by other genes and on how *dpp* acts to elicit region specific responses should provide detailed insights into the regulation and function of this extracellular growth factor-like morphogen. Patterning in the neurogenic ectoderm involves a super-position of axial positional information and local cell–cell interactions, and it should be possible to study how these two kinds of information are integrated.

While the studies of the known zygotic genes have sketched the outlines of how dorsal–ventral embryonic pattern is specified, many experiments must be carried out before we can understand the underlying biochemical mechanisms. We know very little about the regulatory hierarchies involved in these processes. The experiments carried out to date examining this issue, like the studies of the regulation of *zen* expression, have shown how informative these data can be. We have postulated many possible molecular interactions among components, for which there are few, if any, molecular or biochemical data. It is also clear that many crucial components have yet to be identified. Genetic approaches have, to date, not identified the cytoskeletal and cell surface components necessary for early morphogenesis or receptor and other components of the signal transduction pathway for *dpp*. Hopefully, additional genetic and biochemical experiments will ultimately identify the missing components.

The exciting promise of the future is that we have the tools to answer these questions. These answers should allow us to understand several distinct pattern-forming processes and how these processes generate an integrated proportioned animal.

References

Anderson, K. V., and Nüsslein-Volhard, C. (1986). Dorsal-group genes of *Drosophila*. *In* "Gametogenesis and the Early Embryo" (J. Gall, ed.), pp. 177–194. Liss, New York.

Anderson, K. V., Jürgens, G., and Nüsslein-Volhard, C. (1985). Establishment of dorsal–ventral polarity in the *Drosophila* embryo: Genetic studies on the role of the *Toll* gene product. *Cell* **42**, 779–789.

Beer, J., Technau, G., and Campos-Ortega, J. A. (1987). Lineage analysis of transplanted individual cells in embryos of *Drosophila melanogaster*. IV. Commitment and proliferative capacities of mesodermal cells. *Wilhelm Roux's Arch. Dev. Biol.* **196**, 222–230.

Bier, E., Jan, L. Y., and Jan, Y. N. (1990). *rhomboid*, a gene required for dorsoventral axis establishment and peripheral nervous system development in *Drosophila melanogaster*. *Genes Dev.* **4**, 190–203.

Bock, E. (1941). Wechselbeziehungen zwischen den Keimblättern bei der Organbildung von Chrysopa perla. *Wilhelm Roux Arch. Entwicklungsmech.* **141**, 159–247.

Bogaert, T., Brown, N., and Wilcox, M. (1987). The *Drosophila* PS2 antigen is an invertebrate integrin that, like the fibronectin receptor, becomes localized at muscle attachments. *Cell* **51**, 929–940.

Boulay, J. L., Dennefeld, C., and Alberga, A. (1987). The *Drosophila* developmental gene *snail* encodes a protein with nucleic acid binding fingers. *Nature (London)* **330**, 395–398.

Cabrera, C. V., Martinez-Arias, A., and Bate, M. (1987). The expression of three members of the *achaete–scute* gene complex correlates with neuroblast segregation in *Drosophila*. *Cell* **50**, 425–433.

Campos-Ortega, J. A. (1983). Topological specificity of phenotype expression of neurogenic mutations in *Drosophila*. *Wilhelm Roux's Arch. Dev. Biol.* **192**, 317–326.

Crews, S. T., Thomas, J. B., and Goodman, C. S. (1988). The *Drosophila single-minded* gene encodes a nuclear protein with sequence similarity to the *per* gene product. *Cell* **52**, 143–151.

Doyle, H., Harding, K., Hoey, T., and Levine, M. (1986). Transcripts encoded by a homeobox gene are restricted to dorsal tissues of *Drosophila* embryos. *Nature (London)* **323**, 76–79.

Doyle, H., Kraut, R., and Levine, M. (1989). Spatial regulation of *zerknüllt*, a dorsal–ventral patterning gene in *Drosophila*. *Genes Dev.* **3**, 1518–1533.

Ferguson, E. L., and Anderson, K. V. (1991). Positive and negative regulation of the TGF-β family member, *decapentaplegic*, is necessary for dorsal–ventral pattern formation in the *Drosophila* embryo. Manuscript in preparation.

Foe, V. E. (1989). Mitotic domains reveal early commitment of cells in *Drosophila* embryos. *Development* **107**, 1–22.

Frohnhöfer, H. G. (1982). Diplomarbeit, Universität Tübingen, Tübingen, Germany.

Gelinas, C., and Temin, H. M. (1988). The v-*rel* oncogene encodes a cell-specific transcriptional activator of certain promoters. *Oncogene* **3**, 349–355.

Han, K., Levine, M. S., and Manley, J. L. (1989). Synergistic activation and repression of transcription by *Drosophila* homeobox proteins. *Cell* **56**, 573–583.

Hartenstein, V., and Campos-Ortega, J. A. (1984). Early neurogenesis in wild-type *Drosophila melanogaster*. *Wilhelm Roux's Arch. Dev. Biol.* **193**, 308–325.

Ip, Y. T., Kraut, R., Levine, M., and Rushlow, C. A. (1991). The *dorsal* morphogen is a sequence-specific DNA-binding protein that interacts with a long-range repression element in *Drosophila*. *Cell* **64**, 439–446.

Irish, V. F., and Gelbart, W. M. (1987). The *decapentaplegic* gene is required for dorsal–ventral patterning of the *Drosophila* embryo. *Genes Dev.* **1**, 868–879.

Jürgens, G., Wieschaus, E., Nüsslein-Volhard, C., and Kluding, H. (1984). Mutations affecting the pattern of the larval cuticle in *Drosophila melanogaster*. II. Zygotic loci on the third chromosome. *Wilhelm Roux's Arch. Dev. Biol.* **193**, 283–295.

Knust, E., and Campos-Ortega, J. A. (1989). The molecular genetics of early neurogenesis in *Drosophila melanogaster*. *BioEssays* **11**, 95–100.

Knust, E., Tietze, K., and Campos-Ortega, J. A. (1987). Molecular analysis of the neurogenic locus *Enhancer of split* of *Drosophila melanogaster*. *EMBO J.* **6**, 4113–4123.

Kopczynski, C. C., and Muskavitch, M. (1989). Complex spatio-temporal accumulation of alternative transcripts from the neurogenic gene *Delta* during *Drosophila* embryogenesis. *Development* **107**, 623–636.

Lehmann, R., Jimenez, F., Dietrich, U., and Campos-Ortega, J. A. (1983). On the phenotype and development of mutants of early neurogenesis in *Drosophila melanogaster*. *Wilhelm Roux's Arch. Dev. Biol.* **192**, 62–74.

Leptin, M., Bogaert, T., Lehmann, R., and Wilcox, M. (1989). The function of PS integrins during *Drosophila* embryogenesis. *Cell* **56**, 401–408.

Mayer, U., and Nüsslein-Volhard, C. (1988). A group of genes required for pattern formation in the ventral ectoderm of the *Drosophila* embryo. *Genes Dev.* **2**, 1496–1511.

Merrill, P. T., Sweeton, D., and Wieschaus, E. (1988). Requirements for autosomal gene activity during precellular stages of *Drosophila melanogaster*. *Development* **104**, 495–509.

Murre, C., McCaw, P. S., and Baltimore, D. (1989). A new DNA binding and dimerization motif in immunoglobulin enhancer binding, *daughterless*, *myoD* and *myc* proteins. *Cell* **56**, 777–783.

Nambu, J. R., Franks, R. G., Hong, S., and Crews, S. (1990). The *single-minded* gene of *Drosophila* is required for the expression of genes important for the development of CNS midline cells. *Cell,* **63,** 63–75.

Nüsslein-Volhard, C. (1979). Maternal effect mutations that alter the spatial coordinates of the embryos of *Drosophila melanogaster. Symp. Soc. Dev. Biol.* **37,** 195–211.

Nüsslein-Volhard, C., Wieschaus, E., and Kluding, H. (1984). Mutations affecting the pattern of the larval cuticle in *Drosophila melanogaster.* I. Zygotic loci on the second chromosome. *Wilhelm Roux's Arch. Dev. Biol.* **193,** 267–282.

Padgett, R. W., St. Johnston, R. D., and Gelbart, W. M. (1987). A transcript from a *Drosophila* pattern gene predicts a protein homologous to the transforming growth factor-β family. *Nature (London)* **325,** 81–84.

Rao, Y., Jan, L. Y., and Jan, Y. N. (1990). Similarity of the product of the *Drosophila* neurogenic gene *big brain* to transmembrane channel proteins. *Nature (London)* **345,** 163–167.

Roberts, A. B., and Sporn, M. B. (1988). Transforming growth factor β. *Adv. Cancer Res.* **51,** 107–145.

Roberts, A. B., Flanders, K. C., Heine, U. I., Jakowlew, S., Kondaiah, P., Kim, S. J., and Sporn, M. (1990). Transforming growth factor β: Multifunctional regulator of differentiation and development. *Philos. Trans. R. Soc. London, B* **327,** 145–154.

Romani, S., Campuzano, S., and Modolell, J. (1987). The achaete–scute complex is expressed in neurogenic regions of *Drosophila* embryos. *EMBO J.* **6,** 2085–2092.

Roth, S., Stein, D., and Nüsslein-Volhard, C. (1989). A gradient of nuclear localization of the *dorsal* protein determines dorsoventral pattern in the *Drosophila embryo. Cell* **59,** 1189–1202.

Rushlow, C., and Levine, M. (1990). Role of the *zerknüllt* gene in dorsal–ventral pattern formation in *Drosophila. Adv. Genet.* **27,** 277–307.

Rushlow, C., Doyle, H., Hoey, T., and Levine, M. (1987a). Molecular characterization of the *zerknüllt* region of the Antennapedia gene complex in *Drosophila. Genes Dev.* **1,** 1268–1279.

Rushlow, C., Frasch, J., Doyle, H., and Levine, M. (1987b). Maternal regulation of a homeobox gene controlling differentiation of dorsal tissues in *Drosophila. Nature (London)* **330,** 583–586.

Rushlow, C., Han, K., Manley, J. L., and Levine, M. (1989). The graded distribution of the *dorsal* morphogen is initiated by selective nuclear transport in *Drosophila. Cell* **59,** 1165–1177.

Schalet, A., Kernaghan, P., and Chovnick, A. (1964). Structural and phenotypic definition of the *rosy* cistron in *Drosophila melanogaster. Genetics* **50,** 1261–1268.

Schüpbach, T., and Wieschaus, E. (1989). Female sterile mutations on the second chromosome of *Drosophila melanogaster.* I. Maternal effect mutations. *Genetics* **121,** 101–117.

Shimell, M. J., Ferguson, E. L., Childs, S. R., and O'Connor, M. B. (1991). The *Drosophila* dorsal–ventral pattern gene *tolloid* is homologous to Human Bone Morphogenetic Protein-1. Manuscript in preparation.

Simpson, P. (1983). Maternal–zygotic interactions during formation of the dorsoventral pattern in *Drosophila* embryos. *Genetics* **105,** 615–632.

Smith, J. C., Price, B. M. J., van Nimmen, K., and Huylebroeck, D. (1990). Identification of a potent *Xenopus* mesoderm-inducing factor as a homologue of activin A. *Nature (London)* **345,** 729–731.

Spencer, F. A., Hoffman, F. M., and Gelbart, W. M. (1982). *decapentaplegic*: A gene complex affecting morphogenesis in *Drosophila melanogaster. Cell* **28,** 451–461.

Steward, R. (1987). *dorsal,* an embryonic polarity gene in *Drosophila,* is homologous to the vertebrate proto-oncogene, *c-rel. Science* **238,** 692–694.

Steward, R. (1989). Relocalization of the *dorsal* protein from the cytoplasm to the nucleus correlates with its function. *Cell* **59,** 1179–1188.

Steward, R., Zusman, S., Huang, L. H., and Schedl, P. (1988). The *dorsal* protein is distributed in a gradient in early *Drosophila* embryos. *Cell* **55**, 487–495.

St. Johnston, R. D., and Gelbart, W. M. (1987). *decapentaplegic* transcripts are localized along the dorsal–ventral axis of the *Drosophila* embryo. *EMBO J.* **6**, 2785–2791.

Tearle, R., and Nüsslein-Volhard, C. (1987). Tübingen mutants and stocklist. *Drosophila Info. Serv.* **66**, 209–269.

Technau, G. M., and Campos-Ortega, J. A. (1986). Lineage analysis of transplanted individual cells in embryos of *Drosophila melanogaster*. II. Commitment and proliferative capabilities of neural and epidermal cell progenitors. *Wilhelm Roux's Arch. Dev. Biol.* **195**, 445–454.

Technau, G. M., Becker, T., and Campos-Ortega, J. A. (1988). Reversible commitment of neural and epidermal progenitor cells during embryogenesis of *Drosophila melanogaster*. *Wilhelm Roux's Arch. Dev. Biol.* **197**, 413–418.

Thisse, B., El Messal, M., and Perrin-Schmitt, F. (1987a). The *twist* gene: Isolation of a *Drosophila* zygotic gene necessary for the establishment of the dorso-ventral pattern. *Nucleic Acids Res.* **15**, 3439–3453.

Thisse, B., Stoetzel, C., El Messal, M., and Perrin-Schmitt, F. (1987b). Genes of the *Drosophila* dorsal group control the specific expression of the zygotic gene *twist* in presumptive mesodermal cells. *Genes Dev.* **1**, 709–715.

Thisse, B., Stoetzel, C., Gorostiza-Thisse, C., and Perrin-Schmitt, F. (1988). Sequence of the *twist* gene and nuclear localization of its protein in endomesodermal cells of early *Drosophila* embryos. *EMBO J.* **7**, 2175–2183.

Thomas, J. B., Crews, S. T., and Goodman, C. S. (1988). Molecular genetics of the *single-minded* locus: A gene involved in the development of the *Drosophila* nervous system. *Cell* **52**, 133–141.

van den Eijnden-Van Raaij, A. J. M., van Zoelent, E. J. J., van Nimmen, K., Koster, C. H., Snoek, G. T., Durston, A. J., and Huylebroeck, D. (1990). Activin-like factor from a *Xenopus* laevis cell line responsible for mesoderm induction. *Nature (London)* **345**, 732–734.

Vässin, H., Bremer, K. A., Knust, E., and Campos-Ortega, J. A. (1987). The neurogenic gene *Delta* of *Drosophila* is expressed in neurogenic territories and encodes a putative transmembrane protein with EGF-like repeats. *EMBO J.* **6**, 3431–3440.

Wakimoto, B. T., Turner, F. R., and Kaufman, T. C. (1984). Defects in embryogenesis in mutants associated with the Antennapedia gene complex of *Drosophila melanogaster*. *Dev. Biol.* **102**, 147–172.

Wang, E. A., Rosen, V., Cordes, P., Hewick, R. M., Kriz, M. J., Luxenberg, D. P., Sibley, B. S., and Wozney, J. M. (1988). Purification and characterization of other distinct bone-inducing factors. *Proc. Natl. Acad. Sci. U.S.A.* **85**, 9484–9488.

Wieschaus, E., and Sweeton, D. (1988). Requirements for X-linked zygotic gene activity during cellularization of early *Drosophila* embryos. *Development* **104**, 483–493.

Wieschaus, E., Nüsslein-Volhard, C., and Jürgens, G. (1984). Mutations affecting the pattern of the larval cuticle in *Drosophila melanogaster*. III. Zygotic loci on the X-chromosome and fourth chromosome. *Wilhelm Roux's Arch. Dev. Biol.* **193**, 296–307.

Wozney, J. M., Rosen, V., Celeste, A. J., Mitsock, L. M., Whitters, M. J., Kriz, R. W., Hewick, R. M., and Wang, E. A. (1988). Novel regulators of bone formation: Molecular clones and activities. *Science* **242**, 1528–1534.

Zusman, S. B., and Wieschaus, E. (1985). Requirements for zygotic gene activity during gastrulation in *Drosophila melanogaster*. *Dev. Biol.* **111**, 359–371.

Zusman, S. B., Sweeton, D., and Wieschaus, E. (1988). *short gastrulation*, a mutation causing delays in stage-specific cell shape changes during gastrulation in *Drosophila melanogaster*. *Dev. Biol.* **129**, 417–427.

3

Inducing Factors and the Mechanism of Body Pattern Formation in Vertebrate Embryos

Jonathan Cooke
Laboratory of Embryogenesis
National Institute for Medical Research
Mill Hill, London NW7 1AA, England

I. General Introduction

Several complete and scholarly reviews have recently dealt with mesoderm induction and mesoderm-inducing factors in early amphibian development (Smith, 1989; Dawid *et al.*, 1990; Whitman and Melton, 1989). In addition to treating evidence for their normal roles in morphogenesis, these reviews also discuss, and

Current Topics in Developmental Biology, Vol. 25
45

refer readers to literature on, the molecular biology of the relevant families of growth factor peptides and their genes. This chapter makes no claims to completeness of reference to the literature. Instead, it discusses how what we currently know of the cellular responses to these candidates for early morphogenetic signals may match our experimental knowledge of how the beginning of vertebrate development is organized. The accent is on the biology and the logic of development.

A. Gene Products Involved in Early Steps of Vertebrate Patterning

Drosophila is now the complex metazoan embryo whose mechanism is the most understood at the molecular level, and yet knowledge of the precise network of interactions between genes that brings about controlled patterns of cell states lags behind the listing and characterization of the relevant genes themselves. It is clear, however, that prominent among the maternally supplied gene products and first-transcribed genes whose direct interactions regionalize the *Drosophila* blastoderm are those encoding specific DNA-binding proteins of certain classes that exert their effects as "switches" directly at the cell nucleus (Scott and Carroll, 1987; Akam, 1987; Ingham, 1988; Nüsslein-Volhard and Roth, 1989). A network of such genes, whose intracellular products control gene activity, can only control development of a large-scale pattern if, as in the insect blastoderm, the tissue is a syncytium. The evidence is that, after true cellularization, further steps in maintenance and elaboration of the emerging pattern involve genes whose products alter the states of neighboring or more distant cells by projecting from the output cell's surface or by being secreted to activate specific transmembrane signal receptors (Martinez-Arias *et al.*, 1988; Rijsewijk *et al.*, 1987).

The entirety of pattern formation in the general form of vertebrate embryogenesis, and most of it even in the specially rapid version displayed by amphibians such as *Xenopus* (see Section I,B), occurs within truly cellularized tissue. Much of the time the cells concerned are meanwhile displaying energetic locomotory behavior as sheets or cell streams. It is therefore expected that the DNA binding classes of gene products play broadly equivalent roles as components of positional memory, within the established axial pattern in insect and vertebrate embryos, but that earlier steps in generating the vertebrate axial plan are achieved by specific secreted intercellular signals which change the state (including gene activity) in responding cells. Even gap-junctional communication via small molecular signals, while it may play a role in coordinating activity among cells responding to major steps in morphogenetic signaling (Warner, 1986), appears not to be involved in these steps themselves (Warner and Gurdon, 1987).

B. *Xenopus*, an Advantageous but Specialized Experimental Model in Relation to Vertebrate Development Generally

Xenopus, the clawed frog, has rightly become a major experimental model for those seeking to understand vertebrate development. It is robust and regularly available as large batches of synchronously developing embryos amenable to microsurgical and other procedures, as well as to potential functional interference experiments by microinjection of genes and gene products. Its strategy of rapid early development from a giant cell with little or no growth is an experimental advantage, but also a liability in a model from which to generalize to universal vertebrate mechanisms.

The advantage is that, in such a development, an important subset of the earliest-involved gene products with which we are concerned must be present in appreciable quantities (within grams of egg!) as prestored message and/or protein (Kimelman *et al.*, 1988; Tannahill and Melton, 1989). In the true embryo-forming regions of the higher vertebrate (amniote) "blastodisc," these steps are almost certainly part of a controlled program of new gene expression, with the relative inaccessibility of the embryo adding to the difficulties of visualizing directly, or of interfering with, such a program. The liability is that *Xenopus* shows in extreme form—although it probably shares with most other amphibians—a structural mechanism for establishing a reference point for pattern formation at the outset, quite unlike that used in blastodisc-style vertebrate development.

This important early step effectively imprints a map of presumptive fates on the material or tissue that is to form the embryo, probably by arranging the orientation about a particular meridian of a simple bilaterally symmetrical pattern for the origin of particular intercellular signals (see Section I,C). In this way the hitherto radial symmetry is broken. In *Xenopus*-style development this future axial midline is established as a rather direct consequence of spontaneous structural reorganization in the recently fertilized egg (i.e., within a single giant cell). In the blastodisk-style vertebrate, however, a particular region within the tissue acquires midline pattern-organizing status only as the result of more prolonged interactions. These involve unknown cellular physiology and intercellular signals and are probably triggered by small circumstantial asymmetries in the environment (Eyal-Giladi, 1984; Smith, 1985).

From this point, however, we have no reason to believe that the steps in development and the signals involved differ among vertebrates in any more profound way than in geometrical layout and tissue movements—although positive evidence for their identity is not strong. It is also questionable which version of the initiation of body pattern is primitive to the vertebrate subphylum and which is novel. In either case elucidation of the cell biology, whereby a region finally comes to dominate surrounding tissue and initiate induction of the body axis within a blastodisclike structure, must be undertaken in an embryo (e.g., an amniote, or perhaps a teleost fish) with that style of development.

C. Brief Background to Concepts: Induction, Inducers, Morphogens, Pattern Formation, and Regulation

Proper definition, or delimitation, of what experimental embryologists have meant when speaking of "induction" is now so contentious that, like "gene," the word will probably best serve the scientific community if reserved for use when it is irrelevant or positively undesirable to choose various more precise terms. Thus, 30 years ago interactions in which cells at one location caused an instructive change of specification (Slack, 1983) in other cells were all referred to as inductive events, whether cells responding to signal were elsewhere within the same cell layer (Nieuwkoop, 1969) or, as in classically studied events (reviewed by Spemann, 1938), in a separate layer overlying the signaling ones.

In reaction to this, Wolpert (1971) pointed out that development could hardly be well controlled unless influences between cells in the plane of each layer, and those from one layer to a juxtaposed one, involved different mechanisms and signals. Those of the first type were to be considered the mechanism of true pattern formation. The term "induction" could be reserved for the latter type, which effectively allowed the primary pattern of regions established in one cell layer to control the establishment of a set of different, but coordinated, contributions in the other, as in the regionalization of the neural plate following gastrulation. The necessity for the mechanistic distinction remains as obvious as the advantages of being multilayered, but the indiscriminate use of "induction" for all instructive signaling events in development has won the day.

Ironically, the steps in vertebrate development with which this chapter deals are all, essentially, instructions mediating regionalization *within* a cell layer (the blastular wall or the newly involuted mesoderm)—that is, pattern formation— but must be referred to as the primary inductive events. The proteins that simulate them *in vitro* and are strong candidates for their *in vivo* agents are known as "mesoderm-inducing," but, better, just as "inducing" factors (see Section II).

Morphogens (Türing, 1952) are normally defined as the hypothetical chemical agents of pattern formation within a tissue, and in most theory as to the dynamics that lead to spatial patterns of diverse cell states (Wolpert, 1971; Gierer and Meinhardt, 1972), they function as signals whose level, rather than mere presence or absence, is instructive; cells are led to choose between states of specification on the basis of reasonably fine discrimination as to signal concentration. In other words a pattern organized by morphogens, in contrast to one built up by a cascade of successive but simple inductive events, ends up displaying considerably more cell states (or specified regions) than the number of intercellular signal species used in generating it. This apparently arcane distinction is now highly relevant, as seen in Section III,A, in that certain defined inducing signals may or may not function as morphogens *sensu stricto*.

The concept of regulation in the mechanism of embryo formation derives from the observation that the completeness of the body plan, and normal proportions of tissue allocations to regions within it, are buffered against normal variations in conditions attending development. There is also a largely normal performance of the proportioning mechanism after experimental alteration in the extent of tissue where pattern is forming, or where a new second body pattern is instituted in an embryo by a grafting operation. In an era in which the listing of molecular components of the developmental machine is in progress, scant attention is understandably paid to these sophistications of the engineering of pattern formation.

Understanding of the arrangements that bring about quantitative regulation is ultimately essential to an understanding of morphogenesis, nonetheless. In terms of instructive signals spreading within a cell sheet, it is obvious that a sequence of inductions (or a single inducer acting as a morphogen gradient) without any feedback principle is incapable of regulating pattern completeness and proportions against individual embryo size. More concretely, for example, in particularly small amphibian blastulae why is only a normal proportion of animal hemisphere tissue specified as mesoderm by vegetally arising inducers, and only a normal proportion of *this* later converted to dorsal-axial (DA) pattern parts by the organizer (Cooke and Webber, 1985a; Cooke, 1989a)? In Section III,A we see that data on tissue response to known inducers *in vitro* already suggest feedback mechanisms that could regulate pattern formation *in vivo*, although validating these and identifying the other required signals will be challenging indeed.

II. Experimental Embryological Studies

A. Evidence for Early Steps in Regionalization of the Amphibian Embryo

In *Xenopus* and other frogs generally the egg is prestructured to have an animal–vegetal axis that orientates it in gravity, but is otherwise radially symmetrical. This symmetry is broken, to orientate the use of the egg's material in ultimately forming a bilateral body plan, by rotation through some 30° of an outer (~1 μm thick) shell of its cellular structure on the inner core. The rotation is a timed spontaneous part of the schedule of events within the first cell cycle that are initiated by sperm entry/egg activation. It occurs in a plane, including animal and vegetal poles, that is weakly related to the point of sperm penetration, but which itself strongly determines the future plane of pattern symmetry; the dorsal axis forms where vegetal egg cortex has slid furthest upward away from its originally underlying yolky cytoplasm (Vincent *et al.*, 1986; Vincent and

Gerhart, 1987). The process is almost certainly actomyosin driven and micro-tubule organized (Elinson and Rowning, 1988). It controls subsequent development mainly by influencing the character of inductive signals from positions around the vegetal hemisphere as the egg divides to give a 10^2- to 10^4-cell blastula (Gimlich and Gerhart, 1984; Gimlich, 1986).

However, the biochemical steps of this transduction from structural reorganization to specific signal release are quite obscure. The timing of primary inductive signaling, mostly before onset of zygotic transcription, implies that RNA or stored inactive protein precursor for inducers will be within vegetal egg structure. Information on the shifting of dorsal centers or their multiplication, by abnormal application of G force or other means, during various parts of the one-cell stage (Black and Gerhart, 1985, 1986; Scharf et al., 1989), makes the hypothesis of a bulk resituating of specific gene products most unlikely. A potential for the synthesis or deployment of active DA-inducing molecules (see Section II,B) probably exists all around the vegetal zone, but is realized only in the limited sector of greatest rotation in the sense defined above. The undisturbed mechanism is regulative in that the appropriate *relative* extent of DA sector, believed to subtend 45–60°, is set up regardless of egg size. No egg entering the blastula stage with an inappropriately wide or restricted DA sector (see Fig. 1) or more than one such sector can use any regulative mechanism to restore formation of a balanced body pattern (Scharf and Gerhart, 1983; Cooke, 1986; Scharf et al., 1989).

The large yolky urodele amphibian egg is believed to use a similarly "structural" early mechanism of initiating axial pattern, set in motion by fertilization, but not orientated in relation to a plane of sperm entry. It is also unclear whether the DA sector is as absolutely marked off and different in character from the remainder as in the frog egg, or whether stereotypic extent and intensity of such a sector are also required for normal development. Certainly, it is this step in typical amphibian development which can have no direct equivalent in that of higher vertebrates. The higher vertebrates must arrange the first simple patterning of their systems of intercellular inductive signals in other ways.

Knowledge of the next steps in regionalization begins with studies by Nieuwkoop and colleagues (Nieuwkoop, 1969; Sudarwati and Nieuwkoop, 1971; reviewed by Nieuwkoop, 1973) which have more recently been extended in various informative ways (Dale et al., 1985; Dale and Slack, 1987a; Gimlich, 1986; Gurdon et al., 1985; Gurdon and Fairman, 1986). Development of the pattern of structures derived from the animal hemisphere is controlled by the yolky vegetal region of the blastula. This pattern includes the axial and other mesoderm, the pharyngeal and other endoderm having a true structural—as opposed to nutritional—contribution to the body, and the appropriately positioned neural plate. Thus, intercellular signals, emerging from around those blastular regions which, in lineage terms, are largely without contribution to the definitive embryo, respecify up to 50% of the descendants of the remaining more

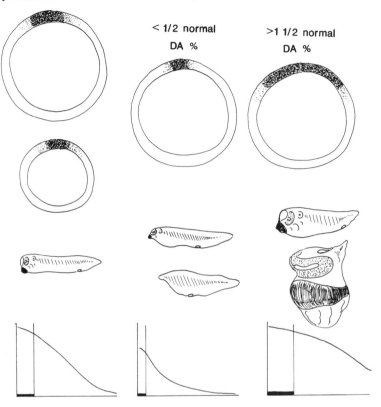

Fig. 1 The nonregulative nature of the earliest patterning events in the frog egg. The left-hand column depicts the normal events of egg symmetrization during the first cell cycle, leading finally to a properly proportional complete larval pattern (second row). The top row shows how the egg re-organization events lead to similarly proportioned major and minor sectors for future inductive events in eggs of all normal sizes. The sectors are seen in plan view from the poles of the egg, and probably reside in subsurface regions. The bottom row depicts a gradient profile that might come from subsequent morphogen interaction between normally proportional dorsal-axial (DA, source) and ventrolateral (VL, sink) mesodermal sectors. In the middle and right-hand columns are shown the morphogenetic consequences of abnormally small or abnormally large DA sectors, respectively, with their possible interpretations in terms of the mesodermal signaling systems. Such imbalances, caused by experimental perturbations during the one-cell stage or surgical recombinations at the late blastula stage, cannot be compensated for by a regulatory system in *Xenopus*.

animal cells away from their "default program" of epidermal differentiation. This occurs in a patterned orientated way, giving rise to the outline plan of the body. The first direct signals specify states leading to endoderm and mesoderm at the marginal zone. Since mesoderm cell types are ultimately those most recognizable in the animal pole/vegetal pole recombinates *in vitro* that demonstrate the existence of this step, it acquired the inaccurate name "mesoderm induction."

Figure 2a depicts schematically the cellular arrangements in the blastula early on, during the time when primary induction *in vivo* is believed to be occurring. "Animal cap" tissue is competent to respond to vegetal induction *in vivo* (as well as to defined factors *in vitro*; see Section II,B) from about the 64-cell stage to the beginning of normal gastrulation, a period of several hours. Thus, although a simple view would be that the natural signals extend only very few cell diameters from the source and operate in the early blastula, a more realistic view is probably that the process is more extended in time, and that signal also penetrates across greater numbers of more advanced, thus older, cells. It might do this by pure diffusion (with attenuation) in the restricted intercellular space, or because of active propagation, whereby recently signaled cells themselves emit signal (classically called "homoiogenetic induction"). Fate mapping by *in situ* lineage labeling (Cooke and Webber, 1985b; Dale and Slack, 1987b) and estimates of the time span across which continued exposure to defined inducers modulates the final response (Cooke et al., 1987; Green et al., 1990) suggest that recruitment of the right proportion of cells into induced states, and achievement of the degree of spatial organization present as gastrulation begins, take much of the blastular period.

Following the more recent clarification of the nature of the initial egg symmetrization i.e., that it set the character of inductive signals around the meridians of the future blastula, it was unclear for a while whether this inductive system was continuously, qualitatively or quantitatively graded, or whether it consisted of sharply different major and minor adjoining sectors (Cooke and Webber, 1985b; Gimlich and Gerhart, 1984). It is now recognized that, for almost the whole time up to the onset of gastrulation, in *Xenopus* at least, the latter is the case (Dale and Slack, 1987a; Stewart and Gerhart, 1990), but, once again, we do not know whether the situation for the equivalent first-induced states in amniote development is similar or is more one of gradation and more regulative.

In *Xenopus* signals arising from most of the vegetal zone specify a state in the overlying tissue that leads, by itself, to formation of ventrolateral (VL)-type mesoderm (i.e., blood, mesothelium, and mesenchyme), with only occasional small amounts of unorganized muscle. The mechanical forces, thus deformations, produced by mesodermal tissue of this type during normal gastrulation are small and transient, resembling the contribution to gastrulation made by only the ventral sector in the normal whole embryo. In the minor ($\sim60°$) sector of the blastula, centered on the dorsal midline as established by the precleavage rotation (see above), the vegetal inductive activity has superimposed on it a different DA character. This specifies a cell state leading autonomously to production of the anterior and dorsal midline contributions to the normal body, that is, axial and pharyngeal endoderm, prechordal and notochord tissue, and segmenting somite. Such tissue, in turn, induces abundant neural tissue in any overlying ectoderm, whereas neural induction is not seen to be associated with isolated VL inductions made by vegetal pole/animal pole blastomere combinations. As a prelude to these differentiations, DA-induced tissue performs energetic force-producing cell

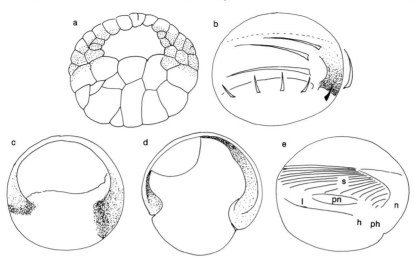

Fig. 2 Induction, gastrulation, and the body plan in frog development. (a) Longitudinal section of an early (125-cell) blastula, with the approximate region normally recruited into induced mesendodermal states shown by stippling. It is meaningful to show portions of blastomeres in different zones at this stage because in the marginal zone subsequent cell division during the period of induction cuts off deep from more superficial cleavage products, and these acquire mesodermal specifications and retain ectodermal ones, respectively. Vegetally, a tier of yolky blastomeres contributes to both extraembryonic nutritive yolk cells and definitive endodermal and mesodermal lineages. Involvement of outer surface in induced (endodermal) structure is much greater on the dorsal (right-hand) side. (b) The three-signal class of model for stepwise diversification, with the surface view orientated as in (a). The short arrowheads represent vegetally arising primary inductions of the two sorts (signals 1 and 2), while the long arrowheads represent further geographical organizations, within the shaded DA sector or between DA- and VL-induced sectors by agency of signals 3, before and during gastrulation. (c and d) Beginning and later stages of gastrulation, with sections orientated as in (a). Density of shading indicates preorganization within the mesoderm, in relation to the time of involution and the presumptive body position, which refines itself as gastrulation proceeds. (e) Fate map to show normal deployment of material from pregastrula stages into the axial pattern, with the surface view orientated as in (b). By comparing (e) with (b), and recalling that only the DA-induced sector spontaneously extends and segments when explanted from the beginning gastrula, the extent of recruitment of originally VL tissue into more posterior DA structure by signal 3 events can be appreciated. Territories: n, notochord; pn, pronephros; l, lateral mesoderm; h, heart; ph, pharyngeal mesendoderm; s, somite segments, with slanting lines depicting the way in which material from around the meridians of the early gastrula is known to find its way into successive segments, from anterior (short strips at right) to posterior (longer higher-positioned strips) in the body plan. Notochord also has an anterior (low and midline) to posterior (higher and more lateral) preorganization in this fate map. Thus, the future tailbud (see Section IV,B) is a broad high marginal zone sector at early stages.

rearrangements—convergent extension (Keller *et al.*, 1985; Keller, 1986)—which characterize the dorsal midline and neighboring sectors during intact gastrulation.

Only as gastrulation time approaches is there any evidence, deduced from careful surgical recombination experiments (Stewart and Gerhart, 1990), that a spontaneous capacity to develop non-VL structures has invaded outward from the original DA-inductive sector in normal development. This rather limited spread could reflect an inductive effect of DA vegetal-inducing cells on neighboring vegetal cells, altering the latter's signaling capacity, or the onset of signaling (inductions) *within* the recently induced zone, whereby DA-induced cells are "dorsalizing" (Smith and Slack, 1983) hitherto VL-induced ones. Certainly, from the onset of gastrulation, an episode of the latter sort of *intra*mesodermal signaling assumes major importance.

This graded respecification of much of the VL tissue sector in relation to proximity of the DA sector, which emits dorsalizing signals, is a major determinant of the axial body plan. There is also self-organization, particularly of the DA sector, into a gradation of states that presages the head-to-tail sequence of mesoderm after gastrulation (Cooke, 1985a,b, 1989b,c) and is crucial in organizing this. Dorsalization, as a large-scale organizing interaction around the gastrula, has been amenable to experimentation (Slack and Forman, 1980; Smith and Slack, 1983), while the more local head-to-tail self-organization within dorsal tissue, which is mainly related to the height of the cells in the blastula wall above the original vegetal-inducing source, has not. Signaling for dorsalization must largely occur after the period of competence by animal cells to respond to the first two inductive signals has ended, and while mesoderm cells are performing gastrulation. It is thus a logically distinct step in spatial diversification, even if the signal(s) whereby DA respecifies formerly VL-induced tissue were to prove molecularly identical to the previous vegetal signals that induced the DA sector in the marginal zone. The reverse interaction, a capacity of VL tissue to "ventralize" DA, does not occur (Cooke and Webber, 1985a; Slack and Forman, 1980). Because of this, production of a complete balanced body sequence in the whole embryo depends on the copresence of VL tissue and one sector of DA tissue, within a reasonably critical range of proportions, at the onset of gastrulation (Cooke, 1985b, 1986; Kao and Elinson, 1988; Stewart and Gerhart, 1990).

B. "Three-Signal" Class of Model and Its Extensions: Origins of Anteroposterior Axial Sequence

Figure 2b represents the scheme suggested by the experimentally revealed sequence of steps discussed in Section II,A. It has been proposed and called the three-signal model by Slack and colleagues (e.g., Dale and Slack, 1987a) and best represents our formal knowledge to date. One set of observations in particular speaks strongly in favor of the idea that there are two qualitatively distinct zones of induction that normally interact, as in the model, and against the notion of a single inductive signal quantitatively concentrated to give dorsal character on one side. These concern the "ultraviolet (UV) embryo," in which the physical reorganizations before the first cleavage have been effectively prevented by prior UV irradiation of the vegetal hemisphere (Vincent *et al.*, 1986). The general cell biology of such embryos can be undisturbed, so that rather normal cleavage occurs, followed by a radially symmetrical set of gastrulation movements having entirely the character of those at the ventral sector of the normal embryo (Scharf and Gerhart, 1980, 1983). These embryos, at "control" larval ages, have an essentially normal amount of mesodermal tissue, even though it is of entirely VL character (Cooke and Smith, 1987). They lack entirely a DA zone of induced mesoderm, however, so that no interaction—thus, large-scale axial patterning—can occur. The removal, or quantitative leveling, of an asymmetrical peak of one inductive signal would not produce such a result. In fact, lineage labeling studies suggest that initially *more* mesoderm, rather than less, is induced ventrolaterally than dorsally, and that the massive final participation of originally ventral mesoderm in the posterior–dorsal axis (Fig. 2e) is entirely caused by late signaling from the latter to the former.

However, in order to account fully for the axial patterning that has occurred by the "official" close of gastrulation in the early neurula stage, the three-signal model requires some supplementation. This need arises mainly from the evidence that an organization *within* mesoderm sectors (see long arrowheads in Fig. 2b), leading to the anteroposterior sequence of position values that sets the character of various derivatives, is underway before the involution of gastrulation commences. Progressive organization in the sequence of mesoderm movement and progress during gastrulation itself are indicated in Fig. 2c and d (Cooke and Webber, 1985b; Keller *et al.*, 1985; Keller, 1976; Kanéda, 1981; Cooke, 1989b). This regionalization is firmly in place by the time this tissue has finished its gastrulation movements (Kieny *et al.*, 1972; Deuchar and Burgess, 1967).

Some principle of spatial organization must operate during the recruitment of cells by at least DA-type induction in the marginal zone, or perhaps during their aggregation there from more scattered origins or in the course of their multiplication during or after induction. This principle must utilize the fact that signal is originating at one edge, the vegetal and future anterior edge, of the field. We know this because, in vertebrates, there is a close reciprocal causal relationship between the cell movements of gastrulation and the elaboration of axial pattern, a relationship which is not evident in, say, *Drosophila* development.

At the level of gross shape and cell rearrangement, the tissue that is to form the mesodermal mantle undergoes massive reorganization as its cells involute (Keller *et al.*, 1985), to change layers and migrate. However, a variety of experimentation shows that the organized time course of gastrulation consists of the successive active participation of cell groups over hours, cell groups which are already in different states, implying ultimate participation in successive parts of the axial plan. At gastrulation itself the induced, but yet uninvoluted, cells are already ranked in relation to position within the marginal zone. Individual embryos whose abnormalities in pregastrular phases have prevented specification of complete body patterns invariably show gastrulation with an incomplete time course; it starts late or ends early. By this normal mechanism, appropriate ordering of already somewhat regionalized tissue is assured immediately after gastrulation. Such early refinements within at least one of the major induced sectors must accompany the basic operation of the three-signal scheme.

The third signaling system of the model, while called dorsalization, is really better described by saying that as gastrulation proceeds, the elongating and converging DA sector progressively recruits adjoining mesoderm into making more and more contribution to the lateral parts of the somite at more posterior levels of axial pattern. There is a great difference, at the late blastula stage, between the simple map describing current specified states in the marginal zone (Fig. 2b) and the fate map for the axial body plan (Fig. 2e). This is due to self-organization within DA, and to the third signal system acting mainly across the meridians of the embryo from dorsal to what is conventionally, but inaccurately, called "ventral" (Keller, 1976; Cooke and Webber, 1985b). The original DA-induced sector may indeed be more restricted, and shorter in the animal-to-vegetal dimension than suggested in Fig. 2b, in which case all of the refinements of specification that make up the fate map are best thought of as due to operation of signal 3 interactions.

Experimentally, this system of interaction between the initial sectors behaves rather as expected for a simple source/sink-controlled gradient in a signal acting as a morphogen, with DA and VL tissue being the uniform source and the (passive) sink, respectively. Thus, as shown in Fig. 1, if too little or too much DA is present in relation to VL, only partial sectors of the normal fate map become specified, as if the range of gradient levels had been restricted, even though proper polarity and coherence of pattern is retained (Stewart and Gerhart, 1990; Scharf and Gerhart, 1983; Cooke, 1986; Sharf et al., 1989). Such partial patterns are observable in vertebrate development of all types, and may entirely lack one or more tissue types seen in the complete body. In other words the signal 3 source cells are not necessarily restricted in differentiation to the tissues they normally contribute to the complete plan. From this we must conclude that although the DA-inducing signal could, in part, function as a morphogen (see Section I,C), its primary role is to specify a cell state which acts as the source for signal(s) 3 of the model. The sequence of tissue types and anteroposterior axial levels result more directly from levels of this subsequent signal.

C. New Evidence on Origins of the Nervous System

Evidence that alters our view of the foundation of the nervous system has recently come along, and must be mentioned here because it may make this pattern element a part of the primary results of inducing signals. In most writing since the time of Hilde Mangold's classic experiments (Spemann and Mangold, 1924), the positioning and overall patterning of the neural plate have been assumed to result from a set of specifically neural-inducing stimuli, acting on competent ectoderm from the DA mesoderm that had migrated beneath.

There is still no doubt that the progressive submigration of this mesoderm, and its own regionalization, are major contributors to neural pattern. However, the presumed neural area on the dorsal side of the embryo is now known to have acquired bias toward neural development ahead of gastrulation or in its absence (Kintner and Melton, 1987; Sharpe *et al.*, 1987; London *et al.*, 1988). This may be because the initial dorsalizing events of the one-cell stage, not completely restricted in their effects to vegetal egg regions, have directly set up such a bias from the outset. More probably, it is because signals traveling tangentially within the blastula wall, and extending beyond the conventionally recognized limits of DA-type induction, function to set up such a preneuralized region (Savage and Phillips, 1989; Dixon and Kintner, 1989; Ruiz i Altaba, 1990).

The detailed structural studies by Keller (1986) reveal a cell group lying animalward of the upper limit of mesodermized tissue in the wall of the beginning gastrula, whose cellular anatomy already differs from that of general ectoderm, although no axial invaginating tissue has yet reached it. Thus, in examining the credentials of proteins put forward as candidate mesoderm-inducing factors, we may actually be looking for agents that mediate the first regionalizations in all three definitive layers of the vertebrate body during one episode of induction.

III. Growth Factor-Related Proteins: Candidates for the Required Component Signals in the Mechanism

A. DA Inducers: Activin Subfamily

Certain members of the activin family of the transforming growth factor β (TGF-β) group of proteins are the only currently identified molecules able to induce the DA state, leading to axial mesodermal and pharyngeal endodermal differentiations preceded by characteristic shape change (convergent extension), when used to treat blastular animal cap tissue *in vitro*. They do this when used as the sole purified protein added to the simple salt culture medium at few nanograms per milliliter (Smith *et al.*, 1988). Activins are dimers, usually homodimers, of very highly conserved (A or B) versions of the β chain, which is, in turn, a component of the α–β heterodimer inhibin. The chains (16 kDa) are thought to be secreted after cleaving at a specific position from a larger original translation product. Positions of cysteines within the secreted product are totally conserved, suggesting their importance to the effective structure.

The factor first purified from a *Xenopus* tissue culture cell line (XTC-MIF) (Smith, 1987), is now known to be either *Xenopus* activin A or an extremely close congener of it (rather than any other named TGF-β superfamily member) (Smith *et al.*, 1990). The closely similar bone morphogenic protein 2 (BMP-2, mammalian origin) is also reported to be a DA inducer *in vitro* in *Xenopus*, while sequences diagnostic of activin and BMP are reported to be present in the RNA of eggs and early embryos. Veg-1, a closely related coding sequence which is not only present in eggs but actively localized to a vegetal subcortical site during oogenesis and translated (Yisraeli and Melton, 1988; Tannahill and Melton, 1989; Dale *et al.*, 1989), is not yet certified to induce the DA state either alone or as an adjunct factor. XTC-MIF is as potent a DA inducer in the axolotl, a distant amphibian species, as in *Xenopus* (Cooke, 1989c), while conversely, but even more strikingly, the inducer WEHI-MIF (Godsave *et al.*, 1988) from murine cells, now believed to be mouse activin A, is indistinguishable from the *Xenopus* molecule in its effects on *Xenopus* (Albano *et al.*, 1990) and also avian blastoderm cells (Cooke and Wong, 1991).

In their other identified roles, at disparate points in the life cycle, the A and B forms of activin seem indistinguishable, but both are specifically and competitively antagonized by the related inhibin protein. These roles are in control of follicle-stimulating hormone secretion from the pituitary gland and in control of terminal erythroid differentiation as well (Vale *et al.*, 1986; Eto *et al.*, 1987). Interestingly, preliminary evidence is that antagonism by inhibin is *not* involved in the case of primary induction, although we will see that there is circumstantial evidence that this cellular response is indeed subject to feedback control at the tissue level. The identification of receptors generally for the TGF-β superfamily and elucidation of their mechanisms of signal transduction are not well advanced (although the latter may not involve protein tyrosine kinase activity). Appropriate receptors have therefore not been identified at relevant positions in the embryo to date, but the proteins act in induction only if supplied as extracellular protein, or intracellularly injected RNA (Cooke *et al.*, 1987).

The XTC-MIF molecule has properties that vary quantitatively in an interesting way according to whether it is applied to freshly excised animal pole tissue explants or to single cells prepared from these explants followed by washing and aggregation. In either case, though, cells are competent to respond from around the 64-cell stage until somewhat after onset of the normal gastrulation schedule, that is, until a time when *in vivo*-induced cells would already be commencing novel behavior as their first overt response (Smith, 1987; Cooke and Smith, 1989). With adequate (i.e., picomolar) concentrations exposure on the order of 10 minutes followed by washing is sufficient, and this can be given well before the expected onset of competence for a transcriptional response, which occurs at midblastula transition some 7–8 hours after fertilization.

This strongly suggests that the response can be recorded, at some level of the mechanism lying between occupancy of receptors and novel RNA synthesis, for some time and through cell cycles. Particularly at the lower inducing concentrations (i.e., few nanograms per milliliter), the level of response (see below) seems to be set by concentration × time exposed. This may help account for the axial patterning of mesodermal tissue types made by animal caps *in vitro*, which progressively round up to occlude the responsive blastocoelic cell membranes from further free inducer during the hour after explantation. It also may be a part of the mechanism of specification of different tissue types *in vivo* (e.g., head versus notochord versus somite muscle), in that normal *in vivo* induction is from a restricted source at one (vegetal) edge of the responding tissue.

Although the outermost original egg cell membrane itself cannot mediate a response (Cooke *et al.*, 1987), cells that inherit this but also acquire newly synthesized membrane and remain in the outer animal cell layer are responsive to this class of inducer. Cells of this origin often participate in axial mesoderm tissue of *in vitro*-induced animal caps. Consistently with this, the pharyngeal and dorsal axial endoderm (Sudarwati and Nieuwkoop, 1971), thought to be specified as part of this DA-inductive zone *in vivo*, originates from the surface cell sheet of the marginal zone (as, indeed, do many mesoderm cells of urodele amphibians). Another major class of inducer (see Section III,B) is apparently unable to act on *Xenopus* outer layer cells.

The responses observed in tissue treated as in animal cap explants will now be contrasted with those seen following treatment of single cells and their reaggregation. Explants exposed to more than a few nanograms per milliliter of XTC-MIF characteristically perform energetic convergent extension movements that are powered by an internal cell population at control gastrulation times (see Keller *et al.*, 1985), followed by differentiation of an axial mass of mesoderm and often a core of immunocytochemically identifiable endoderm (E. Jones and H. Woodland, personal communication). Such mesoderm contains considerable masses of segmenting somite, and often a notochord mass. Notochord tends to occur at the higher concentrations within the 4–10 ng/ml range, but this tendency is too ill defined to term a "threshold." At concentrations of only one or a few times the minimal inducing level (which is perhaps 0.2 ng/ml for *Xenopus* blastular cells) only mild elongation and the differentiation of nonaxial, mesenchymal, or mesothelial inner tissues are seen. As inducing concentrations rise above the 20 ng (100+ U)/ml range, on the other hand, increasing incidence of a third type of outcome is seen, where the inner tissues are not elongated (except sometimes very briefly and extremely, during gastrulation) and are, in fact, a less massive part of the whole, resembling the head mesendodermal structures of whole embryos, which also do not undergo elongation during development.

At all levels of response at which either axial or these supraaxial anterior mesendodermal types are formed, a domain of the remaining ectoderm is induced to neural development whose character corresponds with the general level of body structure represented in the underlying tissues. It is noteworthy that at this whole-tissue level of response the proportion of cells recruited into mesendodermal pathways of development can never be more than 40–50%, and does *not* increase, once low threshold (i.e., few units per milliliter) responses have been passed, even though a systematic tendency to production of first more dorsal and then more anterior (prechordal) character in the responding cells is seen over a broad range, progressing up to perhaps a multiple of 300 over threshold (Smith *et al.*, 1988).

If single-cell suspensions of blastula animal cap are treated for approximately 1 hour with inducing concentrations of XTC-MIF, followed by careful washing and prompt restoration of calcium and magnesium ions, reaggregates are produced in which we can assume that nearly all cells have undergone the initial phases of rather similar levels of response to the factor. This is especially so as imunocytochemical and behavioral studies on such cell suspensions which have not been allowed to reaggregate (Symes *et al.*, 1988) show that essentially all of the cells make the initial response, diverting from the default ectodermal pathway of development, as individuals. Any inherent differences of responsiveness among animal cap cells should be randomized spatially in such aggregates, especially as the original surface layer cells (see above) are specifically omitted from them.

The convergent extension movement within the aggregates at control gastrulation times is, in fact, much less organized and intense than that of intact treated tissue. This could be for some combination of three reasons. Normal globally organized movements could require—indeed, be an expression of—a systematic spatial array of cells which has achieved graded levels of inductive response, an array which is achieved *in vivo* or in whole tissue treated *in vitro*, but not in reaggregates. The movements may require a normal relationship between two components, a surface cell type and a deeper-lying cell type (see, e.g., Keller *et al.*, 1985), which is absent in reaggregates. Finally, treatment of single cells with even low concentrations of the factor may somehow elevate their level of specification to that characteristic of anterior mesendodermal tissue which does not organize such movements.

The final response levels of differentiation seen after the reaggregation procedure are strikingly different from those of whole treated tissue. As shown by RNase protection assay for muscle-specific actin and for a transcript, specific to neural tissue, successive thresholds for tissue types are passed across a narrow range of applied factor concentrations, entirely near the low end of the extended one across which progressive change can be seen in whole-tissue response (Green and Smith, 1990). Thus, with rising numbers of units-per-milliliter (Cooke *et al.*, 1987) inducing activity seen by the single cells, reaggregates successively switch on muscle and notochord formation, switch off these differentiations, and switch on instead a pathway of differentiation which is itself a very strong neural inducer for further ectodermal cells; that is, by implication it is anterior or prechordal mesoderm. The spatial organization within reaggregates is most interesting. Muscle, produced over only a two- or threefold range of concentrations on the order of 5 low-threshold U/ml, occurs as small isolated groups of cells, each characteristically accompanied by a group of notochord cells. A factor concentration range between two thresholds, in which either muscle or notochord differentiation is produced without the other, is difficult to find.

More work must be done in which animal cap material from the same batches of embryos is carefully exposed to particular concentrations of the inducing factor, either as single cells followed by washing and reaggregation or as intact tissue prevented by low divalent cation concentrations from rounding up during exposure, then carefully washed. It already seems hard to account for the differences in response level, however, in terms of access by factor to the cell membranes in single cells versus intact animal caps. Young blastula tissue is only one or two cell layers thick, and intercellular spaces are prominent early in the culture period, whereas the very wide range of factor concentrations over which animal caps finally form muscle and notochord lies almost or entirely above the upper threshold for production of these tissues in reaggregates. It seems more likely that when the response occurs in a whole tissue from the start, feedback signals occur as part of a cascade that diversifies the response to allow large-scale pattern formation, even including epidermis differentiation. These secondary controlling signals are partly bypassed through treatment of disaggregated cells (see also Symes et al., 1988).

An additional indication that the intact inductive system incorporates negative regulatory signals is the even more elevated concentration of the factor required to cause ectopic mesoderm that differentiates as muscle, when factor is injected into the blastocoel cavities of whole embryos to mesodermize the animal pole region (Cooke and Smith, 1989). It is as if the whole embryo, in which induction is, after all, already proceeding, has deployed signals that dampen the response but which are partly bypassed in in vitro isolated cap tissue, and absent when early response phases occur in isolated cells.

It is apparent at this point that there are several experimental indications that concentration of the factor might act instructively in specifying the character of tissue produced, that it might act as a classically proposed morphogen (see Section I,C). This seems especially likely as regards the histotypic differentiations of the mesoderm—the dorsal to ventral series in the body. Because the thresholds are elevated (i.e., responsiveness is depressed) in later blastula aged tissue, the time in development at which signal is received at each position could also be an in vivo principal underlying patterning. We believe currently that a morphogen principal indeed may apply as regards the patterning into the tissue-type differentiations, but that neither this nor timing of induction is likely to be the main mechanism for axial organization in the embryo. Further evidence is discussed in Section III,C.

B. Inducers Apparently Specifying Nonaxial Body Regions: Heparin-Binding and TGF-β Subfamilies

Other effective inducing factors in the Xenopus assay are members of the heparin-binding or fibroblast growth factor (FGF) family (Slack et al., 1987; Kimelman et al., 1988; Godsave et al., 1988; Paterno et al., 1989) and the true TGF-β subfamily within the same superfamily as the activinlike proteins. The

TGF-βs are effective either on their own or as adjunct factors which in some way potentiate the action of FGF-like factors ((Rosa *et al.*, 1988; Kimelman and Kirschner, 1987). It seems that all of these factors and factor combinations induce mesoderm having a general character corresponding to the natural VL sector of *Xenopus* mesoderm as isolated at onset of gastrulation, although more muscle than is normal may be obtainable in the *in vitro* induction. Objective comparison of the results seen in different laboratories with the various factors and their combinations is difficult, mainly because some scientists attach great importance to morphology as indicating the positional character of tissue in early development (e.g., Cooke *et al.*, 1987; Smith *et al.*, 1988; Green *et al.*, 1990), whereas others are more concerned with histologically revealed cell type or even molecular probing for specific gene products (Rosa, 1989; Rosa *et al.*, 1988). Nevertheless, we have not seen evidence that use of the above factors and factor combinations more than occasionally produces the DA vigorously convergently extending induced tissue regularly seen with activinlike molecules. One rather surprising problem of characterization is that the same peptide chain, cloned and expressed in different ways, or perhaps from different sources within a species, may have different levels of activity (Paterno *et al.*, 1989). This could represent the effects of slightly different RNA splicing patterns—thus, sequence—or patterns of secondary modification (e.g., glycosylation) that are important to steric function.

To date acidic and basic FGF (αFGF, bFGF), embryonal carcinoma-derived growth factor (an incompletely characterized member of the family), and the Kaposi sarcoma-derived oncogene (kFGF) have been found to be similarly active *in vitro*. At least the last molecule is distinguished from αFGF and bFGF in possessing a bona fide secretion pathway targeting sequence in the definitive molecule. The *int-2* protooncogene product is weakly but appreciably active, and is more distantly related in sequence to the heparin-binding growth factors. Of the TGF-β molecules TGF-β_1 is reported as active in conjunction with an FGF molecule only, while TGF-β_2 and TGF-β_3 are each reportedly active alone. A molecule with strong homology to mammalian bFGF has been cloned from *Xenopus* and its RNA is present in the oocyte, while the protein is present at plausible concentration in the early embryo, although its *in vivo* localization has not been ascertained (Kimelman *et al.*, 1988). Receptors for FGFs are well characterized, and such high-affinity receptors for αFGF or bFGF indeed are present at times of competence for induction in the *Xenopus* blastula (Gillespie *et al.*, 1989).

The lack of evidence that bFGF is a conventionally secreted protein may not be of concern, since mechanisms of secretion are not understood entirely. Alternatively, a relative having such a mechanism for secretion may, in fact, be the *in vivo* active molecule and have the required avidity for the receptors that have been found. That such may be the case is also indicated by a failure of specific precipitating antibodies to bFGF to prevent passage of the natural VL-inducing signal from vegetal to animal pole cells in transfilter combinations *in vitro*, even though heparin sequesters this signal and prevents induction in the same system (J. M. W. Slack, personal communication).

The more extensive work with FGF and the documentation of appropriate transcripts, protein, and even receptors in the embryo have perhaps diverted attention from the possibility that a TGF-β-like signal molecule is, in fact, the *in vivo* inducer of the more widespread VL-type mesendodermal state in the early gastrula. The veg-1 protein (Yisraeli and Melton, 1988; Tannahill and Melton, 1989; Dale *et al.*, 1989) appears to be an example of an appropriately distributed molecule, and it could also be that the *in vivo* VL inducer works as an adjunct factor with an omnipresent FGF-type signal (Kimelman and Kirschner, 1987; see also Section III,C).

The fully active bFGF cloned from *Xenopus* is only a "weaker" inducer than XTC-MIF (activin A?) if the narrow criterion of quantitation of somite muscle differentiation is adopted. As with the activin subfamily, exposure of animal pole tissue to low picomolar concentrations for fractions of 1 hour is an adequate inductive stimulus, although, unlike XTC-MIF, FGFs do not seem to induce outer-layer cells to participate in mesodermal structure. Appreciable muscle actin RNA transcription is only induced at concentrations on the order of 100-fold the minimal inducing one in intact cap tissue, and is always much less than that present in convergently extending explants such as are produced by XTC-MIF at, say, 20-fold its low-threshold dose. Histologically, the muscle produced rarely spontaneously segments if induction is by pure FGF, and such segmentation as is seen is of small cell groups reminiscent of the normal tailbud. Neural induction in the remaining ectoderm is equally rarely seen, and much of the mesoderm produced is mesenchymal and mesothelial.

The two classes of inducer are most clearly distinct as regards the morphogenetic movements at time of gastrulation, and the final differentiated morphology, of treated animal cap explants. bFGF inductions make only minimal deformations in the hours of gastrulation, and finally differentiate as balloons of stretched normal skin (i.e., epidermis underlain by dermis) over fluid-filled cavities with webs of mesenchyme, mesothelium, and disorganized muscle fibers. In particular the healed site of the original explant edges is usually ruptured by the convergently extending inner mass in DA inductions. In FGF inductions it becomes, instead, the site of a nipple-shaped pore over an inner crater, lined with tissue of endodermal character, but surrounded by tissue resembling the hematopoietic zone in the normal belly midline. This site, in fact, corresponds with a radially symmetrical version of the normal proctodeum, where the primitive gut exits at the real site of the blastopore closure under the tailbud. The mesendodermal inductions characterizing actions of heparin-binding growth factors (and perhaps TGF-βs), on the one hand, and activins, on the other, may thus represent, respectively, ventral/posterior and (in a dose-dependent way) dorsal/anterior zones of body structure. Section III,C deals with proposals as to how enough positional information, for deployment of position-specific gene activity in a stable axial pattern, may be built up by intercellular signaling from such a simple two-part beginning.

C. Proposals for Mapping Experimentally Defined Classes of Inducer Signal onto the Natural Mechanism

A straightforward way in which the findings concerning classes of *in vitro* effective inducers might fit with experimental embryological data (Section II,A) is via the three-signal model (Fig. 2b), with signal molecules of the two classes being, respectively, the vegetally arising inducers of the DA and VL marginal zone sectors. The early egg rotation events might be seen as superimposing the capacity for DA signaling on a universal capacity for VL signaling that can develop all around the blastula, and this could mean that the real *in vivo* DA signal is effective only as an adjunct to the VL one. However, it is noteworthy that the only, and highly effective, purified inducers of the DA state, the activins, are effective alone and dominate the inductive character of any *in vitro* cocktail (Cooke, 1989c). The VL signaling capacity therefore probably becomes redundant in the DA sector. An alternative concept is that the *in vitro* properties of FGFs are somewhat misleading as to real mechanisms, because an FGF ligand–receptor system is ubiquitous in the induction-competent zone (i.e., animal hemisphere), where it functions in an autocrine or paracrine way, but only if one of the genuinely instructive signals, acting at a distance, turns it on.

However, the logical necessity for two initial inducing signals initially from sharply demarcated zones, remains because of the results of the blastular recombination experiments (Dale and Slack, 1987a; Stewart and Gerhart, 1990) and the mesoderm-filled, but radially symmetrical, UV embryo (Cooke and Smith, 1987). The third signal system mediating the creation of a graded series of specifications or body plan from the initial two-zone partitioning has no current molecular candidates, unless the same molecular mechanism should mediate dorsalization (Slack and Forman, 1980; Smith and Slack, 1983) during gastrulation as mediated DA marginal zone specification during blastula phases. This is not an illogical scenario, since development proceeds by steps of specification; animal cap cells that are still ectodermal by the gastrula stage are no longer competent to respond to signal events 1 or 2, so the same signal species are free to have new functions (e.g., the signaling of state 2 cells to their neighbors of state 1 in a dorsalization process). Such a real arrangement could still correctly be described by a three-signal model, where for "signal" read "signaling step."

The need to refine the three-signal model by postulating self-organization within the initial marginal zone sectors, as well as setting up signal gradient systems by interaction between them, has already been mentioned (Section II,B). This need is first seen if we consider the autonomous timing of cell behavior change at different locations in the induced zones during gastrulation. For each of the two functional classes of pure *in vitro* inducer, tissue makes this change (i.e., altered interaction with fibronectin and with other cells) at a particular "age" since fertilization of the egg, corresponding with a particular stage in the precisely orchestrated process of normal gastrulation. This is best seen by watching the behavior of ectopic mesoderm induced in blastocoel roofs after injection of the respective factors (e.g., Cooke and Smith, 1989). That induced by activins acts as if involuting near—although not at—the very beginning of gastrulation, when the first DA convergently extending mesoderm follows the prechordal mesoderm into the involution sequence. That induced by FGF makes its equivalent, although distinctive, involution changes at the onset of normal ventral involution considerably later. These times are separated by more than 1 hour with the schedule of *Xenopus* development, and 3 hours in the larger and slower gastrula of the frog *Rana* (J. Cooke, unpublished results). However, in the normal course of gastrulation, we have seen that tissue within both major zones makes its involution in a sequence or queue over some hours, in relation to position relative to the initial blastopore lip and expected position in a head-to-tail body sequence. This sequence is closely related to future body pattern and is the first expression of the spatial organization leading to that pattern. Furthermore, involution activity spreads smoothly across both initial sectors as well as within each one, showing that, already during gastrulation, spatial organization has proceeded by interaction between the sectors as well as within them.

What is the nature of this preorganization, leading toward axial pattern? Experiments in which the times and the concentrations at which responding cells have received the inducer signals are varied across a wide range have revealed that these two variables are not, in any simple way, those causing the preorganization. When the free signal is presented to the cell sheet in a spatially uniform way, the position value (i.e., the involution time specified) is characteristic and fixed within the gastrulation period in the case of each factor, but independent of prior timing or concentration of the signal (Cooke and Smith, 1989). It can be seen from Fig. 2a and b that either signal concentration or the ages at which cells first receive signal could be variables correlated with distance away from sources in the vegetal hemisphere, and thus be directly read to create the marginal zone preorganization seen. These features indeed may be utilized, but apparently not in such a simple way. Instead, they trigger a more dynamic self-organization.

That DA-type mesoderm at least has an autonomous tendency for self-organization is evident in the later outcomes of development after intrablastocoelic injection of inducer (see above). The area of ectopically induced mesoderm in the original blastocoel roof typically gives rise to imperfect, but very significantly organized, axial formations by larval stages, although, at original induction (homologous to signal 2 of Fig. 2b), the field of tissue must have been almost homogeneously stimulated in space and time. In the normal situation such progressive organization is reliable and predictable in orientation because of the origin of activation from one (i.e., vegetal) edge of a field. Gierer and Meinhardt (1972; see also Meinhardt, 1982), among others, have developed dynamic models whereby propagated inductive events, or simple cascades of such events involving activation and then negative or modulating signals, lead stably to spatial gradations of cell state within a sheet. It seems likely that the first origins of axial patterning, within and across the major induced sectors of the blastula and the gastrula, are of this nature. It is therefore interesting that, for example, TGF-β production in some systems is known to be autocatalytic (Van Obberghen-Schilling et al., 1988).

Potentially conflicting information concerning the relative roles of FGF and activin classes of inducer in axial patterning has come from experiments which assess those factors in simulating the classic dorsal lip, or organizer graft, that leads to twinned body pattern in amphibians. Cooke (1989c) found that small panels of animal pole tissue from donors that had been subinjected with activin (XTC-MIF) were effective grafts in causing second axial organizations, when integrated into the ventral marginal zones of similar-aged hosts near the onset of gastrulation. Donor tissue reached maximal organizer potential within 1 hour of receiving the inducer in the injected donor, and the most nearly complete second patterns were seen after making small (i.e., ~30° of arc around the blastula) grafts that had seen a high (i.e., 500+ inducing units per milliliter) factor concentration.

Although the grafts organized an extensive new series of anteroposterior-axial structures, the factor-stimulated implanted cells themselves made only a restricted contribution at the anterior end of the pattern. In this they contrast with most "natural" dorsal lip grafts (Fig. 3). When the same procedure was followed, but with FGF as the inducing agent, no evidence was seen of disturbance to the host's single axial pattern, and graft-derived mesoderm integrated into those regions of body structure that might result from receipt of signal 1, or signal 1 and then 3, in the three-signal schema of Fig. 2b.

This is all consistent with the idea that FGF and XTC-MIF replicate, respectively, the VL and DA primary signals, that VL is a baseline nonaxial-induced state, and that body pattern is elaborated in anteroposterior and dorsal–ventral aspects by a self-organizing propensity within DA tissue (which is better advanced in natural dorsal lip than in induced blastocoel roof). A third signaling system would then act like a simple source/sink-controlled gradient from the restricted DA territory across the more extensive VL tissue (see Fig. 1).

In another study along similar lines, but using a different operating procedure (Ruiz i Altaba and Melton, 1989a), FGF-stimulated implants were found to organize accessory tail axial formations, whereas XTC-MIF-stimulated ones caused new structure that included head parts as well (i.e., potentially complete patterns). Ruiz i Altaba and Melton concluded that an in vivo principal of coding for the first stage of anteroposterior organization might be the relative degrees of stimulation, in induced marginal zone tissue, via the XTC-MIF (i.e., activin) and FGF pathways, with principally FGF stimulation encoding the DA but posterior

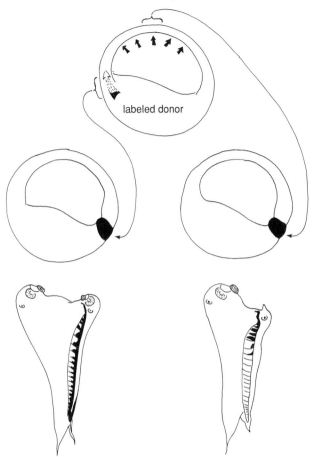

Fig. 3 Ectopically activin-induced animal pole tissue and natural dorsal blastoporal lip compared as "organizers." In (separate) lineage-labeled donor embryos (top), the animal pole region may be homogeneously and synchronously induced by blastocoelic XTC-MIF injection (small black arrows), whereas the natural dorsal lip region has been subject to *in vivo* DA induction from one (vegetal) edge and is already somewhat spatially organized (arrow within marginal zone). Perhaps related to this are their appreciably different lineage contributions to new body patterns when grafted to host blastula ventral marginal zones, and the inferior capacity of the experimentally induced tissue to organize a craniocaudally complete new pattern. Note in the latter case (right) the presence of organized second posterior somite rows, even though these are not contributed to by the tissue which evoked them.

(i.e., tail) position. This view, in simple form, runs into the large problem that the general VL or baseline nonaxial-induced state remains unaccounted for by any known factors, whereas the general properties of FGF-induced tissue (Section III,B) are as required for such a state. The UV embryo, with its extensive mesoderm, must be thought of as a radially symmetrical axisless, or "belly" structure, not as a tail. Very high concentrations of FGF, possibly artifactually high, were used in this study. On the other hand, those segmental formations that are seen rarely in animal pole tissue induced with FGF *in vitro* are tailbud-like. Only future molecular studies that identify the inducers, their distributions, and effective concentrations available *in vivo*, and which ascertain what states of specification these can give rise to *in vitro*, will complete our understanding.

It is probable that the natural mechanism first establishes sharply demarcated zones of reliably different character by deployment of more than one inducer, the inducing species being present at effective concentrations where the programs of activity within cells, which they initiate, do not overlap without subsequent interactions. Thus, the cell differentiations and morphogenesis caused in animal caps by FGF and XTC-MIF at, say, 5 ng/ml concentration are qualitatively different. Abundant somite differentiation can occur within such originally FGF-stimulated tissue, but only if it is subsequently joined to XTC-stimulated tissue from which it must receive some further signal (J. B. A. Green and J. Cooke, unpublished observations). XTC-stimulated tissue joined to previously uninduced but competent tissue produces quite a different region of body structure, with little somite, but massive cement gland and forebrain induction.

This all corresponds with what would be expected from a direct mapping of these classes of inductive signal onto the three-signal arrangement. However, the different specified states caused by initial action of signals 1 and 2 do not require that, at the signal transduction level, they utilize entirely different pathways of second message production, etc. Distortion of the responsiveness of competent tissue during induction by lithium treatment, via an unknown effect, but one possibly involving the scavenging pathway of the inositol/lipid signal transduction mechanisms (Busa and Gimlich, 1989), can obliterate the clear differences seen with the inducer classes *in vitro* (Slack *et al.*, 1988; Cooke *et al.*, 1989). There are corresponding catastrophic effects on the capacity to specify full body pattern *in vivo* (Kao and Elinson, 1988; Cooke and Smith, 1988). This suggests that some—perhaps not all—onward transduction pathways are shared by the receptor mechanisms of the different inducers in the normal mechanism. It remains unclear whether true TGF-βs, which are related in steric structure to activins, produce VL specification because they interact at low efficiency with activin receptors or because they have their own receptor and pathways involved in normal *in vivo* induction of VL sector.

IV. Stable Axial Patterning Closely Follows Primary Induction

A. Early Deployment of Position-Specific but Intracellularly Acting Genes

There is now much evidence that specific DNA-binding proteins of homeobox-containing and zinc finger classes are involved in the recording of axial position, as opposed to the setting of differentiation pathway, for cell groups in the early embryo of vertebrates. Such proteins belong to family groupings homologous to some of the genes in *Drosophila* whose functions in pattern establishment are better understood. In some cases molecular conservation appears to be accompanied by a similar function within the process of segmental patterning, as in the mammalian *Hox2* and the *Drosophila antennapedia/bithorax* complex (Graham *et al.*, 1989; Wilkinson *et al.*, 1989). In other cases no such detailed conservation of roles seems to obtain beyond the involvement in early axial patterning per se. Some of these genes are first transcribed early in mesoderm formation, during gastrulation, although it is currently impossible to say whether their patterns of synthesis remain unchanged in lineage terms while the mesodermal tissue moves into place, or whether these evolve and are refined as time goes on. It is plausible to suggest that certain of these gene products embody, in their spatial patterns, the earliest downstream expression of the preorganization for axial morphogenesis that is brought about by the intercellular inductive signals themselves. Certainly, axial mesoderm tissue that has involuted, but not yet differentiated or segmented, at each point in the time sequence of gastrulation is already quite stably imbued with axial position values (Kieny *et al.*, 1972; Deuchar and Burgess, 1967).

A role of homeobox- and zinc finger-encoding genes at this level is further suggested by recent reports of examples which are either immediate early-response genes to the process of induction *in vitro* (*Mix.1*, Rosa, 1989), responding less than 1 hour after exposure to signal, or at least early participants in the process of response (*Xhox3*, Ruiz i Altaba and Melton, 1989a; *xsna*, Sargent and Bennett, 1990). *xsna* (a homolog of *Drosophila snail*) and *Xhox3* are synthesized during gastrulation and in response to induction. *Mix.1* responds to activin or DA-type induction, but essentially not to VL-inducing factors. Interestingly, *Xhox3* responds with differential intensity to FGF (high) and XTC-MIF (lower) and is spatially graded in expression from posterior to anterior within axial mesoderm *in vivo* in a way that appears linked to positional specification (Ruiz i Altaba and Melton, 1989b,c).

B. Possible Morphogen Role for Retinoic Acid

A conceptual problem has always been that, whereas at the earliest phase of axis formation the dorsal blastoporal lip tissue, specified to give rise to the anterior extreme, obviously has the organizing role (Spemann and Mangold, 1924; Cooke, 1972), the site of the tailbud then develops an organizing capacity (Cooke, 1975) as if it were similar to the "progress zone" that lays down new pattern values in the distal outgrowth of the limb (Summerbell *et al.*, 1973). In the early fate map the site of tail formation, where it can be defined at all, as in the amphibian case, is simply the site of the farthest upward extent, from the vegetal origin, of mesodermal induction in the DA marginal zone (Fig. 1e). It gathers toward it further VL-specified tissue during the movements of gastrulation, and at some point acquires the property of autonomously specifying tail axial pattern when grafted, acting as an organizer of its surroundings in this way just as the dorsal lip did for the axial pattern as a whole at the onset of gastrulation.

It has been shown that retinoic acid, present exogenously at the time of gastrulation, modifies and reduces the anterior axial pattern in all body layers of amphibian (Durston *et al.*, 1989; Sive *et al.*, 1990) and bird embryos (J. Cooke, unpublished observations). The precise way in which this happens is consistent with the notion that endogenous retinoic acid functions as a morphogen, somehow becoming distributed in posteroanteriorly declining gradient fashion during the process of gastrulation, with a high point in posterior structure. Fascinating in this connection is the coordinate and graded retinoic acid inducibility within certain clusters of homeobox-containing genes, recorded in mammal cells *in vitro* and in whole *Xenopus* embryos (Papalopulu *et al.*, 1990; Simeone *et al.*, 1990). Studies of retinoic acid in relation to the effects of the protein inducing factors should be pursued, as it may form a link in the causal sequence lying between whatever organization can be directly achieved by those factors and the subsequent first activation of position-specific genes.

V. Higher (Amniote) Vertebrates

A. Early Steps in Bird Development

Our strongest inferences as to the arrangements and dynamics of axis formation in mammalian development must come from experiments on the bird blastoderm (reviewed by Eyal-Giladi, 1984; Stern and Canning, 1988), which is probably similarly organized, once allowance has been made for the extraembryonic accessory structure which must develop in the mammal. It may be that already, at a very early stage in such embryos, the epiblast layer (i.e., mammalian primitive ectoderm) consists of an intricate mosaic of cells with specific tendencies to participate in each of the three definitive body layers (Stern and Canning, 1990). If so, this probably indicates that inductive events have already occurred, in part, and that a source of the specifying signals, the primary hypoblast, underlies the entire epiblast. Since even this hypoblast [as well as even earlier-emerging populations of cells (Kochav *et al.*, 1980)] has emerged from the blastoderm by polyinvagination, we are faced with a problem in understanding the generation of cell diversity without a clear principle of geographically segregated signal sources and responsive cells, as in *Xenopus*.

The subsequent process of axis formation probably involves the events more closely related to DA induction in *Xenopus*. A special sort of hypoblast forms at an eccentric location, and this induces the primitive streak, by specifying axial-type mesendoderm in overlying epiblast; by causing aggregation of already induced cells to this site within the epiblast, along with effecting a further respecification in such cells (cp. dorsalization; signal 3 in the amphibian model); or by a combination of these processes. The special substreak hypoblast itself may result from an inductive step, or may be directly constructed of cells in which a spontaneous change has occurred at one site in the blastoderm (Eyal-Giladi, 1984; Stern, 1990).

It is this localized first change or inductive signal that sets the meridian about which bilateral symmetry and axis formation occur. It is set up by gradual development, in a system of physiological dominance that eventually leads to stable establishment of one center and suppression of the capacity to form it elsewhere. In exhibiting such dynamics, where environmental gradients or asymmetries are amplified until special cell states exist at one location, the amniote blastoderm resembles such primitive developmental systems as regenerating hydroids or cellular slime mold aggregation fields. This contrasts maximally with amphibian eggs, in which early mechanochemical reorganization in the single cell somehow sets up the inductive sectors in a permanent way. Once symmetrization has occurred, however, the subsequent chain of intercellular signals may be a conserved one, as between all vertebrate types during the late blastula and gastrula stages.

B. Amphibian and Bird: Evidence for Involvement of Homologous Molecules in Related Steps of Specification

We do not have a clear view of the homology of the geographical parts of the very early inductive system, as between the different vertebrate embryo types, although these become clearer in the more advanced stages of gastrulation because of the behavior and contributions of the mesoderm in the streak. In particular, because all of the vegetal yolky cells of conventional amphibian embryos are taken into the interior during gastrulation, we do not know whether there are domains within that general region which are produced by induction, but which are equivalent to parts of the amniote hypoblast that never participate (in lineage terms) in the embryo itself. Given that we expect a conservation of the fundamental mechanism of early development within vertebrates, it may be more useful at this stage to ask whether there is a conserved array of instructive intercellular signals than to look for detailed anatomical correspondences in what is specified by each such signal. In this spirit tests have been made to determine whether particular growth factor family members, of amphibian or mammalian origin, act as inducers or respecifiers of avian blastoderm cells (Cooke and Wong, 1991). These tests have been of three types. First, we have asked whether treatment of epiblast for 3–4 hours *in vitro* causes its cells to flatten and spread on fibronectin, since cells remaining ectodermal do not do this, whereas streak and substreak hypoblast cells of gastrulating embryos do. Second, we have asked whether such treatment of epiblast cells gives them altered properties when they are layered, to sit as does newly ingressed tissue at gastrulation, as a cell suspension onto a host's basal epiblast surface. Are chimeras formed, and, if so, is the donor cells' contribution within them affected by prior factor treatment? Third, we have preincubated whole blastoderms in very low concentrations of candidate inducing factors before setting them up to develop in an *in vitro* culture system (New, 1955) that normally permits advanced axial development.

bFGF, TGF-β_2, and activin A, or a close relative as purified from amphibian or mammalian sources (i.e., XTC-MIF, Smith *et al.*, 1990; WEHI-MIF, Albano *et al.*, 1990), have all been tested and on all three criteria cause massive respecification of epiblast from prestreak ages. Platelet-derived growth factor, which was originally negative in tests for inductive activity in *Xenopus* (Slack *et al.*, 1987), is also negative in the bird system. Differences in the state specified by different families or subfamilies of the effective signals do not emerge clearly in this study, although Mitrani and Shimoni (1990) have reported that XTC-MIF, but not FGF, restores significant axial development to a partial bird blastoderm culture, an observation consistent with a homologous role for this signal in amphibian and avian development (see Cooke and Smith, 1989, for blastocoelic injection of XTC-MIF).

VI. Postscript

During much of the present century, the feeling reigned that early development was a phase in the life of the organism when a unique mechanism was in play, whose study was an autonomous discipline even though embryo cells had mitotic cycles, locomotory apparatus, metabolism, etc., much like those in later stages of the life cycle. For the present at least, with the discoveries of the last decade and especially the past 5 years, this feeling has evaporated, along with the concepts of embryonic fields, chreodes, epigenetic landscapes, and canalization (Waddington, 1956). Developmental biology currently appears to be just the study of the cell biological events occurring in early embryos (see also Wolpert, 1990). The intercellular signals involved, and their receptors and transducing mechanisms, as well as the molecular components of the control of gene activity, offer no evidence of being different from those operating in the organism generally.

One aspect of cellular activity does remain, however, as being possibly distinctive to early embryonic life. This is the capacity to record, and to organize changes of activity within, an absolute developmental time schedule (Cooke and Smith, 1990). Cells make the changes dictated by particular histories of specification events at particular ages, counting from some initiation point within development, regardless of the prior times of the events. In *Xenopus*-style vertebrate development this is particularly striking because the time schedule starts effectively at fertilization. Early phases of amniote vertebrate development may be more loosely organized, so that the timer in individuals starts after variable early periods, but it may then run just as inflexibly. We have little idea as to what the molecular mechanism of such timekeeping might be (although it has little to do with cell cycles), but it probably has a major role in organizing the formation of a body plan.

References

Akam, M. (1987). *Development* **101,** 1–22.
Albano, R. M., Godsave, S. F., Huylebroeck, D., Van Nimmen, K., Isaacs, H. V., Slack, J. M. W., and Smith, J. C. (1990). *Development* **110,** 439–444.
Black, S. D., and Gerhart, J. C. (1985). *Dev. Biol.* **108,** 310–324.
Black, S. D., and Gerhart, J. C. (1986). *Dev. Biol.* **116,** 228–240.
Busa, W. B., and Gimlich, R. L. (1989). *Dev. Biol.* **132,** 314–324.
Cooke, J. (1972). *J. Embryol. Exp. Morphol.* **28,** 27–46.
Cooke, J. (1975). *Nature (London)* **254,** 196–199.
Cooke, J. (1985a). *J. Embryol. Exp. Morphol.* **88,** 135–150.
Cooke, J. (1985b). *J. Embryol. Exp. Morphol., Suppl.* **89,** 69–87.
Cooke, J. (1986). *Nature (London)* **319,** 60–63.
Cooke, J. (1989a). *Development* **106,** 519–529.
Cooke, J. (1989b). *Ciba Found. Symp.* **144,** 187–200.
Cooke, J. (1989c). *Development* **107,** 229–241.
Cooke, J., and Smith, J. C. (1987). *Development* **99,** 197–210.
Cooke, J., and Smith, E. J. (1988). *Development* **102,** 85–99.
Cooke, J., and Smith, J. C. (1989). *Dev. Biol.* **131,** 383–400.
Cooke, J., and Smith, J. (1990). *Cell* **60,** 891–894.
Cooke, J., and Webber, J. A. (1985a). *J. Embryol. Exp. Morphol.* **88,** 113–134.
Cooke, J., and Webber, J. A. (1985b). *J. Embryol. Exp. Morphol.* **88,** 85–112.
Cooke, J., and Wong, A. (1991). *Development* **111,** 197–212.
Cooke, J., Smith, J. C., Smith, E. J., and Yaqoob, M. (1987). *Development* **101,** 893–908.
Cooke, J., Symes, K., and Smith, E. J. (1989). *Development* **105,** 549–558.
Dale, L., and Slack, J. M. W. (1987a). *Development* **100,** 279–295.
Dale, L., and Slack, J. M. W. (1987b). *Development* **99,** 197–210.
Dale, L., Smith, J. C., and Slack, J. M. W. (1985). *J. Embryol. Exp. Morphol.* **89,** 289–312.
Dale, L., Matthews, G., Tabe, I., and Colman, A. (1989). *EMBO J.* **8,** 1057–1065.
Dawid, I. B., Sargent, T. D., and Rosa, F. (1990). *Curr. Top. Dev. Biol.* **24,** 261–288.
Deuchar, E., and Burgess, A. M. C. (1967). *J. Embryol. Exp. Morphol.* **17,** 349–358.
Dixon, J. E., and Kintner, C. R. (1989). *Development* **106,** 749–757.
Durston, A. J., Timmermans, J. P. M., Hage, W. J., Hendriks, H. F. J., De Vries, N. J., Heideveld, M., and Nieuwkoop, P. D. (1989). *Nature (London)* **340,** 140–144.
Elinson, R. P., and Rowning, B. (1988). *Dev. Biol.* **128,** 185–197.
Eto, Y., Tsuji, T., Takezawa, M., Takano, S., Yokogawa, Y., and Shibai, H. (1987). *Biochem. Biophys. Res. Commun.* **142,** 1095–1103.
Eyal-Giladi, H. (1984). *Cell Differ.* **14,** 245–255.
Gierer, A., and Meinhardt, H. (1972). *Cybernetics (Engl. Transl.)* **12,** 30–39.
Gillespie, L. L., Paterno, G. D., and Slack, J. M. W. (1989). *Development* **106,** 203–208.
Gimlich, R. L. (1986). *Dev. Biol.* **115,** 340–352.
Gimlich, R. L., and Gerhart, J. (1984). *Dev. Biol.* **104,** 117–130.
Godsave, S. F., Isaacs, H. V., and Slack, J. M. W. (1988). *Development* **102,** 555–566.

Graham, A., Papalopulu, N. J., and Krumlauf, R. (1989). *Cell* **57**, 367–378.

Green, J. B. A., and Smith, J. C. (1990). *Nature (London)* **347**, 391–394.

Green, J. B. A., Howes, G., Symes, K., Cooke, J., and Smith, J. C. (1990). *Development* **108**, 173–183.

Gurdon, J. B., and Fairman, S. (1986). *J. Embryol. Exp. Morphol., Suppl.* **97**, 75–84.

Gurdon, J. B., Fairman, S., Mohun, T. J., and Brennan, S. (1985). *Cell* **41**, 913–922.

Ingham, P. W. (1988). *Nature (London)* **335**, 25–34.

Kanéda, T. (1981). *Growth Differ.* **23**, 553–564.

Kao, K. R., and Elinson, R. P. (1988). *Dev. Biol.* **127**, 64–77.

Keller, R. E. (1976). *Dev. Biol.* **51**, 118–137.

Keller, R. E. (1986). *In* "The Cellular Basis of Morphogenesis" (L. Browder, ed.), pp. 241–328. Plenum, New York.

Keller, R. E., Danilchik, M., Gimlich, R. L., and Shih, J. (1985). *J. Embryol. Exp. Morphol., Suppl.* **89**, 185–209.

Kieny, M., Mauger, A., and Sengel, P. (1972). *Dev. Biol.* **28**, 142–161.

Kimelman, D., and Kirschner, M. (1987). *Cell* **51**, 869–877.

Kimelman, D., Abraham, J. A., Haaparenta, T., Palisi, T. M., and Kirschner, M. (1988). *Science* **242**, 1053–1056.

Kintner, C. R., and Melton, D. A. (1987). *Development* **99**, 311–326.

Kochav, S., Ginsberg, M., and Eyal-Giladi, H. (1980). *Dev. Biol.* **79**, 296–308.

London, C., Akers, R., and Phillips, C. (1988). *Dev. Biol.* **129**, 380–389.

Martinez-Arias, A., Baker, N. E., and Ingham, P. W. (1988). *Development* **103**, 157–170.

Meinhardt, H. (1982). "Models of Biological Pattern Formation." Academic Press, New York.

Mitrani, E., and Shimoni, Y. (1990). *Science* **247**, 1092–1094.

New, D. A. T. (1955). *J. Embryol. Exp. Morphol.* **3**, 326–331.

Nieuwkoop, P. D. (1969). *Wilhelm Roux's Arch. Dev. Biol.* **162**, 341–373.

Nieuwkoop, P. D. (1973). *Adv. Morphog.* **10**, 2–39.

Nüsslein-Volhard, C., and Roth, S. (1989). *Ciba Found. Symp.* **194**, 37–54.

Papalopulu, N., Hunt, P., Wilkinson, D., Ephaham, A., and Krumlauf, R. (1990). *In* "Advances in Neural Regeneration Research," pp. 291–307. Wiley-Liss, New York.

Paterno, G. D., Gillespie, L. L., Dixon, M. S., Slack, J. M. W., and Heath, J. K. (1989). *Development* **106**, 79–84.

Rijsewijk, F., Schuerman, M., Wagenaar, E., Parren, P., Weigel, D., and Nuss, R. (1987). *Cell* **50**, 649–657.

Rosa, F. M. (1989). *Cell* **57**, 965–974.

Rosa, F. M., Roberts, A. B., Danielpour, D., Dart, L. L., Sporn, M. B., and Dawid, I. B. (1988). *Science* **239**, 783–785.

Ruiz i Altaba, A. (1990). *Development* **108**, 595–604.

Ruiz i Altaba, A., and Melton, D. A. (1989a). *Nature (London)* **341**, 33–38.

Ruiz i Altaba, A., and Melton, D. A. (1989b). *Development* **106**, 173–183.

Ruiz i Altaba, A., and Melton, D. A. (1989c). *Cell* **57**, 317–326.

Sargent, M. G., and Bennett, M. R. (1990). *Development* **109**, 967–974.

Savage, R., and Phillips, C. R. (1989). *Dev. Biol.* **133**, 157–168.

Scharf, S. R., and Gerhart, J. C. (1980). *Dev. Biol.* **79**, 181–198.

Scharf, S. R., and Gerhart, J. C. (1983). *Dev. Biol.* **99**, 75–87.

Scharf, S. R., Rowning, B., Wa, M., and Gerhart, J. C. (1989). *Dev. Biol.* **134**, 175–188.

Scott, M. P., and Carroll, S. B. (1987). *Cell* **51**, 689–698.

Sharpe, C. R., Fritz, A., De Robertis, E. M., and Gurdon, J. B. (1987). *Cell* **50**, 749–758.

Simeone, A., Acampora, D., Arcioni, L., Andrews, P. W., Boncinelli, E., and Mavilio, F. (1990). *Nature (London)* **346**, 763–766.

Sive, H., Draper, B. W., Harland, R. M., and Weintraub, H. (1990). *Genes Dev.* **4**, 932–942.

Slack, J. M. W. (1983). "From Egg to Embryo: Determinative Events in Early Development." Cambridge Univ. Press, Cambridge, England.

Slack, J. M. W., and Forman, D. (1980). *J. Embryol. Exp. Morphol.* **56,** 283–299.

Slack, J. M. W., Darlington, B. G., Heath, J. K., and Godsave, S. F. (1987). *Nature (London)* **326,** 197–200.

Slack, J. M. W., Isaacs, H. V., and Darlington, B. G. (1988). *Development* **103,** 581–590.

Smith, J. C. (1987). *Development* **99,** 3–14.

Smith, J. C. (1989). *Development* **105,** 665–677.

Smith, L. J. (1985). *J. Embryol. Exp. Morphol.* **89,** 15–35.

Smith, J. C., and Slack, J. M. W. (1983). *J. Embryol. Exp. Morphol.* **78,** 299–317.

Smith, J. C., Yaqoob, M., and Symes, K. (1988). *Development* **103,** 591–600.

Smith, J. C., Price, B. M. J., Van Nimmen, K., and Huylebroeck, D. (1990). *Nature (London)* **345,** 729–731.

Spemann, H. (1938). "Embryonic Development and Induction" [Reprinted by Hafner, New York, 1967.]

Spemann, H., and Mangold, H. (1924). *Wilhelm Roux's Arch. Dev. Biol.* **100,** 599–638.

Stern, C. D. (1990). *Development* **109,** 667–682.

Stern, C. D., and Canning, D. R. (1988). *Experientia* **44,** 61–67.

Stern, C. D., and Canning, D. R. (1990). *Nature (London)* **343,** 273–275.

Stewart, R. M., and Gerhart, J. C. (1990). *Development* **109,** 363–372.

Sudarwati, S., and Nieuwkoop, P. D. (1971). *Wilhelm Roux Arch. Entwicklungsmech. Org.* **166,** 189–204.

Summerbell, D., Lewis, J. H., and Wolpert, L. (1983). *Nature (London)* **224,** 492–495.

Symes, K., Yaqoob, M., and Smith, J. C. (1988). *Development* **104,** 609–618.

Tannahill, D., and Melton, D. A. (1989). *Development* **106,** 775–785.

Türing, A. M. (1952). *Philos. Trans. R. Soc. London, B* **237,** 37–72.

Vale, W., River, J., Vaughan, J., McClintock, R., Corrigan, A., Wood, W., Karr, D., and Spiess, J. (1986). *Nature (London)* **321,** 776–779.

Van Obberghen-Schilling, E., Roche, N. S., Flanders, K. C., Sporn, M. B., and Roberts, A. B. (1988). *J. Biol. Chem.* **263,** 7741–7746.

Vincent, J.-P., and Gerhart, J. C. (1987). *Dev. Biol.* **123,** 526–539.

Vincent, J.-P., Oster, G., and Gerhart, J. C. (1986). *Dev. Biol.* **113,** 484–500.

Waddington, C. H. (1956). "Principles of Embryology." Cambridge Univ. Press, Cambridge, England.

Warner, A. (1986). *Ciba Found. Symp.* **125,** 154–162.

Warner, A., and Gurdon, J. B. (1987). *J. Cell Biol.* **104,** 557–564.

Whitman, M., and Melton, D. A. (1989). *Annu.. Rev. Cell Biol.* 93–117.

Wilkinson, D. G., Bhatt, S., Cook, M., Boncinelli, E., and Krumlauf, R. (1989). *Nature (London)* **341,** 405–409.

Wolpert, L. (1971). *Curr. Top. Dev. Biol.* **6,** 183–223.

Wolpert, L. (1990). *Biol. J. Linn. Soc.* **39,** 109–124.

Yisraeli, J. K., and Melton, D. A. (1988). *Nature (London)* **336,** 592–595.

4

Patterning of Body Segments of the Zebrafish Embryo

Charles B. Kimmel, Thomas F. Schilling, and Kohei Hatta
Institute of Neuroscience
University of Oregon
Eugene, Oregon 97403

I. Introduction

The past decade has seen a renaissance of interest in an old issue in biology, namely, the significance of segments, or metameres, in establishing the body plan of metazoans. Segments form the framework underlying, in part, both the pattern of metazoan development and its evolution into the many complex forms of today, such as the vertebrates. Bateson (1894) clearly defined segmentation nearly 100 years ago "as a more or less coincident repetition of elements belonging to most of the chief systems of organs along an axis which corresponds to the long axis of the body." This definition remains useful today (Stent, 1985), even considering that the serially reiterated "elements" now include individual types of cells, macromolecules, and patterns of development. Recent evidence is causing a revision in our ideas about segment evolution, as we briefly consider, and use as a framework to review more comprehensively, our understanding of segments in a single vertebrate species, the zebrafish *Brachydanio rerio*. Descriptive

Current Topics in Developmental Biology, Vol. 25

studies in zebrafish have provided exceptionally clear information, often at the level of individual cells, about the structure, extent in the body, and development of segments. Experimental analyses, including the use of mutations, have begun to reveal cellular interactions required for segmentation. We expect that information from zebrafish will provide a useful background for understanding how genes make vertebrate segments, an issue for the future, and for which this species also holds some promise (Streisinger *et al.*, 1981; Kimmel, 1989). We develop the theme that, despite the pronounced differences between segments in the head, on the one hand, and the trunk and the tail, on the other, "body metameres" (Goodrich, 1930) might be patterned as a single series, as are the thoracic and abdominal segments of *Drosophila*.

II. Genes and Evolution of Segments

The foundations of the renewed interest in segmentation are unusually clear. They are in landmark studies (Lewis, 1978; Nüsslein-Volhard and Wieschaus, 1980) that used mutations to identify and characterize the action of genes that establish segments and their identities in *Drosophila*. This work was followed by the discoveries of the homeobox that many of these genes contain (McGinnis *et al.*, 1984b; Scott and Weiner, 1984), and its wide conservation among diverse animals, suggesting (McGinnis *et al.*, 1984a) "that the segmentally organized animals in both the protostome and deuterostome classes had a common ancestor, and that the metameric body plan has evolved only once in evolution."

Recent support for this hypothesis has been striking: The *Drosophila* homeotic (*HOM*) genes are clustered together on the chromosome and expressed along the anteroposterior (AP) axis of the embryo in a region-specific pattern that matches their linear arrangement within the gene cluster. Their homologs in mice, *Hox* genes, preserve the clustering, gene arrangement within the cluster, and AP expression pattern (Graham *et al.*, 1989; for a review see Kessel and Gruss, 1990). As for insect *HOM* genes, boundaries of expression of at least some mouse *Hox* genes (Murphy *et al.*, 1989; Wilkinson *et al.*, 1989) and their counterparts in birds (Sundin and Eichele, 1990) and zebrafish (Molven *et al.*, 1990) are segment boundaries (Fig. 1). *HOM* genes encode segment identity, and *hox* genes may have the same role (Holland, 1988), as suggested by recent evidence in *Xenopus* (Wright *et al.*, 1989) and in the mouse (Balling *et al.*, 1989). Although *hox* genes are not as well characterized in zebrafish as in mice, what is known suggests that the gene structure, their clustered arrangement, and their expression patterns have been highly conserved in vertebrates (see Njølstad *et al.*, 1990, and references therein).

Such striking similarities leave little doubt that a common ancestor of vertebrates and arthropods possessed a *HOM/hox* gene cluster and probably used it to pattern the AP body axis. However, many questions remain. If the common ancestor were segmented, does this mean that anterior trunk segments in the fish,

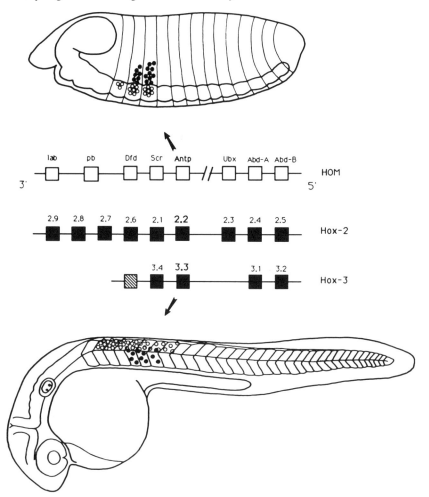

Fig. 1 *Drosophila* (upper) and zebrafish (lower) express equivalent genes, *Antp* and *hox-3.3*, in similar patterns. Whole mounted embryos are shown diagrammatically in left side view. Between the embryos are the gene clusters that appear to control segment identity in both of these creatures. The gene *Antp* is located within the homeotic (HOM) complex in the fly. Gene structure and arrangement in the HOM complex is conserved within vertebrate hox clusters, such that the genes *Hox-2.2* and *Hox-3.3* are vertebrate equivalents of *Antp*. The *Hox-2* and *Hox-3* clusters are shown according to current understanding in the mouse (only two of the four known complexes are included). Less is known about the zebrafish genes, but zebrafish *hox-2.1* and *hox-2.2* are arranged similarly to their murine counterparts (Njølstad *et al.*, 1990), and preliminary evidence suggests the same for *hox-3.3* and *hox-3.4* (A. Fjose, personal communication). All of the *HOM/hox* genes are expressed during embryogenesis in spatially restricted domains, with anteroposterior positions along the body axis that correspond to the gene location, 3' to 5', within the cluster. Solid circles indicate expression in the mesoderm; open circles, that in neurectoderm. The *Drosophila* and zebrafish expression patterns are from Bermingham *et al.* (1990) and Molven *et al.* (1990), respectively, and the gene arrangements are from Gaunt and Singh (1990).

where *hox-3.3* is expressed, are the homologs of the thoracic segments in the fly, where *Antp* is expressed (Fig. 1)? Or, during evolution, can expression of a particular *HOM/hox* gene jump from one segment to another, meaning that homologous body parts do not express homologous genes? Or yet, within the domain of expression of a particular *HOM/hox* gene, can individual segments be added or lost during evolution, meaning that homology does not usually extend to individual segments, but might extend to blocks of them? Among vertebrates the approximate AP level of expression of a particular *hox* gene is highly conserved; more studies are needed to learn just how precise the conservation is, but a striking example is *hox-3.3*. The equivalent genes are expressed in a gradient in the ventral part of the forelimb bud of the mouse, chicken, and frog, and in the same pattern in the zebrafish pectoral fin, which is the homolog of the tetrapod forelimb (Harrison, 1918).

Comparisons of expression of another homeobox gene family that has been widely studied, homologs of the segmentation gene *engrailed* of *Drosophila*, show that interpretations about homology based on genes and their expression patterns need to be made cautiously. Many aspects of *engrailed* gene expression are, like *hox* genes, similar among different vertebrates; for example, mice, chickens, frogs, and fish all express *engrailed* genes in cells located in a stripe across the same location in the brain. The stripe, shown for the zebrafish genes (so-called *eng* genes) in Fig. 2, is only one component of a rather complex spatiotemporal pattern of expression present in this and other vertebrates. As can also be seen in Fig. 2, in addition to the brain stripe, *eng* is segmentally expressed along the body. This pattern, discussed in detail below (Section V, B), is reminiscent of *Drosophila engrailed*, which is also expressed in subsets of cells in each segment. However, in *Drosophila*, expression comes early in development, before the segments form, and mutational analysis reveals that *engrailed* is part of the gene network that establishes segmentation itself. In zebrafish *eng* expression begins only after the segments appear, and thus could not be having an equivalent role. Homologous homeobox genes can evidently be usurped for different functions in different animals; presumably, the acquisition of such regulatory genes into new developmental programs is one of the ways that evolutionary change comes about. Just as for morphological comparisons among animals, it will take careful analyses to reveal what seem to be equivalent expression patterns of conserved genes. Such comparative molecular analyses are only

---

Fig. 2 Zebrafish *eng* genes, homologous to the segmentation gene *engrailed* of *Drosophila*, are expressed in a complex pattern, as revealed by antibody labeling, shown in a dorsal-view whole amount of an embryo at 22 hours. The earliest and most prominent expression is in a transverse stripe of cells in the central nervous system, at the midbrain–hindbrain junction (arrow). Subsequently, segmental "muscle pioneers" (MP) located in the center of each somite-derived myotome express *eng*. Later yet, expression is present in a number of other cell types, and among them are segmentally arranged neural cells present in the hindbrain (arrowheads) and continuing into the spinal cord. (From Hatta *et al.*, 1991.)

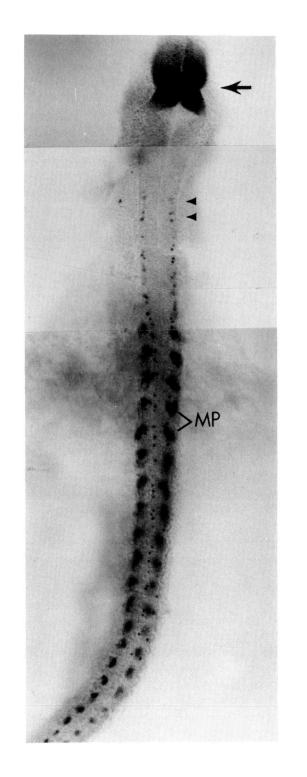

beginning, and it will be most interesting to see how far they will take us, particularly in deciphering evolutionary relationships that have proven enigmatic in the past.

Whether the common ancestor of insects and vertebrates had segments or not is controversial, in part, because of the traditional view from morphological evidence that metamerism arose separately and independently in the chordate and annelid/arthropod lineages. If the common ancestor were unsegmented, then during subsequent evolution the expression of *HOM*/*hox* genes must have been linked to segmentation convergently in the two lineages (Akam, 1989; Holland, 1990; Wilkinson and Krumlauf, 1990). However, as organ rudiments form in the *Drosophila* embryo, the domain of *Antp* expression in the neurectoderm is broader and extends more anteriorly than in the mesoderm (Bermingham *et al.*, 1990), and it seems remarkably coincident that *hox-3.3* expression in zebrafish shares both of these features (Fig. 1).

The traditional view of separate origins of segmentation in the chordate and arthropod/annelid lineages could well be incorrect. For understanding segment evolution comparisons of the morphology of segments of modern animals, or their development (reviewed by Kimmel, 1990), can be deceiving because of the tremendous differences that are present among the different phyla. This fact does not necessarily mean that arthropods and chordates established segmentation independently, for their lineages have been separate for a long time. As we now understand from fossil evidence from the Cambrian period, particularly from Burgess Shale, they were separate more than 500 million years ago.

Segmentation was widespread among diverse animal groups in the Cambrian era, including many that left no modern survivors (reviewed by Gould, 1989). Thus, it was not just present in isolated forms long separated on two major forks (i.e., protostome versus deuterostome) of a supposed metazoan evolutionary tree, as is the traditional view. Traditionally, the chordate ancestor of vertebrates was thought to be unsegmented, but among these Cambrian creatures is *Pikaia*, the earliest known chordate (Fig. 3). *Pikaia* possesses V-shaped segments that look like those of *Amphioxus* or a fish. Segmentation seems to have been an extremely successful invention, possibly a single invention in part responsible for the Cambrian explosion of metazoan lineages.

An argument raised against the phylogenetic soundness of the common segmented ancestor idea surrounds the question of the *extent* of body segmentation in chordates. Along with annelids and arthropods vertebrates were considered by Bateson (1894) to be animals in which segmentation reaches its highest development. Other authors treated the issue rather differently: "Annelids and arthropods are fundamentally metameric animals. . . . [and] while chordates do possess some serially repeated structures, most prominent of which are the somites, they are in no real sense metameric. . . ." (Raff and Raff, 1985). However, as we consider below, this view is overly skeptical. Recent work strengthens the already substantial evidence for vertebrate metamerism and adds credence to the argument for common ancestry.

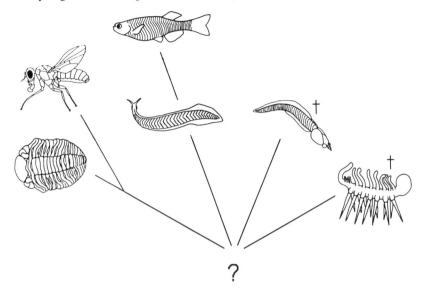

Fig. 3 Fossil evidence from the Burgess Shale reveals that segmentation was widespread during the Cambrian era. The fossil reconstructions (shown from left to right) are *Phacops* (a trilobite), *Pikaia*, *Arthrochordata*, and *Hallucigenia*. Trilobites are arthropods, and *Pikaia* is thought to be a chordate. *Arthrochordata*, with a head like an arthropod and fin arrangements like a chordate, has no known modern relatives, nor are fossil relatives known after the Cambrian era. The same is the case for *Hallucigenia*, whose name tells it all. The fossils are redrawn from Gould (1989).

III. Goodrich Hypothesis of Body Metamerism

Segmented structures in vertebrates extend from at least the region of the mouth caudally to the end of the tail. Throughout this long extent some, but not all, tissues are segmented. The segmentally organized cells are derived from both ectoderm and mesoderm and are present in both the central nervous system (CNS) and the periphery. We describe zebrafish segmentation in the head and the trunk, but ignore tail segments, which are essentially the same as those of the trunk. On the other hand segmented structures differ morphologically between the head and the trunk. In the head is an iterated series of pharyngeal arches, the anterior members forming jaw structures and the posterior ones carrying gills. Brain segments are recognized during embryonic stages as a series of prominent swellings, or neuromeres. Well-defined boundaries separate individual hindbrain neuromeres, also called rhombomeres. In the trunk is a series of vertebrae and the associated segmented body wall musculature. Spinal cord segments do not form neuromeres, and are recognized only by examining the neurons they contain. In a simplifying hypothesis that we call the "body metamere hypothesis," all of the segmental structures, including both the head and the trunk, are parts of a single series (Goodrich, 1930).

For the body metamere hypothesis to have developmental significance requires that the separate tissue components, mesodermal and ectodermal, that comprise a single metamere, are somehow patterned *together*, either independently by something like a patterning wave that passes through all of them, or more likely interdependently by cell interactions. In either case tissues of the same segment should lie spatially together along the AP axis (i.e., in the primordium of the same metamere), at least during key developmental stages when the patterning would occur. Alternatively, in what we term the "tissue segment hypothesis," the separate tissue components of individual metameres are patterned separately and come to lie in register along the body axis only as the result of passive positional shifts of progenitor cells to the same AP level. Accurate information about the early developmental origins of metameres was not available to Goodrich.

Furthermore, according to Goodrich (1930), differences between head and trunk segmentation are the ". . . result of a process of cephalization of the anterior segments in an originally uniform series. . . ." The major differences are of two sorts: The "consensus" plan of organization (i.e., the generalized segment structure) differs substantially between the head and the trunk, and individual segments vary stereotypically from the consensus plan in the head, but not, at least to such a marked extent, in the trunk. As we see here, both differences are related to the functions of the segments, and if the body metamere theory is correct, then one might expect to find *conserved* features of development between the head and the trunk in spite of these adaptations. Alternatively, head and trunk segmentation might arise by completely separate mechanisms (Stern, 1990). Thus, in considering the information that follows, one would like to understand whether there is a long single series of body metameres, versus separate series of tissue segments that are present in the CNS and the periphery of both the head and the trunk. We next consider evidence that in both body regions segmental patterning involves interactions between the germ layers. If this is the case, then segmental development of a tissue would depend, at least in part, on influences extrinsic to that tissue.

IV. Extrinsic Programming of Segments

A. Characteristics of Trunk Segments

The most prominent segmentation in fish is of body wall muscle (Fig. 1). It is arranged in myotomes[1] that are the major components of the embryonic somites, and the first ones to differentiate. Vertebral cartilages, also present segmentally,

[1]As often used in the older literature, "myotome" referred collectively to the whole segmental set of body wall muscles, with individual muscle segments being termed "myomeres." The meaning we give the word here seems to fit with current general usage. Myotomes and somites are unilateral

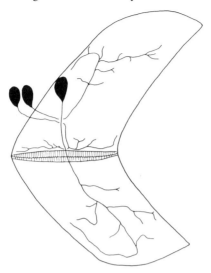

Fig. 4 Muscles in a single segment, or myotome, are innervated in a stereotyped pattern by identified primary motoneurons present in a single cluster in the spinal cord. Left side view as in Fig. 1. Muscle cells span the myotome, as shown for two muscle pioneers located at its center. The motoneurons, according to their anteroposterior positions within the spinal segment, innervate middle, dorsal, and ventral muscle, respectively. (From Myers *et al.*, 1986.)

differentiate relatively late in fish, well into the larval stages, and probably not from the notochord, as recently claimed (Stern, 1990), but from the sclerotomes, as in other vertebrates. The zebrafish sclerotomal progenitors are present early as a relatively small subset of somitic cells (A. Wood and G. Bobrowicz, personal communication). Other segmentally organized components of the trunk periphery include blood vessels and sensory ganglia which develop in the late embryo, from mesoderm and neural crest, respectively.

Centrally, in the spinal cord, single clusters of early-arising "primary neurons" develop in an identical pattern in each spinal segment (as defined with reference to the overlying myotomes; segmental boundaries cannot be recognized directly in this region of the CNS). Each neuronal cluster contains three or four identified primary motoneurons with axons that collect together into a single ventral root and innervate a single myotome (Fig. 4). Primary motoneurons have axonal arbors strictly confined to muscles of their own segment and, within the segment, innervate the dorsal and ventral muscle masses in a stereotyped nonoverlapping pattern that is related to, and appears to be specified by, soma position within the cluster (Eisen, 1991). At least one class of ventrally located primary interneuron

structures, whereas body segments are bilateral. Since segmented components we know of are symmetrical across the midline, we ignore bilaterality for the sake of simplicity. Thus, "one cell per segment" should be understood to mean "one pair of bilateral homologous cells per segment."

is also segmentally arranged (Kuwada *et al.*, 1990), one or two of the same class being present in the same clusters that house the primary motoneurons.

Other spinal neurons may not be arranged segmentally, although, of course, some of them might *function* segmentally, according to the distribution of their processes. Secondary motoneurons arise only hours after the primary motoneurons and form a continuous column of cells in the ventral spinal cord, but their axons group segmentally to follow those of the primary motoneurons in the ventral roots. Primary interneurons located dorsal to motoneurons may not be segmentally arranged (Kuwada *et al.*, 1990). More dorsal yet are primary sensory neurons, which are present within the spinal cord and function transiently, before the definitive sensory neurons that arise 1 day later in dorsal root ganglion. These early neurons, termed "Rohon–Beard cells," occur in variable numbers and positions in each segment and their axons exit the cord individually along it, and are not collected into segmental dorsal roots (Metcalfe *et al.*, 1990).

B. Somitic Mesoderm Is Required for Spinal Cord Segmentation

The components of trunk segments are patterned interdependently. In amphibian and avian embryos segmental patterning of peripheral neural structures, ventral roots and spinal ganglia, are determined by interactions with somitic mesoderm (reviewed by Keynes and Stern, 1987). For example, rotating somites to produce an AP reversal leads to corresponding changes in the locations of nerves and sensory ganglia. Recent evidence in zebrafish suggests that the segmented mesoderm controls not only the distribution of peripheral motor nerves, but also the central segmental arrangements of spinal neurons. The mesodermal and neuroectodermal components of trunk segments develop together in a highly coordinated interactive fashion. The first cells to differentiate in both germ layers arise segmentally and interact with one another. The first demonstrable segmentation in the embryo is the formation of somites, beginning in the anterior trunk shortly after gastrulation and continuing in a posterior-going wave.

Even before the somites form, a few cells, called muscle pioneers, in each presumptive segment develop distinctive features, including the expression of acetylcholinesterase (Hanneman and Westerfield, 1989), and then, shortly after somite formation, expression of *eng* (Patel *et al.*, 1989; Hatta *et al.*, 1991), that is, one or more members of the *engrailed* homeobox gene family discussed earlier. The muscle pioneers, labeled in Fig. 2, may be important for patterning the characteristic chevron shape of the myotome and for proper growth cone navigation of the pioneering motoneurons. They differentiate exactly in the middle of the segment, where both the apex of the chevron forms and later the connective tissue appears that forms the horizontal myoseptum separating dorsal and ventral muscle masses. The muscle pioneers elongate horizontally, to span the segment (Fig. 4), and they form myofibrils hours earlier than other muscle cells in the same segment (Felsenfeld and Curry, 1991). As the muscle pioneers differentiate the chevron shape of the myotome becomes recognizable, and within 1 hour or so the first motor axons appear in the periphery. Irrespective of which part of the muscle segment the motor axons later innervate, their growth cones first grow directly to the muscle pioneers and interact with them specifically, for the muscle pioneers begin to twitch neurogenically (Myers *et al.*, 1986) and they develop clusters of acetylcholine receptors at the time they are innervated (Liu and Westerfield, 1991). If the primary motor neurons are ablated by laser-microbeam irradiation before axogenesis, the muscle pioneers in that segment do not develop receptor clusters, at least on schedule (Liu and Westerfield, 1991), suggesting that neuronal signaling is required for their formation.

Signals in the opposite direction, from the muscles to the neurons, appear to be required for segmental development of the spinal cord. In zebrafish, as in other organisms, a brief heat shock applied to the embryo locally disrupts patterning in mesodermal segments that form 2 hours following the treatment. Disruption of segmental patterning of the spinal cord occurs at exactly the same AP level as in the mesoderm, as evidenced by local disorganization of its motoneuronal clusters (Kimmel *et al.*, 1988). This finding suggests that mesodermal and spinal cord segmentation are coordinated by the time the heat shock exerts its effects, 2–2.5 hours before overt segmentation. One interpretation is that heat shock interferes with both mesodermal and ectodermal segmentation directly and coordinately. Alternatively, the effect in one tissue (e.g., the spinal cord) could be indirect, the disturbance propagated to it from the other tissue (e.g., the somite).

Mutational analysis supports the second alternative. The *spadetail* mutation, *spt-1(b104)*, massively disrupts segmental patterning in the trunk of the body, reducing the number of muscle segments there and disturbing patterning of those that do form (Kimmel *et al.*, 1989). The disruptions result from incorrect morphogenetic movements of somitic precursor cells in the paraxial mesoderm during gastrulation (Warga and Kimmel, 1990), which leave the trunk depleted of the somite-forming cells. The gastrulation movements of neuroectodermal cells occur normally in *spt-1*, yet, just as in the heat-shock experiments, segmental patterning of the spinal cord is disrupted in the mutant, here in the entire trunk (Eisen and Pike, 1991). The neurons that are normally segmental in organization are dislocated and reduced in number in a manner corresponding to the changes in mesodermal segmentation; other spinal cord cell types not normally arranged segmentally are unperturbed. Further, primary motoneurons present in the trunk segments of the mutant have abnormal axons; in many instances axonal outgrowth appears to have arrested where the growth cones would normally encounter the muscle pioneers.

Complementing the heat-shock experiments, these findings suggest that a patterning disturbance in mesoderm is propagated to the ectoderm, and in this case this idea could be further examined by mosaic analysis, to learn in which cell types, mesoderm and/or ectoderm, the mutation exerts its direct effects.

Transplanting mutant mesodermal cells into wild-type hosts failed to rescue their gastrulation movements (Ho *et al.*, 1989), and in the reciprocal transplantation wild-type mesodermal cells were shown to gastrulate in a mutant environment as they would have in a wild-type environment. Thus, *spt-1* autonomously disrupts mesodermal cell movement (Ho *et al.*, 1989). Conversely, its effect on primary motoneuron morphology is nonautonomous (Eisen and Pike, 1991b): Transplantation of single postmitotic primary motoneuronal precursors from mutant to wild-type embryos rescues their phenotypes, and the reciprocal transplant makes genetically wild-type motoneurons mutant-looking. Together, the two studies suggest that the cell-autonomous domain of *spt-1* function is limited to mesodermal precursor cells and, consequently, that spinal cord segmental patterning is under mesodermal control.

Experiments have not revealed which somitic cells are important for spinal cord segmentation. A possibility is that the muscle pioneers play a major role, for the trunk myotomes that form in *spt-1* mutants are defective not only in shape and muscle cell arrangement, but also in that muscle pioneers are missing, again, specifically in the trunk (Hatta *et al.*, 1991). The analyses do suggest about *when* the interactions must take place: As revealed by the heat-shock experiments, they must occur well after gastrulation, at some stage after the heat shock-sensitive period. To appreciate the time scale involved, consider a representative trunk somite, number 10 in the series. It is depatterned by a heat shock given at about 12 hours, partitions from the segmental plate and forms muscle pioneers by about 14 hours, and is innervated by primary motor axons by 18 hours. The patterning interactions might occur at any time over this 6-hour period, for Eisen (1991) has shown by transplantation experiments in wild-type embryos that postmitotic primary mononeuronal precursors can switch their identities, from one identified type of motoneuron to another, up to the stage their axons grow. This degree of developmental plasticity is remarkable.

Stern (1990), in a provocative article, has argued that the notochord might imprint segmental information onto the adjacent paraxial mesoderm and the neural tube. However, we have obtained no evidence for notochord segmentation, and the notochord appears to be unessential for the segmentation of other tissues. Zebrafish lacking a notochord, except occasionally for a few cells in the tail, are easily produced by applying hydrostatic pressure to one-cell embryos, presumably by interfering with events required for mesodermal dorsalization in the same manner as that well studied in *Xenopus* (Gerhart *et al.*, 1981). These monsters are severely depleted in head structures, but their bodies are segmented (Fig. 5). Imperfect rounded somites are present throughout the trunk and the tail,

---

Fig. 5 Mesodermal segmentation does not depend on the presence of a notochord. (A and B) Left side views (dorsal up), at shallow and deep planes of focus, of a normal 24-hour embryo. (C and D) Corresponding views of an embryo lacking the notochord (NC) and the floor plate (FP), after treatment with hydrostatic pressure at the one-cell stage (see Streisinger *et al.*, 1981, for method). Somites (S) are present, but misshaped and bilaterally fused beneath the spinal cord (SC).

the usual pairs now fused together into a single bilateral structure. The fusion occurs in the midline ventral to the CNS, where the notochord would normally lie. The spinal cord contains segmental ventral neurons, revealed by antibody staining (S. H. Pike, unpublished observations). It lacks a central canal and a floor plate, for which, like the notochord, there is also no evidence for segmental organization. Thus, the floor plate may absolutely require inductive signaling from the notochord for its development (Jessell et al., 1989), but segmentation does not.

C. Segmented Tissues Are Aligned in the Head

Segmentation in the posterior part of the zebrafish head is readily recognized by the series of gill arches. They derive from a set of a seven embryonic pharyngeal arches, complex organ primordia whose early development has recently been examined by fate-mapping experiments (Schilling et al., 1989). Each arch has cartilages and connective tissue derived from the neural crest, muscles derived from mesoderm, and a blood channel (i.e., an aortic arch) whose walls also are mesodermal. Cranial sensory ganglia associated with each arch have neurons that are ectodermal, derived from neural crest and probably sensory placodes. At about the same AP level along the body axis, the hindbrain primordium forms a linear series of prominent swellings, the rhombomeres. The detailed structure of the rhombomeres is considered in Section VI,A, but we note here that they contain cranial motor nuclei, several of which supply the innervation to the arch musculature in a serial, but not 1:1, pattern, as shown in Fig. 6. Tetrapod embryos share all of these embryonic features with bony fishes; thus, the early development of the head segmental tissues has been highly conserved among vertebrates. As in tetrapods the first and second arches in zebrafish are incorporated into jaw structures (maxillary–mandibular and hyoid, respectively). In fish the more posterior arches make the definitive gills.

A longstanding idea (Goodrich, 1930; Jarvik, 1980) is that in the head, as we have discussed for the trunk, innervation of the periphery is segmentally based. In particular, motoneurons could innervate muscles that arise from the same body metamere. However, at advanced stages of embryogenesis target muscles in the head periphery are generally present at levels in the head *anterior* to the motoneurons that innervate them (Fig. 6). To rescue the body metamere hypothesis, one can propose that this out-of-register relationship arises secondarily, through morphogenetic rearrangement of an earlier, simpler, and segmental pattern. The first critical examination of the early origin of head muscles was made in avian embryos by Noden (1988), using chick–quail chimeras to fate map muscle precursor cells to the paraxial cranial mesoderm. Importantly, he found that the precursors of specific muscles lie in approximate AP register with the brain segments supplying their innervation. Subsequent studies in zebrafish con-

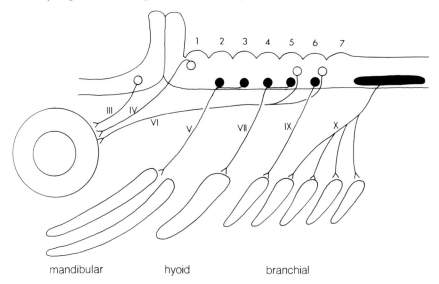

Fig. 6 Cranial motor nerves (Roman numerals) connect segments of the brain (upper) and the head periphery (lower). Left side view. Hindbrain segments (rhombomeres) are numbered 1–7. Open circles show cranial motor nuclei innervating the extrinsic muscles of the eye (the "donut" to the left); solid circles show motor nuclei innervating pharyngeal arch muscles of the jaws (V and VII) and the gills (IX and VII).

firmed Noden's findings and extended them to show that the early AP alignment of the positions of precursors of a particular muscle and the rhombomere containing the precursors of the motoneurons that innervate that muscle is precise (Schilling *et al.*, 1989).

In zebrafish gastrulation, cell movements deliver cells to the head in two separate layers, an outer ectodermal primordium and an inner mesodermal (and endodermal) one (Warga and Kimmel, 1990). As in avian embryos head muscles derive from paraxial mesoderm. To show this, and to learn the axial level of origin of specific muscles, involved dye labeling of early postgastrula precursor cells simultaneously at the same AP level in both the neurectoderm and the paraxial mesoderm. Subsequently, their labeled derivatives were found in positions predicted by the body metamere theory. For example, if the labeled neuroectodermal cells later were present in the second hindbrain neuromere, then muscle labeling was in the jaw, according to Fig. 6. The eventual anterior displacement of head muscles, relative to their innervating motoneurons, is due to shifting after this period, as directly determined by observing the labeled cells as the shift occurred.

Observations of these cell movements and fates were extended for two specific jaw muscles that, in the embryo, are the only cells in the head periphery to express eng homeodomain proteins (Hatta *et al.*, 1990). The mesodermal precursors of these muscles begin to express the gene as undifferentiated loosely associated mesenchymal cells, near the end of the stage that the mesoderm and the neurectoderm lie in segmental register. The findings suggest that *eng* is involved in coding the eventual specific fates of the precursor cells (Hatta *et al.*, 1990), and if this idea is correct, the timing of initial expression of *eng* means that specification of cell fate occurs during the stages when the ectoderm and the mesoderm are in segmental register, as the metamere theory would require. Direct evidence for early segment-specific neuromuscular interactions was obtained from the same study; trigeminal motor axons were found to grow to the precursors of their jaw muscle targets within a few hours of the time of *eng* expression.

As noted above, neural crest cells contribute prominently to the segmented structures in the head periphery. The body metamere theory predicts that premigratory crest that contributes to an arch again comes from the corresponding neuromere, and such is roughly the case in the avian embryo (Couly and Le Douarin, 1990), the medaka fish (Langille and Hall, 1988), and zebrafish (T. F. Schilling, unpublished observations). For example, crest and ectodermal placodal cells derived from the AP level of the second hindbrain neuromere contribute specifically to the trigeminal sensory ganglion associated with the mandibular arch, and also specifically to the mandibular arch cartilages and the mesenchyme. This arch forms the jaw, and, as has been discussed, jaw muscles and the motoneurons that innervate them all come from populations of cells from the same axial level.

We argued in Section IV,B that, in the trunk, spinal cord segmentation is absolutely dependent on interactions from segmented mesoderm. Segments in the head could also be patterned by mesoderm, but this idea has not been investigated experimentally. In the later embryo, and with respect to development of features specific to individual segments, experiments in the avian embryo (Noden, 1988) suggest that the neural crest exerts a major patterning influence. Similarly, Schilling *et al.* (1990) have characterized a mutation in zebrafish, *chw-1*, and seem to have revealed cellular interactions in the same direction. In mutant embryos the jaw fails to appear. The neural crest and the mesoderm both migrate to form the mandibular arch, such that segmentation occurs apparently normally, but then development fails, for the mandibular arch specifically. Transplantation analysis revealed that the mutation affects the crest autonomously, but that the mesodermal defect is nonautonomous, such that mutant mesoderm can form jaw muscle in a wild-type host. The mesodermal failure occurs after the stage when the mesoderm and the neural crest are associated together in the mandibular arch, suggesting that it is due to a missing interaction from the crest, in which the *chw-1* acts directly.

Whereas these experiments suggest that the neural crest plays a major influence at a stage after segments form, they do not argue one way or the other for an

early importance of head mesoderm, which some workers claim is overtly segmented as a series of "somitomeres" (reviewed by Jacobson, 1988). Particularly
prominent in shark embryos (Balfour, 1878), these "head somites" are thought to
be transient mesodermal segments that eventually break up into mesenchyme.
Somitomeres may develop before neuromeres are present in the brain and before
crest cells migrate from their early positions at the top of the neural tube. In
particular, Anderson and Meier (1981) have argued that somitomeres influence
migration of the cranial neural crest in much the way that is now well understood
for somites in the trunk, as mentioned in Section IV,B. The role of mesoderm in
interactions underlying patterning of head segments must be regarded as an open
question.

In summary, so far we have reviewed studies that generally support the body
metamere hypothesis. In the trunk, segmented mesoderm clearly influences ectodermal segmentation. In the head, descriptive analyses reveal that at early stages
the ectoderm and the mesoderm that contribute to a segment are in register with
one another, as the hypothesis predicts, and the experimental analyses so far have
suggested a role of the neural crest in patterning the segment-specific differentiation of the mesoderm. Thus, in both the trunk and the head, body metameres
seem to assemble as predicted. We now examine cell-intrinsic features of segmental development, cell lineage, and *eng* homeobox gene expression, which
also support the body metamere hypothesis.

V. Intrinsic Programming of Segments

A. Cell Lineage May Specify Aspects of Segmentation

Fraser *et al.* (1990; reviewed by Lumsden, 1990) have shown that, in the chick
embryo, a clone of cells arising from a progenitor present in a segment of the
hindbrain primordium at or after the time segment borders form, remains confined to that segment. Cells mix between rhombomeres before the border forms,
and they continue to mix together *within* a single rhombomere after the border
forms, suggesting that the border is a special region that restricts cell movement.
Similarly, analysis of somite development in the zebrafish (Kimmel and Warga,
1987) and the mouse (Tam, 1988) revealed that, during somitogenesis, mesodermal precursor cells mix extensively within the segmental plate mesoderm such
that clonal descendants of a cell can contribute to adjacent somites before, but
not after, the somites form. Somite formation occurs in an AP-going wave, and it
was clear from the zebrafish study that the restricted mixing was linked to somite
formation, rather than stage of development. Progeny of cells present in a newly
formed somite were restricted to that somite, whereas at the same stage cells
located more caudally, in the segmental plate where somite borders were not yet
present, were unrestricted. Thus, segment boundaries, chick rhombomere or fish

and mouse somite, appear to provide a kind of partition that prevents cell movement across them, and possibly serves to establish the segment as a unit of developmental patterning, as in the fashion of segmental lineage compartment boundaries in the *Drosophila* epidermis (Garcia-Bellido *et al.*, 1973).

Cell lineage analysis has also been used to examine earlier aspects of development in the zebrafish. The mesodermal and ectodermal components of single segments come from progenitors that are spatially separate in the early gastrula and subsequently migrate to the same AP level (Kimmel *et al.*, 1988). For each germ layer the cells that form the segments normally arise from tissue-specific lineages in patterns that, particularly in the case of the CNS, are highly stereotyped. Cells derived from blastula-stage or early gastrula-stage progenitors that will populate any AP region of the CNS mix with one another in an extremely regular fashion with cells from many different clones. This cell intercalation, occurring during and just after the gastrula stage, produces an elongated neuraxis (Warga and Kimmel, 1990) in which the cells of a single clone are highly dispersed along the axis. Several non-CNS lineages—for example, those producing the somite mesoderm (Kimmel and Warga, 1987)—exhibit similar behavior, but what is remarkable about the CNS lineages is that the cell divisions and interminglings result in cells of a single clone becoming periodically distributed along the neuraxis and bilaterally distributed across the CNS midline (Kimmel and Warga, 1986). In some clones the periodicity at which the cells or cell clusters disperse along the axis corresponds to a segment length or a multiple of a segment length, such that in these clones cells derived from single early gastrula progenitors occupy homologous positions in several spinal segments.

Segmental periodicity in clones suggests a role of cell lineage in establishing segmental patterning of the nervous system. However, in other neural clones period length is not ordinarily related to segment length, such that the related cells occupy noncorresponding positions in different segments. The fact that only certain types of cells in the spinal cord may be organized segmentally provides a possible explanation for the segmental versus nonsegmental clonal arrangements; we can suppose that the clones that disperse segmentally generate the ventral (i.e., basal plate) cell types that themselves are segmentally arranged, and the other clones generate other, nonsegmental, cell types (e.g., dorsal ones). This hypothesis has not been examined systematically, but it is true that segmentally (as well as bilaterally) homologous primary motoneurons are frequently produced by the same early progenitor (see, e.g., Myers *et al.*, 1986; Kimmel and

Fig. 7 A blastomere clone forms segmentally organized clusters in the hindbrain. Dorsal views, at (A) dorsal and (B) more ventral planes of focus of a whole mounted embryo, 2 days after fertilization. A single blastomere was intracellularly injected with biotin during the late blastula stage, and its progeny appear as darkly labeled cell clusters, one bilateral pair in each of several rhombomeres (A). Labeled commissural axons that arise from these clusters of neurons are visible in (B). The commissures are present in the rhombomere border regions (see Fig. 8).

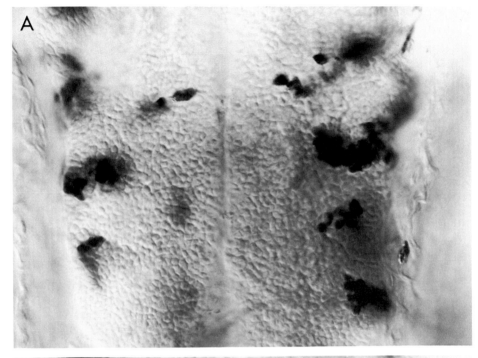

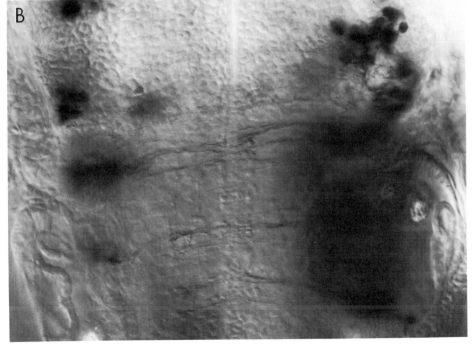

Warga, 1988). Furthermore, the hypothesis predicts that hindbrain cell lineages would be segmental more frequently than spinal ones, since segmental organization seems to include many more types of neurons in the hindbrain than in the spinal cord. We have, indeed, observed many segmentally organized clones in the hindbrain (C. B. Kimmel, T. F. Schilling, K. Hatta, and R. Warga, unpublished observations). Furthermore, by labeling the clones with a marker that allows detailed examination of their axonal morphology, and allowing them to develop long enough so that substantial numbers of cells are differentiating, we frequently observe that the segmental clusters in the hindbrain do contain the same type of neurons, as is also predicted by the hypothesis (Fig. 7).

Thus, as early as the gastrula stage, cells may acquire some kind of programming, heritable through cell lineage, that specifies the segmental patterning of their neuronal progeny. This programming, if it occurs at all, does not rigidly commit the cells to a single course of development, for if it did, we would expect to see clusters of lineally related cells in successive segments that are exact copies of one another, as in the segmental lineages produced by teloblasts in the leech (Weisblat and Shankland, 1985). Such rigidly organized lineages do not occur in zebrafish. The copies are imperfect, whole segments being skipped. Furthermore, as reviewed above, Eisen's (1991) transplantation experiments reveal clearly that motoneuronal commitment does not occur until cells are postmitotic and beginning axogenesis. Lineage programming must therefore reversibly or "conditionally *specify*" (Davidson, 1990) a cell such that its behavior and that of its progeny are biased (Jacobson and Moody, 1984) but adaptable. Acquisition of reversible biases appears to be an important and usually unrecognized feature of animal development (discussed by Kimmel *et al.*, 1991), and we suggest that it plays a significant role in segmental development in zebrafish.

B. CNS Expression of Engrailed-Type Homeoproteins

We have already noted two aspects of expression of eng homeodomain proteins in the mesoderm. Expression in the iterated set of muscle pioneers may specify the boundary between dorsal and ventral muscle of each myotome. Expression in precursors of two specific muscles of the jaw may establish the region-specific, perhaps segment-specific, identity of the cells. *eng* is also expressed in the embryonic CNS, in what seem to be at least two basic patterns that appear to reveal separate aspects of its segmental organization.

The first expression of *eng*, occurring just after gastrulation, appears as a single prominent transverse stripe in the brain primordium (Njølstad and Fjose, 1988; Patel *et al.*, 1989) that, within its borders, appears to include every cell in the neural tube (Hatta *et al.*, 1991). Later, at the center of the stripe, the midbrain–hindbrain boundary forms. This position is of interest, considering that the boundary seems to be the anterior segmental boundary of the first rhombomere.

Furthermore, the midbrain itself might be another brain segment; it is somewhat larger than a single hindbrain segment, but, like a hindbrain segment, it has a motor nucleus and a single cluster of reticulospinal cells (see Section VI,A). By this interpretation *eng* expression would delimit, and by its early expression perhaps serve to specify (Hatta *et al.*, 1991), a specialized CNS segmental boundary.

On each side of the boundary, the stripe is about a half-segment wide. That is, the anterior limit of *eng* expression is *within* the midbrain and includes only its caudal half, and the posterior limit of expression is within the first rhombomere and includes only its anterior half, not the whole rhombomere, as suggested for the mouse (Wilkinson, 1990). Thus, the whole strip is the width of a single segment, but phase-shifted in the fashion of the relationship between segments and parasegments in *Drosophila* (Lawrence, 1988). The expression of *eng* may be important in specifying not only the segment boundary, but also the fates of the cells within its domain, for the midbrain cells form particular segmental nuclei, and the hindbrain cells form part of the cerebellum. In the mouse two *engrailed* genes are expressed in the stripe, and deletion of one of them, *En-2*, by mutation produces phenotypic defects in the cerebellum (Joyner *et al.*, 1991).

After rhombomeres form, a second pattern of *eng* expression appears in the CNS that includes a subset of its cells extending in a discontinuous row through the length of both the hindbrain and the spinal cord (Hatta *et al.*, 1991). The identities of these cells are unknown, but from their locations we suspect they are interneurons. They are all positioned at roughly, but not exactly, the same dorso-ventral level in the neural tube, approximately subdividing the tube into dorsal and ventral halves recognized by the alar and basal plates, similar to the manner in which the muscle pioneers subdivide the myotomes into dorsal and ventral halves. Also, like the muscle pioneers, the *eng*-expressing cells in the CNS are apparently organized segmentally (Fig. 2).

Segmental arrangement is clearest in the rhombomeres, where even many hours after expression begins one can easily locate most of the groups of eng^+ cells to the rhombomere centers. The overall pattern is complex and bilaterally symmetrical, suggesting that several types of cells are included. Segmental pat-terning is harder to discern in the spinal cord. Here, *eng* expression develops in an AP wave, and to observe the segmental organization, one needs to examine the segments where the expression is just beginning. Usually, a single cell on each side of the midline, located approximately at the center of the segment (as related to the myotomes), expresses *eng* at this stage. Shortly thereafter, ex-pression begins in cells located at AP levels between the first ones, and they fill in the row until the periodicity is essentially lost. This spatiotemporal pattern of development, a segmental one giving way to a nearly continuous row of cells, is like that observed in the pattern of differentiation of ventral spinal neurons, as revealed by probes for neuron-specific markers (Hanneman *et al.*, 1988). However, the *eng*-expressing cells, located more dorsally, are not the same neurons. Thus, spinal cord segmentation would seem to include more cell types than previously recognized.

The presence of this distinctive AP column of *eng*-expressing cells extending through both the hindbrain and the spinal cord is one of the features *shared* by segments in both of these CNS regions. Further study should permit identification of the cells to see whether they share other features (e.g., similarities in the pathways of their axons).

VI. Features of Hindbrain Segments

Similarities in the early lineages of cells that form the hindbrain and the spinal cord, and the shared pattern of *eng* expression, might suggest that head and trunk segments are both parts of a single linear series, as required by the body metamere hypothesis. When rhombomeres form in the hindbrain, they are the same length as trunk somites (Hanneman *et al.*, 1988), which also supports the hypothesis. However, as is clear from the discussion so far, major differences are present between the head and trunk, which argues against the hypothesis. The changes in the periphery have been summarized already. Recently, much new information has become available concerning brain segmentation, and we will need to consider it in depth for a fuller comparison of the brain and the spinal cord. Differences might mean that segmentation in the head and the trunk are basically different processes (Stern, 1990), or, as we argue, they may have arisen adaptively because of the different functional requirements between the head and the trunk.

A. Rhombomeres Have a Rich Internal Structure

Seven rhombomeres are conspicuous in the hindbrain, each one subdivided along its length into center and border regions that contain functionally distinctive subsets of neurons separated from one another by a curtainlike row of glial fibers (Fig. 8). The segment centers contain motor and premotor neurons derived from the basal plates. The motoneurons are grouped into segmental clusters (Kimmel *et al.*, 1985; Trevarrow *et al.*, 1990). Most early premotor interneurons project axons posteriorly into the spinal cord, and, since they are present in the so-called reticular formation of the hindbrain, they are known as reticulospinal neurons. A single cluster of these neurons is present in each neuromere center (Metcalfe *et al.*, 1986; Hanneman *et al.*, 1988). The neuromere border regions flank the boundaries between adjacent neuromeres. Their most prominent neurons are dorsally located, derived from the alar plate, and situated so as to directly receive sensory information entering the brain via the sensory roots of cranial nerves.

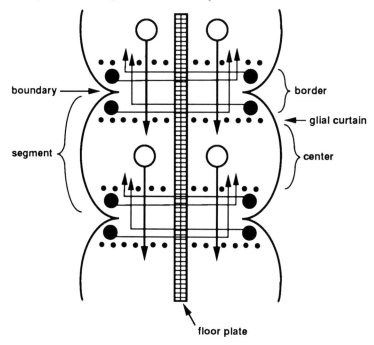

boundary

border

glial curtain

segment

center

floor plate

Fig. 8   The consensus structure of a zebrafish rhombomere. Reticulospinal cells (open circles) in the rhombomere centers have axons that project caudally to the spinal cord. Motoneurons (not shown) are also located in the rhombomere centers. Commissural neurons (solid circles) have axons that cross the midline near the segment boundaries and then project rostrally to the midbrain. The crossing axons are closely associated with a curtainlike structure formed by processes of neuroglia cells, which seems to form a partition between the center and border regions within each rhombomere. The floor plate, located in the midline, does not appear to be segmented. (From Trevarrow et al., 1990.)

The axons of the dorsal neurons relay this information, many of them collecting into bundles that course ventrally in close association with the glial curtains, and cross the midline in commissures located just adjacent to the segment boundaries (Trevarrow et al., 1990).

Thus, as compared with the spinal cord, hindbrain segmentation is more prominent. The only morphologically nonsegmented component known in this region of the CNS is the floor plate. A key difference between the hindbrain and the spinal cord is the prominence of the interneurons, many more of them being present in the hindbrain than in spinal segments, and most certainly their functions are more diverse. That segmental organization is more apparent in the hindbrain than in the spinal cord may reflect this richness in diversity, particularly with respect to the organization of the axonal pathways of the interneurons. The curtainlike arrangement of glial cells may serve to guide the commissural axons, with which the curtains are closely associated (Trevarrow et al., 1990).

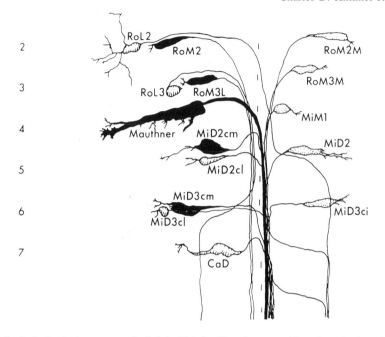

Fig. 9   Reticulospinal neurons are included within families of segmental homologs, but have individual segment-specific identities. Dorsal view 5 days after fertilization. Three families of cells are indicated by the solid, hatched, and stippled cell bodies. Each cell is actually bilaterally paired, but is shown on only one side of the midline (dashed line) or the other, according to its family membership. The axons of all of the neurons project caudally (down) to the spinal cord, some in a medial pathway and others switching to the more lateral pathway; this and the cell body position within the segment are used to define family membership. Most of the segments (numbered 2–7) have one member of each family, but not always; a hatched cell is missing in the fourth segment, and only a hatched cell is present in the seventh. Other segment-specific features include cell size, dendrite branching pattern, and whether or not the axon crosses the midline. (From Metcalfe *et al.*, 1986.)

The axons of certain reticulospinal neurons appear to use segmentally repeating cues as guidance choice points; in Fig. 9 certain axons can be seen to switch from a medial to a lateral pathway, and these switches occur in the segment centers (see also Metcalfe *et al.*, 1986). In contrast axon pathways in the spinal cord seem not so segmentally based.

B. Rhombomeres Have Individual Identities

Also unlike the spinal cord is that specific rhombomeres differ from one another stereotypically. The differences include features of their innervation of the periphery via the motor and sensory roots of separate cranial nerves, whose differences in humans every medical student has been forced to memorize for the past several decades; the situation is not much less complex in fish (Fig. 6). Individual rhombomeres project motor nerves to either pharyngeal arch or eye muscle, or, in the case of the fifth segment, from separate motor nuclei to both target organs. Primary sensory input is also complex. The second segment uniquely receives fibers mediating tactile sensibility (Metcalfe *et al.*, 1990), and the next three segments are the only ones to receive input from hair cells, fibers from the lateral line system entering the brain anterior and posterior to those from the ear. These facts make little sense if one is attempting to deduce the plan of a consensus rhombomere; the organization seems highly derived.

With interneurons one can consider segment diversity at the level of single identified cells. By morphological similarities one can assign particular neurons to one or another family of segmental homologs, three of which are shown in Fig. 9. However, the families have no representatives in some of the segments, and many individual neurons, while meeting the rules for membership to a particular family (Metcalfe *et al.*, 1986), vary in a segment-specific fashion in size, shape, and axonal projection. In segmented invertebrates differences between segmentally homologous neurons often arise as secondary modifications after a common early pattern of development (reviewed by Kimmel, 1990), such as neurite retraction and regrowth. Study of reticulospinal neuronal development has revealed no such remodeling among identified neurons in the zebrafish hindbrain (Mendelson, 1986; Mendelson and Kimmel, 1986; W. K. Metcalfe, unpublished observations).

This morphological diversity underlies functional specializations of segments that is more pronounced in the case of the hindbrain than in the spinal cord. For example, considering the motor output, all spinal segments swim, but hindbrain segments stare, chew, or breathe, according to their positions in the series. In the brain's commanding role over spinal activity, a reticulospinal neuron in the fourth rhombomere, the Mauthner cell, usually functions in avoidance behavior, but if it is deleted from the circuit, some other reticulospinal neuron, possibly one of its segmental homologs, takes its place (Eaton *et al.*, 1982).

C. Pairs of Rhombomeres May Be Patterned Together

Motoneurons supplying cranial nerves V, VI, and VII are each present as clusters in two adjacent segments. Because of this pattern, Kimmel *et al.* (1985) mistakenly assumed that a single hindbrain segment was twice as large as we now understand it to be. Rather, in a fashion analogous[2] to the segment pairs defined

---

[2]We purposely use the term "analogous," rather than "homologous," here. It seems rather unlikely, from the information available at present, that *Drosophila* pair-rule gene homologs are used for segmental patterning even in other insects (Tear *et al.*, 1988), let alone in vertebrates.

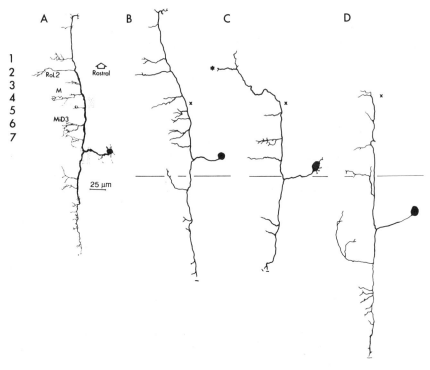

Fig. 10 T-reticular interneurons, located in the caudal hindbrain of a 5-day-old larva, have segment-specific axonal branching and termination patterns. Rhombomeres are numbered 1–7. The asterisk marks the position of the the RoL2 neuron and the x's mark the position of the crossing Mauthner axon. (A and B) Two examples of neurons located in the seventh rhombomere. Their axons terminate in the midbrain, giving rise to collateral branches in each of the seven rhombomeres. The more prominent branches are in the even-numbered rhombomeres, where the reticulospinal neurons RoL2, Mauthner (M), and MiD3 are located (see Fig. 9). (C) The axon of a T-reticular interneuron located about a segment more caudally terminates in the second rhombomere. (D) The axon of a yet more caudal T-reticular interneuron terminates in the fourth rhombomere. (From Kimmel *et al.*, 1985.)

by pair-rule gene expression patterns in *Drosophila*, brain segment pairs could represent another level of axial patterning, segmentally based, but at a level higher than the segments themselves, in a hierarchy of patterning interactions. This interpretation was made by Lumsden and Keynes (1989), principally based on the arrangement of motoneurons in the chick embryo, and also on the timing of their development, earlier in even- than in odd-numbered rhombomeres (see also Lumsden, 1990).

If segment pairs are really an important element in hindbrain patterning, then one might expect to find additional structures, besides motoneurons, to be patterned segment-pair-wise. This, in fact, is the case in zebrafish. The odd-numbered rhombomeres are reproducibly larger than the even-numbered ones

(Hanneman *et al.*, 1988 and C.B.K., unpublished observations). Identified reticulospinal neurons located in even-numbered rhombomeres are displaced lateral relative to their segmental homologs in odd-numbered rhombomeres (Fig. 9). Branching and terminations of the rostral axons of successive T-reticular neurons, which are serially repeating neurons of the caudal hindbrain, occur in a segment pair fashion (Fig. 10). Like specific cranial motoneurons, some kinds of reticulospinal neurons seem to be present only in each of two successive segments; for example, single MiR neurons are present uniquely at the 3–4 and 4–5 segment border regions. These observations all strengthen the case for segment pairs being generally meaningful in terms of hindbrain AP organization.

So far there is no hint of segment pairs in spinal cord patterning. They might be present cryptically, but since differences between adjacent spinal segments have not been described, extensive analyses will be required to find them if they are present.

D. Posterior Hindbrain Is a Region of Transition to the Spinal Cord

The connection between the hindbrain and the spinal cord is of clear importance with respect to the issue of body metamerism. Hindbrain tissue continues caudal to the region where the seven prominent neuromeres that we have been considering are present. An eighth brain segment was described here by Lumsden and Keynes (1989) in the chicken, and two segments, eight and nine, were tentatively assigned in the corresponding region in the zebrafish (Hanneman *et al.*, 1988), based on the length of the region and the positions of large (but unidentified) neuronal cells. Whether a real species difference exists cannot yet be decided; the organization of the region and the level of the spinal cord–hindbrain boundary are simply not well understood. However, it is clear that a pattern transition occurs in both the bird and the fish, abruptly after the seventh rhombomere. In zebrafish reticulospinal cells disappear. The apparently single large motor nucleus of the vagus nerve extends through the posterior hindbrain and into the anterior spinal cord, innervating not a single gill arch, but four of them (Fig. 6)! Evidence that this brain region is segmented comes from its interneurons. T-reticular interneurons, prominent dorsolateral interneurons of the morphologies shown in Fig. 10, recur serially here at about six successive AP levels. Ventromedial "ic" interneurons also recur with the same spacing, but they are not so periodic as the T-reticular interneurons. This repeat of both classes is at two neurons per segment, if one assumes that a segment length in this posterior hindbrain region is the same as the length of a rhombomere more anteriorly.

Antibody labeling studies show that, in the fish, the organization of a number of antigens in the posterior hindbrain is much more similar to that of the spinal cord than to that of the more anterior hindbrain (Trevarrow *et al.*, 1990). For example, glial fibers are present in two rows per segment anteriorly, but here and in the spinal cord glial fibers are present more continuously and segmental organization is not apparent. On the other hand, not all features of the spinal cord extend into the region; the most anterior primary motoneurons are found in the first spinal segment. The posterior hindbrain and the first few segments of the spinal cord thus form a transitional zone in which patterning is spinal, but not entirely so, in character. It is interesting that characteristics that are overtly spinal extend into the head, anterior to the level of the first myotome. This out-of-register pattern could be specified by *hox* genes, the expression of which in the CNS and the mesoderm is typically offset in the same fashion (Fig. 1).

VII. Zebrafish Metameres?

Considering the foregoing analyses, what can we now say about the outstanding issues concerning segmentation in vertebrates that were raised at the beginning of this chapter? Are segments patterned independently in the different segmented tissues, or is a vertebrate a metameric creature, whose body segments encompass several tissues? Further, if vertebrate metameres are present, do those in the head correspond to those of the lower body?

The body metamere theory predicted that the different tissue components of metameres should lie in register, and be patterned together, independently or interactively. The recent analyses strengthen the argument made previously (Kimmel *et al.*, 1988) that trunk and tail segments are patterned interactively, as metameres. Programming the segmental patterning of the spinal cord might involve lineage-dependent biases of the neuronal progenitor cells, but the expression of segmental patterning appears to be rigidly dependent on the mesoderm. Trunk metameres thus are formed interactively by cells present in two germ layers, and in fact by a restricted "paraxial" subset of cells in each of them. We propose that they arise from corresponding paraxial zones of cells in the gastrula stage fate map, shown in Fig. 11. The most dorsal axial cells in the gastrula include the prospective notochord (i.e., the mesoderm) and, immediately above it, the prospective floor plate (i.e., the ectoderm). Neither the notochord nor the floor plate is overtly segmented, and neither cell type is required for establishing segmentation. In the paraxial zone, adjacent to the axial tissue precursors, precursors of segmental plate mesoderm and basal plate ectoderm form the metameres. As yet unrecognized interactions could be occurring while the cells are in these positions that underlie segmental patterning. More laterally still is the intermediate and lateral plate mesoderm and the overlying prospective alar plate, neural crest, and skin ectoderm. While many cell types derived from these precursors seem not to be segmentally arranged, some of them are, including sensory ganglia from the ectoderm and blood vessels from the splanchnic mesoderm. Like the basal plate neuroectodermal cells, these cell types are probably dependent at a later time on the somitic mesoderm for segmentation, as is

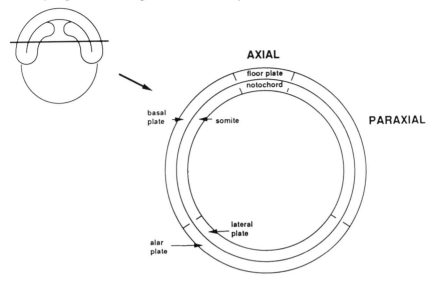

Fig. 11 Segmented neurectoderm and mesoderm arise from corresponding regions of the gastrula. Shown is the midgastrula fate-map arrangement of certain tissue precursors, seen in transverse section, with dorsal to the top. The outer ring of cells forms the neurectoderm; the inner one, mesoderm. In both layers the paraxial tissues are prominently segmented, while the axial ones are not.

known for the neural crest derivatives in amphibian and avian embryos (Keynes and Stern, 1987). Learning how trunk metameres are established may thus require focusing on a single subset of early cells in a single germ layer, namely, paraxial mesoderm.

The head is more mysterious, and more controversial. On the one hand is the notion that head segments are special derivatives of an initially uniform series of body metameres (Goodrich, 1930), such that cranial nerves are the anterior homologs of spinal nerves (see also Jarvik, 1980). On the other hand is the idea that the vertebrate head is a brand new structure in evolution, the invention of which depended on a new kind of patterning in which the key player is the neural crest (Gans and Northcutt, 1983), not the paraxial mesoderm. What has become much clearer from the recent work, including cell-level studies in the chicken (Lumsden and Keynes, 1989; Fraser *et al.*, 1990; Lumsden, 1990) and the zebrafish, is that segmentation figures very prominently in head patterning. The new molecular studies of *hox* gene expression in rhombomeres in the mouse (Wilkinson *et al.*, 1989) suggest that, whether the head is old or new, it uses ancient genes to pattern the identities of segments it contains.

The recent fate-mapping studies show that at an early postgastrula stage in both avian (Noden, 1988) and fish (Schilling *et al.*, 1989) embryos, the mesodermal precursors of the segmented periphery are found in a linear arrangement along the AP axis, in phase with the neural segments that later supply their innervation and the premigratory crest that supplies their cartilages. These relationships were unknown, but were supposed by Goodrich (1930), and discovering that they are so strongly supports the proposition that the head is metameric.

We also argue for the homology of head and trunk segments that the Goodrich model requires, but we admit that our position requires some hand waving, and that we are playing a devil's advocate role, for the consensus of current understanding would seem to suggest otherwise. The developmental relationships between the CNS neuromeres, mesoderm, and neural crest are not nearly so well understood in the head as in the trunk. In the head the neural crest seems to have taken on a more prominent role in segmentation; perhaps it is segmentally organized even before it migrates [within crest "ectomeres" (see Couly and Le Douarin, 1990)], which seems unlike the situation in the trunk. Crest clearly contributes in a major way to the head segmented periphery, and could be a major player in segmental patterning in the head periphery; it is principally this increased role of the crest in the head that led to the suggestion that the head is a new structure in evolution (Gans and Northcutt, 1983) and, more recently, that the head uses a basically different mechanism than the trunk for segmentation, in which the ectoderm, not the mesoderm, has the dominant role (Stern, 1990). On the other hand, the paraxial mesoderm is present in the head before the crest migrates, and may already be segmented, as somitomeres. This view is controversial, for head somitomeres apparently can be seen only in the preotic part of the head, using a single technique, scanning electron microscopy, and apparently only by some who try to find them. The paraxial mesoderm is as reduced in the head as the crest is expanded.

However, the differences in contribution of the mesoderm and the neural crest to the head and the trunk segment can be understood considering the functional differences between them, as contrasted with their development. For a larval fish to swim requires extensive musculature (i.e., the mesoderm), since the whole body must be propelled, yet swimming segments require no cartilage, for what is being pulled on by the muscles is the notochord, the vertebrae developing very late. In contrast breathing segments use cartilages (i.e., the head neural crest) to move the gills, and since only gill arches are being moved, not the whole body, a good deal less muscle is required in a breathing segment than in a swimming one.

Thus, different functional adaptations of head and trunk segments may be obscuring developmental similarities. Experiments to critically examine the role of the head mesoderm in segmentation are lacking, and the extent to which a given primordium contributes to a segment could make little difference developmentally. For example, the notochords in birds and mammals are small, as compared to those of lower vertebrates that have swimming larvae. However, the notochord seems to play the same developmental role during neural induction in all vertebrates.

Goodrich's (1930) idea of body metameres being present in a single continuous series has received support in much of the recent work. If he is correct, then some apparent differences will need to be worked out, such as pair-rule patterning being rather clear in the head segments but not, so far, in the trunk. But there are similarities. Rhombomeres have the same length as trunk somites when they first appear, which suggests that the same underlying patterning mechanism might be operating. In the mouse, and possibly in the zebrafish, the anterior levels of expression of successive *hox* genes within a single locus pass through hindbrain segments into and through spinal ones, in what seems to be a continuous series. *eng* expression turns on in the zebrafish brain and continues into and through the spinal cord without a gap in pattern. The periodically dispersed progeny of early neuroectodermal precursor cells frequently contribute to both hindbrain and spinal cord segments, again without a break in pattern. It may be worthwhile not to discard the unifying concept of a vertebrate body segment as a remarkably plastic structure that has been adapted for different functions according to AP location along the body, as is clearly the case in insects.

In closing we reconsider the issue of the origin of vertebrate segmentation. As pointed out in Section II, there are many parallels between insect *HOM* and vertebrate *hox* genes, and the parallels increase as our studies continue. For example, the fact that somitic expression of *hox-3.3* in zebrafish begins exactly at a segment border (Molven *et al.*, 1990) is the first such case we know of for the mesoderm, the discovery coming only 1 year following the first demonstrations of mouse *Hox* gene expression boundaries fall on neuromere boundaries (Murphy *et al.*, 1989; Wilkinson *et al.*, 1989). It will be interesting to learn whether other *hox* genes exhibit segmentally based expression patterns, as they should according to the hypothesis that their common ancestor was segmented. New findings in *Drosophila* have also revealed new parallels; thus, before the work by Bermingham *et al.* (1990), a difficulty for the common segmented ancestor hypothesis was the out-of-register expression of *hox* genes in the neurectoderm and the mesoderm. This has been observed in all but one case examined (De Robertis *et al.*, 1989), and did not seem to fit with the "in-register" pattern of *HOM* genes described for *Drosophila*. However, Bermingham *et al.* (1990) found that, early in *Drosophila* development, mesodermal and ectodermal cells expressing *Antp* are only lined up during early development. As the tissue primordia arise during gastrulation, the expression of *Antp* changes to match the vertebrate out-of-register pattern shown in Fig. 1. It will be interesting to learn whether regulatory pathways patterning vertebrate *hox* gene expression (Gaunt and Singh, 1990) are shared with *Drosophila*.

As we have emphasized throughout this chapter, the developmental studies of zebrafish strengthen the notion that vertebrates seem to be metameric creatures. Attempts to dispel this notion in the past have pointed up the limited extent of vertebrate body segmentation. We agree that segmentation does indeed seem to be limited, but it is even limited in annelids, which are certainly segmented animals and which show no hint of segmental organization in lineages that produce the gut or the skin, organs that also appear unsegmented in vertebrates. Accordingly, the presence of nonsegmented tissues within a segmented body plan does not seem particularly problematic for the common segmented ancestor hypothesis; a most interesting question for both development and evolution is how the apparently unsegmented axial sets of cells, the notochord and the floor plate (Fig. 11), come to be insinuated into the metameres. These axial tissues have dominant developmental roles (Jessell *et al.*, 1989), and certainly have also been extremely important in chordate evolution.

That extrinsic influences are important in segmental patterning is also not unique to vertebrates. We have discussed evidence that patterning of ventral neurons of the zebrafish spinal cord might involve lineage-dependent biases of the neuronal progenitor cells, but certainly seems rigidly dependent on mesoderm. The situation here seems exactly analogous to what we now know is the case in the leech. Ectodermal teloblasts intrinsically generate segmental sets of neuronal precursors in the leech (Stuart *et al.*, 1989), but patterning instructions from the mesoderm are essential for expression of the pattern (Torrence *et al.*, 1989). As for the molecular studies the parallels between these distantly related metazoans, here at the cellular level, were unsuspected before the experimental investigations of segmental development were carried out.

Acknowledgments

We thank G. Bobrowicz, J. S. Eisen, D. W. C. Liu, S. H. Pike, M. Westerfield, and A. Wood for sharing unpublished observations. Pat Edwards helped in preparing the manuscript, and Reida Kimmel helped with the figures. Original work from our laboratory was supported by National Science Foundation grant BNS-8708638 and National Institutes of Health grants NS17963 and HD22486.

References

Akam, M. (1989). *Cell* **57,** 347–349.
Anderson, C. B., and Meier, S. (1981). *Dev. Biol.* **85,** 385–402.
Balfour, F. M. (1878). "A Monograph on the Development of Elasmobranch Fishes" (*J. Anat. Physiol.* 1876–1877 and 1878). Macmillan, London.
Balling, R., Mutter, G., Gruss, P., and Kessel, M. (1989). *Cell* **57,** 337–347.
Bateson, W. (1894). "Materials for the Study of Variation," p. 598. Macmillan, London.
Bermingham, J. R., Martinez-Arias, A., Petitt, M. G., and Scott, M. P. (1990). *Development* **109,** 553–566.
Couly, G., and Le Douarin, N. M. (1990). *Development* **108,** 543–558.
Davidson, E. H. (1990). *Development* **108,** 365–389.
De Robertis, E. M., Oliver, G., and Wright, C. V. E. (1989). *Cell* **57,** 189–191.
Eaton, R. C., Lavender, W. A., and Nissanov, J. (1982). *J. Comp. Physiol., A* **144,** 521–531.
Eisen, J. S. (1991). *Science* **252,** 569–572.
Eisen, J. S., and Pike, S. H., (1991). *Neuron* **6,** 767–776.

Felsenfeld, A.L., Curry, S., and Kimmel, C.B. (1991). Manuscript in preparation.

Fraser, S. E., Keynes, R. J., and Lumsden, A. (1990). *Nature (London)* **344,** 431–435.

Gans, C., and Northcutt, R. G. (1983). *Science* **220,** 268–273.

Garcia-Bellido, A., Ripoll, P., and Morata, G. (1973). *Nature (London), New Biol.* **245,** 251–253.

Gaunt, S. J., and Singh, P. B. (1990). *Trends Genet.* **6,** 208–212.

Gerhart, J., Ubbels, G., Black, S., Hara, K., and Kirschner, M. (1981). *Nature (London)* **292,** 511–516.

Goodrich, E. S. (1930). "Studies on the Structure and Development of Vertebrates." Macmillan, London.

Gould, S. J. (1989). "Wonderful Life: The Burgess Shale and the Nature of History." Norton, New York.

Graham, A., Papalopulu, N., and Krumlauf, R. (1989). *Cell* **57,** 367–378.

Hanneman, E., and Westerfield, M. (1989). *J. Comp. Neurol.* **284,** 350–361.

Hanneman, E., Trevarrow, B., Metcalfe, W. K., Kimmel, C. B., and Westerfield, M. (1988). *Development* **103,** 49–58.

Harrison, R. G. (1918). *J. Exp. Zool.* **25,** 413–461.

Hatta, K., BreMiller, R. A., Westerfield, M., and Kimmel, C. B. (1991). *Development.* In press.

Hatta, K., Schilling, T. F., BreMiller, R. A., and Kimmel, C. B. (1990). *Science* **250,** 802–805.

Ho, R. K., Kane, D. A., and Kimmel, C. B. (1989). *Soc. Neurosci. Abstr.* **15,** 809.

Holland, P. W. H. (1988). *Development, Suppl.* **103,** 17–24.

Holland, P. W. H. (1990). *Semin. Dev. Biol.* **1,** 135–145.

Jacobson, A. G. (1988). *Development, Suppl.* **104,** 209–220.

Jacobson, M., and Moody, S. A. (1984). *J. Neurosci.* **4,** 1361–1369.

Jarvik, E. (1980). "Basic Structure and Evolution of Vertebrates." Academic Press, New York.

Jessell, T. M., Bovolenta, P., Placzek, M., Tessier-Lavigne, M., and Dodd, J. (1989). *Ciba Found. Symp.* **144** 255.

Joyner, A. L., Herrup, C. A., Auerbach, C. A., and Rossant, D. J. (1991). *Science* **251,** 1239–1243.

Kessel, M., and Gruss, P. (1990). *Science* **249,** 374–379.

Keynes, R. J., and Stern, C. D. (1987). *In* "Molecular Biology of Invertebrate Development" (J. D. O'Connor, ed.), p. 177. Liss, New York.

Kimmel, C. B. (1989). *Trends Genet.* **5,** 283–288.

Kimmel, C. B. (1990). *In* "Molecular Approaches toward Supracellular Phenomena" (S. Roth, ed.). pp. 137–174. Univ. of Pennsylvania Press, Philadelphia, Pennsylvania. In press.

Kimmel, C. B., and Warga, R. (1986). *Science* **231,** 365–368.

Kimmel, C. B., and Warga, R. M. (1987). *Nature (London)* **234,** 234–237.

Kimmel, C. B., and Warga, R. M. (1988). *Trends Genet.* **4,** 68–74.

Kimmel, C. B., Metcalfe, W. K., and Schabtach, E. (1985). *J. Comp. Neurol.* **233,** 365–376.

Kimmel, C. B., Sepich, D. S., and Trevarrow, B. (1988). *Development, Suppl.* **104,** 197–207.

Kimmel, C. B., Kane, D. A., Walker, C., Warga, R. M., and Rothman, M. B. (1989). *Nature (London)* **337,** 358–362.

Kimmel, C. B., Kane, D. A., and Ho, R. K. (1991). *Symp. Soc. Dev. Biol.* **49,** in press.

Kuwada, J. Y., Bernhardt, R. R., and Chitnis, A. B. (1990). *J. Neurosci.* **10,** 1299–1308.

Langille, R. M., and Hall, B. K. (1988). *Anat. Embryol.* **177,** 297–305.

Lawrence, P. A. (1988). *Development* **104,** 61–65.

Lewis, E. B. (1978). *Nature (London)* **276,** 565–570.

Liu, D. W. C., and Westerfield, M. (1991). Manuscript in preparation.

Lumsden, A. (1990). *Trends NeuroSci. (Pers. Ed.)* **13,** 329–339.

Lumsden, A., and Keynes, R. (1989). *Nature (London)* **337,** 424–428.

McGinnis, W., Garber, R. L., Wirz, J., Kuroiwa, A., and Gehring, W. J. (1984a). *Cell* **3,** 403–408.

McGinnis, W., Levine, M. S., Hafen, E., Kuroiwa, A., and Gehring, W. J. (1984b). *Nature (London)* **308**, 428–433.

Mendelson, B. (1986). *J. Comp. Neurol.* **251**, 172–184.

Mendelson, B., and Kimmel, C. B. (1986). *Dev. Biol.* **118**, 309–313.

Metcalfe, W. K., Mendelson, B., and Kimmel, C. B. (1986). *J. Comp. Neurol.* **251**, 147–159.

Metcalfe, W. K., Myers, P. Z., Trevarrow, B., Bass, M. B., and Kimmel, C. B. (1990). *Development* **110**, 491–504.

Molven, A., Wright, C. V. E., BreMiller, R., De Robertis, E. M., and Kimmel, C. B. (1990). *Development* **109**, 279–288.

Murphy, P., Davidson, D. R., and Hill, R. E. (1989). *Nature (London)* **341**, 156–159.

Myers, P. Z., Eisen, J. S., and Westerfield, M. (1986). *J. Neurosci.* **6**, 2278–2289.

Njølstad, P. R., and Fjose, A. (1988). *Biochem. Biophys. Res. Commun.* **157**, 426–432.

Njølstad, P. R., Molven, A., Apold, J., and Fjose, A. (1990). *EMBO J.* **9**, 515–524.

Noden, D. M. (1988). *Development, Suppl.* **103**, 121–140.

Nüsslein-Volhard, C., and Weischaus, E. (1980). *Nature (London)* **287**, 795–801.

Patel, N. H., Martin-Blanco, E., Coleman, K. G., Poole, S. J., Ellis, M. C., Kornberg, T. B., and Goodman, C. S. (1989). *Cell* **58**, 955–968.

Raff, E. C., and Raff, R. A. (1985). *Science* **313**, 185.

Schilling, T. F., Warga, R. M., and Kimmel, C. B. (1989). *Soc. Neurosci. Abstr.* **15**, 810.

Schilling, T. F., Hatta, K., Walker, C., and Kimmel, C. B. (1990). *J. Cell Biol.* **111**, 238a.

Scott, M. P., and Weiner, A. J. (1984). *Proc. Natl. Acad. Sci. U.S.A.* **81**, 4115–4119.

Stent, G. S. (1985). *Philos. Trans. R. Soc. London, B* **312**, 3–19.

Stern, C. D. (1990). *Semin. Dev. Biol.* **1**, 109–116.

Streisinger, G., Walker, C., Dower, N., Knauber, D., and Singer, F. (1981). *Nature (London)* **291**, 293–296.

Stuart, D. K., Torrence, S. A., and Law, M. I. (1989). *Dev. Biol.* **136**, 17–39.

Sundin, O. H., and Eichele, G. (1990). *Genes Dev.* **4**, 1267–1276.

Tam, P. P. L. (1988). *Development* **103**, 379–390.

Tear, G., Bate, C. M., and Martinez-Arias, A. (1988). *Development, Suppl.* **104**, 135–145.

Torrence, S. A., Law, M. I., and Stuart, D. K. (1989). *Dev. Biol.* **136**, 40–60.

Trevarrow, B., Marks, D. L., and Kimmel, C. B. (1990). *Neuron* **4**, 669–679.

Warga, R. M., and Kimmel, C. B. (1990). *Development* **108**, 569–580.

Weisblat, D. A., and Shankland, M. (1985). *Philos. Trans. R. Soc. London, B* **312**, 39–56.

Wilkinson, D. G., Bhatt, S., Cook, M., Boncinelli, E., and Krumlauf, R. (1989). *Nature (London)* **341**, 405–409.

Wilkinson, D. G. (1990). *Semin. Devel. Biol.* **1**, 127–134.

Wilkinson, D. G., and Krumlauf, R. (1990). *Trends NeuroSci. (Pers. Ed.)* **13**, 335–339.

Wright, C. V. E., Cho, K. W. Y., Hardwicke, J., Collins, R. H., and De Robertis, E. M. (1989). *Cell* **59**, 81–93.

5

Proteoglycans in Development

Paul F. Goetinck
La Jolla Cancer Research Foundation
La Jolla, California 92037

I. Introduction

Proteoglycans are complex macromolecules that consist of a core protein to which one or more glycosaminoglycan (GAG) side chains attached. Differences in proteoglycan structure can result from differential expression of genes encoding their core proteins as well as from variation in the number, length, and types of GAG chains attached during the posttranslational modifications of the core proteins. GAG chains are polymers of repeating disaccharides and they may consist of chondroitin sulfate (*N*-acetylgalactosamine–glucuronic acid), dermatan sulfate (*N*-acetylgalactosamine–iduronic acid), keratan sulfate (*N*-acetylglucosamine–galactose), and heparan sulfate or heparin (*N*-acetylglucosamine–iduronic acid). The attachment of the GAG chains is through a linkage region which consists of xylose, galactose, galactose, and a uronic acid residue followed by the repeating disaccharide units that make up the GAG chain proper. Several sequences involving serine residues of the core protein have been reported as attachment sites of xylose by xylosyltransferase (Bourdon *et al.*, 1987; Doege *et al.*, 1987; Huber *et al.*, 1988; Zimmerman and Ruoslahti, 1989; Krueger *et al.*, 1990a). The addition of each of the carbohydrate residues of both the linkage region and the GAG chain is mediated by glycosyltransferases specific with regard to both the receptor and added sugar. In addition to their GAG chains, proteoglycans may also have N- and O-linked oligosaccharides, and

Current Topics in Developmental Biology, Vol. 25

Spiro *et al.* (1989) have suggested that the processing of N-linked oligosaccharides may play an important role in the addition of GAG chains to certain core proteins. Therefore, to synthesize a proteoglycan, a number of genes must be active. At a minimum, these consist of the genes that encode the core protein, the glycosyltransferases, and the enzymes involved in the activation and transfer of sulfate. All of these genes provide potential sites for regulation of the synthesis and, therefore, the generation of variation in the structure of proteoglycans. A number of reviews on proteoglycans have been published (Evered and Whelan, 1986; Gallagher, 1989; Goetinck and Winterbottom, 1991; Hassell *et al.*, 1986; Ruoslahti, 1988, 1989; Wight, 1989). Each places a different emphasis on the many structural and functional aspects of proteoglycans.

The large amount of heterogeneity in proteoglycan structure provides a number of means of classifying macromolecules. They can be classified either on the basis of their GAG chains or on the basis of the core proteins. In this chapter the proteoglycans are divided on the basis of emerging gene families that encode the different core proteins. Emphasis is placed on the proteoglycans that are clearly involved in developmental processes.

II. Methods of Analysis

The divergent structural features of the proteoglycans imparted by their protein and carbohydrate components provide these molecules with the potential for a wide variety of functions. Clear evidence of the functions of specific proteoglycans in developmental processes, however, is evident only for a relatively small number of these macromolecules. Initial analyses of proteoglycans have usually involved the characterization of these macromolecules extracted from tissues which have been exposed to radiolabeled sulfate. This precursor is incorporated preferentially into the GAG chains of the proteoglycans. Enzymatic and chemical characterizations of the GAG chains are performed easily on relatively small quantities (Schmidtchen *et al.*, 1990). Analysis of the core protein requires more material, although sufficient quantities can be purified easily to generate antibodies, thus enabling immunolocalization of specific proteoglycans.

Changes in the temporal and spatial distribution of proteoglycans in the embryo can often be correlated with events which suggest that they are developmentally relevant (Kitamura, 1987; Bianco *et al.*, 1990; Habuchi *et al.*, 1986; Couchman *et al.*, 1989; Perris *et al.*, 1991; Hoffman *et al.*, 1988; Tan *et al.*, 1987). However, to demonstrate unequivocally a specific role for a proteoglycan in a developmental process, it is necessary to alter some functional property of the molecule and analyze the developmental consequences of the alteration. Such perturbation can be done by genetic means or by experimental manipulations. In the case of genetic interventions, one has the added experimental possibility that mutants can be rescued by reintroducing the normal gene, thus formally establishing that the developmental changes were caused by the mutation. The genetic approach to the study of the role of proteoglycans during development has involved the analysis of spontaneous mutations (Esko et al., 1985; Goetinck, 1983). More recently, investigations have used gain of function and loss of function experiments with cDNAs that provide the expression of core proteins of specific proteoglycans (Kato and Bernfield, 1990; Jalkanen et al., 1990; Yamaguchi and Ruoslahti, 1988).

Experimental interventions can make use of either compounds that alter the structure of the proteoglycan or immunological probes that can block specific functional domains of a structurally normal proteoglycan. One series of compounds that is particularly suitable for testing the potential roles of proteoglycans is the xylosides (Brett and Robinson, 1971). These compounds act as acceptors for the assembly of GAG chains that are normally linked to the core protein of proteoglycans (Fig. 1). The end result of the treatment is xylosylated core proteins and free GAG chains bound to the xyloside. Such an approach has demonstrated the importance of proteoglycans in a number of developing systems, such as the skin (Goetinck and Carlone, 1988) and the kidney (Lelong et al., 1988; Platt et al., 1987). A limitation of this experimental approach, however, is that all proteoglycans synthesized during exposure to the xyloside are affected. As a result, the developmental role of a single proteoglycan cannot be evaluated by this method.

III. Extracellular Proteoglycans

A. Large Aggregating Proteoglycans

One of the more extensively studied proteoglycans is the large aggregating proteoglycan, a major component of the extracellular matrix of cartilage (Heinegård et al., 1986a). In view of its ability to form aggregates with hyaluronic acid, this proteoglycan has been called aggrecan. Figure 2 is an electron micrograph of an avian aggrecan molecule from embryonic cartilage which has been subjected to rotary shadowing. Three globular domains are evident. G_1 and G_2 make up the amino terminus of the core protein, and G_3 is at

|
Serine — **xylose** — galactose — galactose — uronic acid — (GAG)
|

xyloside — galactose — galactose — uronic acid — (GAG)

Fig. 1 Linkage region of glycosaminoglycans (GAGs) to serine residues in the core protein of proteoglycans (top) and the effect of xylosides on the synthesis of GAGs (bottom).

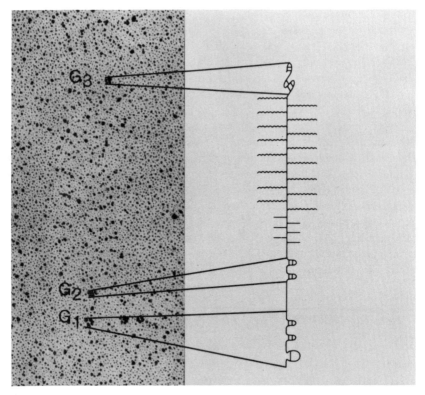

Fig. 2 Rotary shadowing preparation of chick embryonic aggrecan monomer. Three globular domains are identified. (Right) Diagrammatic representation of the electron micrograph based on the sequence of rat chondrosarcoma aggrecan (Doege *et al.*, 1987).

the carboxy terminus. Between domains G_2 and G_3 is the GAG attachment region of the core protein. The disulfide bridges in all three domains have been firmly established from peptides (Sandy *et al.*, 1990). Large proteoglycans from tendon and sclera have domain structure similar to that of aggrecan (Mörgelin *et al.*, 1989). Next to the electron micrograph in Fig. 2 is a diagrammatic representation of aggrecan based on the amino acid sequence of the core protein derived from cDNA clones of rat chondrosarcoma aggrecan (Doege *et al.*, 1987). The structures of the globular domains of the core protein of aggrecan may be similar in different species. Differences, however, have been reported with respect to the GAG attachment region of various aggrecans (Krueger *et al.*, 1990b; Antonsson *et al.*, 1989). For example, the keratan sulfate attachment region is more extensive in bovine aggrecan than in that of the rat chondrosarcoma (Antonsson *et al.*, 1989). Differences also exist in the GAG attachment region between the avian and the rat aggrecan core proteins (Krueger *et al.*, 1990a). The developmental and physiological consequences of these structural differences are not understood. It is clear, however, from genetic studies, that aggrecan plays an important structural role in the development of cartilaginous structures.

Mutants have been described which disrupt the structure of aggrecan at the level of the core protein, its glycoslation, and sulfation. At the level of the core protein, these are nanomelia in the chicken (Landauer, 1965; Palmoski and Goetinck, 1972; Goetinck, 1988; O'Donnell *et al.*, 1988; Stirpe *et al.*, 1987) and cartilage matrix deficiency in the mouse (Kimata *et al.*, 1981). The chondrodystrophy mutation in the turkey results in an underglycosylated aggrecan (Dannenberg *et al.*, 1983), and brachymorphism in the mouse is a mutation in which the proteoglycans are undersulfated (Orkin *et al.*, 1976; Schwartz *et al.*, 1982). Although all three types of mutants have cartilaginous rudiments of a reduced size, the mutants that result from alterations at the level of the core protein, or its glycosylation, are more severely affected than the sulfation-defective mutants. The aggrecan-deficient or -defective mutants have a reduced space between their chondrocytes. This results from the absence or reduction of the hydrophilic proteoglycan molecule in these extracellular spaces. Analysis of the mutants, therefore, has revealed that growth of cartilaginous rudiments results from increases in both the extracellular and cellular compartments of the embryonic rudiments (Goetinck, 1983, 1985).

The amino acid sequence of the core protein of aggrecan, deduced from cDNA sequences, reveals that it is made up of a number of discrete modules (Sai *et al.*, 1986; Doege *et al.*, 1987). Similar modules exist in the core protein of versican, a large proteoglycan synthesized by fibroblasts (Krusius *et al.*, 1987; Zimmerman and Ruoslahti, 1989). The modular makeup of these two proteoglycan core proteins is compared in Fig. 3. At the amino-terminal end of the mature core protein of both proteoglycans, there is an immunoglobulin-like module (Williams, 1987) and two tandemly repeated modules. For aggrecan these three modules represent the G1 domain identified by electron microscopy. The G1 domain has the same structural motif as an entire link protein molecule, a protein of cartilage that interacts with the G1 domain of aggrecan and hyaluronic acid to form a ternary complex (Deák *et al.*, 1986; Neame *et al.*, 1989). By analogy to the interactions of link protein with hyaluronic acid (Goetinck *et al.*, 1987), the interaction of aggrecan with hyaluronic acid is likely to occur through the tandemly repeated domains of the G1 domain. Clearly, these functions indicate that the core proteins of proteoglycans are more than vehicles for the attachment of GAGs. Since versican has the same structural motif at its amino terminus as aggrecan, it is possible that this proteoglycan also interacts with hyaluronic acid. The tandemly repeated modules of the G1 domain of aggrecan are repeated in aggrecan where they represent the G2 domain. In spite of the structural similarity of the tandem repeats of the G2 domain and those of the G1 domain and the link protein, they do not seem to interact with hyaluronic acid (Hardingham *et al.*, 1986). Other similarities between the structure of the core proteins of aggrecan and versican are also evident. The G3 domain of aggrecan (Sai *et al.*, 1986; Doege *et al.*, 1987) consists of two regions: one that has homology with carbohydrate recognition domains of a number of proteins (Drickamer, 1988) and another that shows homology to regions of proteins that bind complement proteins (Kristensen and Tack, 1986; Schulz *et al.*, 1986).

Although the modular structures of versican and aggrecan are similar, there are some major differences. Versican has two modules with high homology to domains within the epidermal growth factor precurson (Gray *et al.*, 1983; Scott *et*

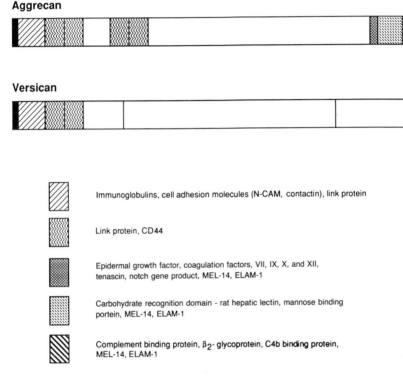

Fig. 3 Comparison of the domain structures of aggrecan (Doege *et al.*, 1987) and versican (Zimmerman and Ruoslahti, 1989). The various domains found in the core proteins are shared with a number of other molecules, such as immunoglobulins (Williams, 1987), N-CAM (Cunningham *et al.*, 1987), contactin (Ranscht, 1988), link protein (Deák *et al.*, 1986; Neame *et al.*, 1986), CD44 (Goldstein *et al.*, 1989; Stamenkovic *et al.*, 1989; Wolffe *et al.*, 1990), epidermal growth factor precursor (Gray *et al.*, 1983; Scott *et al.*, 1983), coagulation factor VII (Hagen *et al.*, 1986), coagulation factors IX and X (Doolittle *et al.*, 1984), tenascin (Pearson *et al.*, 1988), *notch* gene product (Wharton *et al.*, 1985), the homing receptor MEL-14 (Lasky *et al.*, 1989), the endothelial leukocyte adhesion molecule, ELAM-1 (Bevilacqua *et al.*, 1989), rat hepatic pectin (Drickamer *et al.*, 1984), mannose-binding protein (Drickamer *et al.*, 1986) β_2-glycoprotein (Lozier *et al.*, and C4b-binding protein as described by Siegelman *et al.* (1989), Lasky *et al.* (1989), and Bevilacqua *et al.* (1989). The black domain on the left is the signal peptide of the molecule.

al., 1983) on the amino-terminal side of the carbohydrate recognition domain. The inclusion of one epidermal growth factor-like module in the aggrecan model in Fig. 3 is derived from human aggrecan cDNA clones (Baldwin *et al.*, 1989). This domain might be included through alternative splicing of exons.

Although the absence of the entire aggrecan molecule has drastic effects on the development of cartilaginous structures (Goetinck, 1983, 1988), it is not clear what the developmental consequences would be if a mutation were to abolish a function performed by a specific domain. The outcome of such mutations would probably depend on which function is altered and whether the mutation affects the integrity of the rest of the molecule. The G3 domain of aggrecan, for example, has homology with carbohydrate recognition domains, and this homology may suggest that this domain is involved in carbohydrate binding, perhaps in the extracellular matrix. However, a hypothesis has been advanced from investigations on chondrocytes from nanomelic chick embryos which suggest an intracellular role for the G3 domain (O'Donnell *et al.*, 1988). As indicated above, nanomelic chondrocytes fail to produce aggrecan. The analysis of intracellular protein pools of the mutant chondrocytes suggests the possible existence of a truncated form of the core protein of aggrecan. If there is indeed a truncated form of the aggrecan core protein, it is not glycosolated, even though the size of the synthesized protein suggests that it is long enough for the GAG attachment region to be present. One explanation of these results is that the G3 domain may be involved in directing the core protein to appropriate glycosylation sites within the chondrocyte. If this suggestion can be substantiated, the nanomelia mutation would be an example of deletion of a single domain that affects the entire molecule. It will become important, therefore, to investigate the developmental roles of the different domains and to evaluate their relative contributions to the function of the entire molecule. Estimates of the steady-state levels of mRNA for the core protein of aggrecan in nanomelic cartilage indicate that they are only about 6% of normal levels (Stirpe *et al.*, 1987). The relationship between the reduced levels of transcripts and the presence of a truncated form for the core protein of aggrecan in nanomelic chondrocytes remains to be elucidated.

A number of groups have reported that certain embryonic mesodermal tissues, such as limb bud (Royal *et al.*, 1980; Kimata *et al.*, 1986) or skin (Lever-Fischer and Goetinck, 1988), contain a large chondroitin sulfate proteoglycan which can aggregate with hyaluronic acid. These proteoglycans are not aggrecan. It has been proposed that the mesodermal hyaluronic acid binding proteoglycan may be versican (Zimmerman and Ruoslahti, 1989).

B. Basement Membrane Proteoglycan

A major component of basement membranes is a large low-buoyant-density heparan sulfate proteoglycan that has three heparan sulfate side chains located at one end of a large core protein (Dziadek *et al.*, 1985; Hassell *et al.*, 1985; Paulsson, 1987; Paulsson *et al.*, 1987). Structural information from two non-overlapping cDNA clones (Noonan *et al.*, 1988) indicates that one region of the core protein consists of cysteine-free and cysteine-rich domains. The cysteine-rich domains display homology to the cysteine-rich domains of the B1 and B2 chains of laminin (Sasaki *et al.*, 1987; Sasaki and Yamada, 1987). The second cDNA clone encodes a portion of the core protein that consists of eight immunoglobulin-like domains (Williams, 1987). Like laminin, the basement membrane heparan sulfate proteoglycan binds to collagen type IV (Laurie *et al.*, 1986). Whether these interactions with collagen are a reflection of the structural homologies between laminin and the proteoglycan is not known. The core protein of this proteoglycan also binds to fibronectin (Heremans *et al.*, 1990). Clearly, the basement membrane heparan sulfate proteoglycan interacts with several basement membrane macromolecules, and its core protein is also recognized by a cell surface-binding protein present in a number of cells (Clément *et al.*, 1989).

Fibroblast growth factor (FGF) binds to heparin and heparan sulfate (Gospodarowicz, 1990) and has been localized in basement membranes (Saksela *et al.*, 1988; Vlodavsky *et al.*, 1987). It has been proposed that the heparan sulfate proteoglycans of basement membranes may serve as a reservoir for FGF (Gospodarowicz, 1990). In developing systems that depend on inductive interactions between epithelial and mesenchymal components across a basement membrane, a local release of growth factors may be important.

C. Leucine-Rich Repeat Family

The leucine-rich repeat family of proteoglycans consists of three members: decorin, biglycan, and fibromodulin. All three proteoglycans have relatively short core proteins which are homologous to each other and which contain a leucine-rich motif that has been reported in other proteins of vertebrates (Fig. 4) (Lopez *et al.*, 1987; Takahashi *et al.*, 1985), *Drosophila* (Hashimoto *et al.*, 1988; Reinke *et al.*, 1988), and yeast (Kataoka *et al.*, 1985). Tissue-specific variation in GAG composition has been reported for both decorin and biglycan. In skin, tendon, cartilage, and sclera decorin has dermatan sulfate side chains, whereas in bone it has chondroitin sulfate chains (Rosenberg *et al.*, 1985; Choi *et al.*, 1989). A similar situation exists for biglycan. For both decorin and biglycan the GAG side chains are situated at the amino-terminal end of the mature proteins, and in both instances they are attached to serine residues in the core protein (Chopra *et al.*, 1985; Day *et al.*, 1987; Fisher *et al.*, 1989; Krusius and Ruoslahti, 1986). Fibromodulin, which was originally isolated from cartilage, is also present in tissues such as sclera, tendon, and cornea (Heinegård *et al.*, 1986b). In contrast to the other two members of the family, fibromodulin has keratan sulfate side chains (Oldberg *et al.*, 1989) which are attached to the core protein at asparagine residues situated in four different leucine-rich repeats (Plaas *et al.*, 1990). Both decorin and fibromodulin interact with collagen types I and II and inhibit the fibrillogenesis of both of these collagens *in vitro* (Vogel and Trotter, 1987; Hedbom and Heinegård, 1989). Decorin binds to the surface of collagen fibrils at the d-band of the gap region. The site of interaction of fibromodulin with collagen is not known. However, it is believed to be different from the binding site of decorin, since decorin and fibromodulin have an additive effect in fibrillogenesis inhibition assays (Hedbom and Heinegård, 1989). These proteoglycans may, therefore, have different functions in the organization of collagen fibrils.

The association of decorin with collagen fibrils suggests that this proteoglycan plays a structural role in the organism. However, this proteoglycan may play a role in the regulation of cellular proliferation as well (Yamaguchi and Ruoslahti, 1988). The overexpression of decorin in Chinese hamster ovary cells leads to a reduction in the proliferation of these cells and to a restoration of a normal morphology (Yamaguchi and Ruoslahti, 1988). Recent results indicate that the inhibition of cell proliferation in the decorin overexpressors results from the binding and neutralization of transforming growth factor β (TGF-β) by the proteoglycan (Yamaguchi *et al.*, 1990).

A recent investigation (Bianco *et al.*, 1990) of the expression of decorin and biglycan in developing human tissues indicates that these proteoglycans have

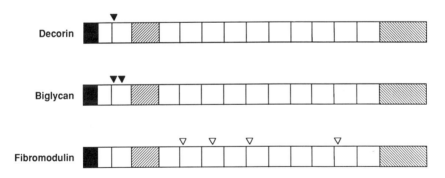

Fig. 4 Comparison of the domain structures of decorin (Krusius and Ruoslahti, 1986), biglycan (Fisher *et al.*, 1989), and fibromodulin (Oldberg *et al.*, 1989). The signal peptides are represented by the solid boxes to the left. The domains to the right of the signal peptides represent the propeptides. The mature core protein begins with the domains marked by solid arrowheads above the decorin and biglycan models. The solid arrowheads represent the serine residues that are substituted with GAGs. There is no GAG substitution in the corresponding domain of fibromodulin. The hatched domains are characterized by intradomain disulfide bonds. Between the two cysteine-containing domains are the leucine-rich repeats. The open arrowheads over the leucine-rich repeats of fibromodulin indicate the positions of asparagine residues substituted with keratan sulfate (Plaas *et al.*, 1990).

divergent and often mutually exclusive localizations in developing organs. Decorin seems to be present in relation to fibrous environments. This distribution is consistent with the role or function of this molecule as established from *in vitro* experiments. The distribution of biglycan has led Bianco *et al.* to propose that this proteoglycan may have a more general function related to cell regulation. They point out that the common structural feature of decorin, biglycan, and fibromodulin resides in the leucine-rich repeats. In other molecules with these repeats they have been shown to bind to other macromolecules. The product of the *toll* gene of *Drosophila* has been shown to be involved in cell adhesion and to play a role in embryonic patterning of the dorsal–ventral axis (Hashimoto *et al.*, 1988). The *chaoptin* gene product of *Drosophila* is a cell surface glycoprotein which plays a role in the development of photoreceptor cells (Reinke *et al.*, 1988; Van Vactor *et al.*, 1988). In *Drosophila*, therefore, the leucine-rich repeats of certain proteins have been implicated in morphogenetic processes. Whether the repeats found in proteoglycans play a similar role in the development of vertebrates remains to be established.

D. Collagen Type IX Proteoglycan

The collagen fibril of cartilage consists of collagen types II, XI, and IX. The latter collagen is situated on the outside of the fibril (Mendler *et al.*, 1989). It is also present in the primary corneal stroma and vitreous of the chick embryo (Fitch *et al.*, 1988). This molecule has several interesting features. Each of the three chains has three collagenous (Col1–3) and three noncollagenous (NC1–3) domains. In addition, the α_1 chain has a fourth noncollagenous (NC4) domain at its amino terminus. Collagen type IX is also a proteoglycan. The α_2 chain carries a single chondroitin sulfate chain attached to the NC3 domain of that chain (Bruckner *et al.*, 1985; Huber *et al.*, 1988; Konomi *et al.*, 1986). The sequence around the serine residue to which the GAG is attached was determined to be Val—Glu–Gly–Ser–Asp (Huber *et al.*, 1986). This is different from the Ser–Gly sequence normally substituted in proteoglycans. Tissue variability has been reported for the structure of collagen type IX which involves both the structure of the protein and the GAG chain (Yada *et al.*, 1990; Svoboda *et al.*, 1988). The NC4 domain is present in some tissues (e.g., hyaline cartilage and early embryonic vitreous), but absent in others (e.g., primary corneal stroma and adult vitreous). The presence or absence of the NC4 domain results from differential use of promoters in these tissues (Nishimura *et al.*, 1990). The GAG chain for both the embryonic and adult vitreous is very large ($\sim$350,000 Da), in contrast to that of other tissues ($\sim$50,000 Da). The role of collagen type IX proteoglycan is not known, but it is thought to be involved in fibril structure and to interact with other extracellular matrix components (Mayne, 1990). The role of the extremely large chondroitin sulfate on type IX of the vitreous has been proposed to contribute to the gel-like consistency of this matrix (Yada *et al.*, 1990).

IV. Membrane-Associated Proteoglycans

Another major class of proteoglycans is associated with the cell surface. These proteoglycans may be associated with the cell membrane through a hydrophobic segment of their core protein, through a glycosyl-phosphatidylinositol anchor or through a receptor that interacts noncovalently with either the core protein or the GAG side chains of the proteoglycan. Membrane-associated proteoglycans have been described for a large number of cell types, such as hepatocytes (Fedarko *et al.*, 1989; Ishihara and Conrad, 1989; Kjellen *et al.*, 1981), epithelial cells (David and Van den Berghe, 1985, 1989; Rapraeger and Bernfield, 1983), fibroblasts (David *et al.*, 1990; DeBoeck *et al.*, 1987; Heremans *et al.*, 1988; Lories *et al.*, 1986, 1987), marrow stromal cells (Gordon and Greaves, 1989; Gordon *et al.*, 1987; Keating and Gordon, 1988; Roberts *et al.*, 1988), ovarian granulosa cells (Yanagishita and Hascall, 1984a,b), glial precursor cells (Stallcup *et al.*, 1990), and Schwann cells (Carey *et al.*, 1987).

A comparison of normal and GAG-deficient cells (Esko *et al.*, 1985) suggested a role for cell surface-associated heparan sulfate proteoglycan in cell–substrate adhesion. When normal cells are plated on a substrate containing intact fibronectin, they attach and form focal adhesions and F-actin-containing stress fibers. Normal cells do not form focal adhesions or stress fibers when they are plated on substrata containing only the heparin binding or cell binding domain of fibronectin, even though they do attach to these substrata. Normal and GAG-deficient mutant cells attach equally well to intact fibronectin, but only the normal, not the mutant, cells form focal adhesions and stress fibers. It seems, therefore, that the cell surface proteoglycan plays a role in establishing a connection between the intracellular cytoskeleton and the extracellular matrix (Woods *et al.*, 1986; LeBaron *et al.*, 1988). The cell surface-associated heparan sulfate proteoglycan(s) involved in these cellular events has not been identified.

Structural information has been obtained from cDNA clones for three membrane-associated proteoglycans: syndecan (Saunders *et al.*, 1989; Mali *et al.*, 1990; Kiefer *et al.*, 1990), fibroglycan (Marynen *et al.*, 1989; David, 1990), and glypican (David *et al.*, 1990). The first two are intercalated in the membrane, and the latter is attached to the membrane through a phosphatidylinositol linkage. Based on their nucleotide and deduced amino acid sequences, the core proteins of syndecan and fibroglycan are the products of different genes. Their core proteins, however, share several structural features: (1) They have similar transmembrane and cytoplasmic domains (Fig. 5) and (2) both possess a potential protease cleavage site immediately external to the transmembrane domain. The

Fig. 5 Alignment of the transmembrane (top) and cytoplasmic (bottom) domains of syndecan (Saunders *et al.*, 1989) and fibroglycan (Marynen *et al.*, 1989).

deduced amino acid sequence of glypican (David *et al.*, 1990) differs from those of both syndecan and fibroglycan, indicating that this proteoglycan is unique.

The developmental role of cell surface proteoglycans has been studied most extensively with syndecan. The unique temporal and spatial distribution of this proteoglycan implies that it has important developmental functions. In adult tissues syndecan is restricted primarily to epithelial tissues (Hayashi *et al.*, 1987). In embryonic tissues, however, syndecan is also expressed in the mesoderm during epithelial–mesenchymal interactions, as in the development of the teeth (Thesleff *et al.*, 1988) and the kidneys (Vainio *et al.*, 1989). Similarly, changes in the expression of syndecan are observed during B lymphocyte maturation. When these cells are associated with the extracellular matrix, first as pre-B or immature B cells in the marrow and again as differentiated plasma cells in the extracellular matrix of lymph nodes, they express syndecan on their surfaces. Between these two stages in their differentiation, when the B lymphocytes are released into the circulation, the expression of syndecan is lost (Sanderson *et al.*, 1989).

The structure of syndecan is highly polymorphic as a result of variations in the size, number, and relative proportion of chondroitin sulfate and heparan sulfate side chains (Rapraeger *et al.*, 1985; Sanderson and Bernfield, 1988). The polymorphism correlates with cell type and the state of differentiation of cells (Brauker *et al.*, 1988) and can result, in part, as a response of cells to growth factors such as TGF-β (Rasmussen and Rapraeger, 1988).

The changes in syndecan structure during B cell maturation have been interpreted to reflect the interactions of the cells with the extracellular matrix that they encounter. This interpretation is entirely consistent with the observations that syndecan behaves as a matrix receptor that can interact, through its heparan sulfate side chains, to a number of extracellular matrix molecules, including fibrils of collagen types I, III, and V; fibronectin; and thrombospondin (Koda and Bernfield, 1984; Koda *et al.*, 1985; Saunders and Bernfield, 1988; Kaesberg *et al.*, 1989). The mechanism of interaction between heparan sulfate and these extracellular matrix macromolecules remains to be established, but the consensus sequences XBBXBX and XBBBXXB (where B and X are basic and hydropathic residues, respectively) for the recognition of heparan sulfate have been identified in fibronectin and thrombospondin (Cardin and Weintraub, 1989).

Lung fibroblasts express syndecan, fibroglycan, and glypican (David, 1990). It is not known whether there are other cell surface-associated proteoglycans and whether all are found on the cell surface of every cell. However, since it has been shown that syndecan can bind to a number of extracellular matrix components through its heparan sulfate side chains, one might expect that other heparan sulfate proteoglycans may share the same property. Why then, are there different kinds of heparan sulfate proteoglycans? One explanation may be found in the mode of attachment to the cell surface. There could be a selective release of these proteoglycans from the cell surface either by a protease for syndecan (Jalkanen *et al.*, 1987) and fibroglycan or a phospholipase for glypican (David *et al.*, 1990). Alternatively, the two types of linkage might reflect different mechanisms for internalization of the cell surface molecules. Both explanations, however, would only account for the necessity of two types of cell surface heparan sulfate proteoglycans. Consideration must be given, therefore, to the possibility that there are as yet unidentified functions associated with the ectodomain of the core proteins. Syndecan and fibroglycan have similar transmembrane and cytoplasmic domains. For syndecan the cytoplasmic domain has been shown to be connected, directly or indirectly, to cytoskeletal actin (Rapraeger *et al.*, 1986). Proteoglycans with transmembrane core proteins that have very different ectodomains but similar cytoplasmic domains might represent receptors for ligands of differing extracellular specificity, but with similar intracellular effects.

In adult epithelial cells syndecan is polarized at the basolateral surface where the cells interact with the extracellular matrix (Hayashi *et al.*, 1987). It has been suggested that these interactions are necessary for the maintenance of epithelial morphology. Recent evidence from transfection experiments with either antisense or sense cDNAs for syndecan support this view. Antisense constructs introduced into mouse mammary epithelial cells result in a loss of epithelial morphology. These syndecan-"deficient" cells become fusiform and lose their cytoskeletal organization and also E-cadherin and β-$_1$-integrin expression (Kato and Bernfield, 1990). Kato and Bernfield have suggested that syndecan, in addition to being a matrix receptor, may also organize other adhesion molecules. Also, when transformed mouse mammary tumor cells are transfected with the syndecan cDNA, they replace their fibroblastic phenotype with an epithelial one (Jalkanen *et al.*, 1990).

Cell surface heparan sulfate proteoglycans also bind basic FGF (bFGF) to their heparan sulfate side chains. This interaction has been demonstrated for syndecan (Kiefer *et al.*, 1990), but presumably occurs with other heparan sulfate proteoglycans as well. The binding of bFGF to heparan sulfate protects this growth factor from proteolysis (Saksela *et al.*, 1988), but does not affect its biological activity. Therefore, heparan sulfate proteoglycans may serve as growth factor reservoirs either at the cell surface or in the extracellular matrix. A mechanism for the release of bFGF–heparan sulfate complexes involving plasminogen activator-mediated proteolysis has been proposed (Saksela and Rifkin, 1990). Since this proteolytic activity is a pericellular process, it may be a mechanism to provide growth factors over relatively short distances. Developmentally, such a mechanism may be important in tissue organization and remodeling. The interaction of growth factors with heparan sulfate is not restricted to bFGF, since heparan sulfate can also bind to the hematopoietic growth factors granulocyte/macrophage colony-stimulating factor and interleukin 3 (Roberts *et al.*, 1988).

One important aspect of development is the regulation of cellular proliferation. Heparin and heparan sulfate have been shown to inhibit cellular proliferation, and a series of reports on the effect of heparan sulfate on hepatoma cells indicates that the proteoglycan is internalized and that some GAG reaches the nucleus and may have its effect there (Ishihara and Conrad, 1989; Fedarko *et al.*, 1989). Recent reports also indicate that heparin inhibits transcription of the protooncogenes c-*fos* and c-*myc* in fibroblasts (Wright *et al.*, 1989) and vascular smooth muscle cells (Pukac *et al.*, 1990). The expression of both genes is believed to be necessary for cellular proliferation. Whether the antiproliferative effect of heparan sulfate is entirely through the control of these protooncogenes remains to be established.

The type III receptor for TGF-β is a cell surface-associated proteoglycan (Segarini and Seyedin, 1988; Cheifetz *et al.*, 1988; Cheifetz and Massagué, 1989). In contrast to the interactions of bFGF with heparan sulfate chains of cell surface proteoglycans, studies with GAG synthesis-deficient mutant cells indicate that the binding of TGF-β is to the core protein.

V. Intracellular Proteoglycans

Mast cells contain a relatively high concentration of small proteoglycans in their secretory granules (Stevens and Austen, 1989). These proteoglycans have a very short core protein characterized as having several repeat sequences of serine and glycine residues. Base on this structural feature, they have been named serglycin (Ruoslahti, 1989). Information on the structure of the core protein of serglycin was first derived from a rat yolk sac tumor cell line. These proteoglycans are synthesized as a preproform and processed to a relatively short core protein (Bourdon *et al.*, 1985, 1986). Although the Ser–Gly repeat is a characteristic of the core protein of this proteoglycan, the lengths of the regions with this repeat can vary among species (Avraham *et al.*, 1988; Stevens *et al.*, 1988). The GAG side chains on the serglycin core protein can be either heparin, as in connective tissue mast cells, or a highly sulfated form of chondroitin sulfate, as in mucosal or bone marrow-derived mast cells. The type of GAG associated with the core protein has been shown to be regulated by the microenvironment and the state of differentiation of the mast cells (Stevens and Austen, 1989).

VI. Part-Time Proteoglycans

Although the type III receptor for TGF-β is a proteoglycan (Cheifetz et al., 1988; Segarini and Seyedin, 1988), it does not need its GAG chain to function as a receptor (Cheifetz and Massagué, 1989). Whether or not both the proteoglycan and the protein form are found on cells is not clear. There is evidence, however, that certain molecules can exist either as unsubstituted core proteins or as proteoglycans. Such proteoglycans have been termed part-time proteoglycans (Ruoslahti, 1989). Cell surface-associated part-time proteoglycans include the invariant chain of the class II antigens (Sant et al., 1985), thrombomodulin (Bourin et al., 1986), and the lymphocyte homing receptor, CD44 (Jalkanen et al., 1988). What effect the GAG chains have on the biological activity of these proteins is not known. CD44 has a module in its ectodomain which is related to the tandem repeats of link protein, aggrecan, and versican (Goldstein et al., 1989; Stamenkovic et al., 1989; Wolffe et al., 1990). In addition to being a lymphocyte homing receptor (Butcher, 1990), CD44 has also been identified as a hyaluronic acid receptor (Aruffo et al., 1990). Whether or not the interaction with hyaluronic acid is through the link protein module has not been established. Now that CD44 has been identified as a hyaluronic acid receptor, its role in developmental processes must be evaluated wherever hyaluronic acid has been shown to be involved (Toole, 1991).

VII. Conclusion

In the beginning of this chapter, it was stated that clear evidence of a developmental role for specific proteoglycans was rather limited. Collectively, however, proteoglycans have clearly been demonstrated to be developmentally important. With the progress being made in the molecular biology of proteoglycans, more detailed information will become available on the structure of their core proteins. With the knowledge of the primary structure, as well as of the nucleic acid sequences that encode them, it will be possible to analyze in detail and in a systematic manner functions of core proteins of individual proteoglycans and even specific domains within individual proteoglycans. The studies on decorin (Yamaguchi and Ruoslahti, 1988) and syndecan (Kato and Bernfield, 1990; Jalkanen et al., 1990) are the first examples of such studies with proteoglycans. Modifications can be introduced by site-directed mutagenesis in regions of the core protein which are to be tested for a specific function. When expressed in appropriate eukaryotic systems, they could act as dominant negative mutations (Herskowitz, 1987). This can be done at the level of the cell or in whole animals, where the effect on organogenesis can be evaluated (Stacey *et al.*, 1988). The characterization of the genomic sequences will allow the study of regulatory events at the transcriptional level and may begin to explain the mechanisms for tissue-specific expression of proteoglycans (Nishimura *et al.*, 1990). The availability of genomic sequences will also allow the targeting of mutations to specific chromosomal regions by homologous recombination (Capecchi, 1989).

Antibodies to defined regions of core proteins, such as synthetic peptides, or monoclonal antibodies whose epitope has been identified will also be unique tools to investigate the structure–function relationship of proteoglycans. Monoclonal antibodies to GAGs (Caterson *et al.*, 1987; Sorrell *et al.*, 1990; Mark *et al.*, 1990) are beginning to identify novel epitopes in the GAG structure. Since these GAG epitopes have a unique tissue distribution, they may be developmentally important. The availability of such monoclonal antibodies will allow study of the structural and functional aspects of the posttranslational modifications of the core proteins.

Acknowledgments

I thank G. David, L. W. Fisher, A. H. K. Plaas, J. D. Sandy, N. B. Schwartz, and B. Toole for sharing results from their laboratories prior to publication. The original work from the author's laboratory was supported by National Institutes of Health grants HD 22016, HD 22050, and HD 22938.

References

Antonsson, P., Heinegård, D., and Oldberg, Å. (1989). *J. Biol. Chem.* **264,** 16170–16173.

Aruffo, A., Stamenkovic, I., Melnick, M., Underhill, C. B., and Seed, B. (1990). *Cell* **61,** 1303–1313.

Avraham, S., Stevens, R. L., Gartner, M. C., Austen, K. F., Lalley, P. A., and Weis, J. H. (1988). *J. Biol. Chem.* **263,** 7292–7296.

Baldwin, C., Regmato, A. M., and Prockop, D. I. (1989). *J. Biol. Chem.* **264,** 15747–15750.

Bevilacqua, M. P., Stengelin, S., Gimbrone, M. A., Jr., and Seed, B. (1989). *Science* **243,** 1160–1165.

Bianco, P., Fisher, L. W., Young, M. F., Termine, J. D., and Robey, P. G. (1990). *J. Histochem. Cytochem.* **38,** 1549–1563.

Bourdon, M. A., Oldberg, Å., Pierschbacher, M., and Ruoslahti, E. (1987). *Proc. Natl. Acad. Sci. U.S.A.* **82,** 1321–1325.

Bourdon, M. A., Shiga, M., and Ruoslahti, E. (1986). *J. Biol. Chem.* **261,** 12534–12537.

Bourdon, M. A., Krusius, T., Campbell, S., Schwartz, N. B., and Ruoslahti, E. (1987). *Proc. Natl. Acad. Sci. U.S.A.* **84,** 3194–3198.

Bourin, M.-C., Boffa, M.-C., Björk, I., and Lindahl, U. (1986). *Proc. Natl. Acad. Sci. U.S.A.* **83,** 5924–5928.

Brauker, J. H., Trautman, M. S., and Bernfeld, M. (1988). *J. Cell Biol.* **107,** 157a.

Brett, M. J., and Robinson, H. C. (1971). *Proc. Aust. Biochem. Soc.* **4,** 92.

Bruckner, P., Vaughan, L., and Winterhalter, K. H. (1985). *Proc. Natl. Acad. Sci. U.S.A.* **82,** 2608–2612.

Butcher, E. C. (1990). *Am. J. Pathol.* **136,** 3–11.

Capecchi, M. R. (1989). *Trends Genet.* **5,** 70–76.

Cardin, A. D., and Weintraub, H. J. R. (1989). *Arteriosclerosis* **9,** 21–32.

Carey, D. J., Rafferty, C. M., and Todd, M. S. (1987). *J. Cell Biol.* **105,** 1013–1021.

Caterson, B., Calabro, T., and Hampton, A. (1987). *In* "Biology of Proteoglycans" (T. Wight and R. Mecham, eds.), pp. 1–26. Academic Press, Orlando, Florida.

Cheifetz, S., and Massagué, J. (1989). *J. Biol. Chem.* **264,** 12025–12028.

Cheifetz, S., Andres, J. L., and Massagué, J. (1988). *J. Biol. Chem.* **263,** 16984–16991.

Choi, H. U., Johnson, T. L., Pal, S., Tang, L.-H., and Rosenberg, L. (1989). *J. Biol. Chem.* **264,** 2876–2884.

Chopra, R. K., Pearson, C. H., Pringle, G. A., Frackre, D. S., and Scott, P. G. (1985). *Biochem. J.* **230,** 181–194.

Clément, B., Segui-Real, B., Hassell, J. R., Martin, G. R., and Yamada, Y. (1989). *J. Biol. Chem.* **264,** 12467–12471.

Couchman, J. R., King, J. L., and McCarthy, K. J. (1989). *J. Invest. Dermatol.* **92,** 65–70.

Cunningham, B. A., Hemperly, J. J., Murray, B. A., Prediger, E. A., Brackenbury, R., and Edelman, G. M. (1987). *Science* **236,** 799–806.

Dannenberg, A., Buss, E. G., and Goetinck, P. F. (1983). *Prog. Clin. Biol. Res.* **110B,** 85–95.

David, G. (1990). *J. Cell Biol.* **3,** 28a.

David, G., and Van den Berghe, H. (1985). *J. Biol. Chem.* **260,** 11067–11074.

David, G., and Van den Berghe, H. (1989). *Eur. J. Biochem.* **178,** 609–617.

David, G., Lories, V., Decock, B., Marynen, P., Cassiman, J.-J., and Van den Berghe, H. (1990). *J. Cell Biol.* **111,** 3165–3176.

Day, A. A., McQuillan, C. I., Termine, J. D., and Young, M. R. (1987). *Biochem. J.* **248,** 801–805.

Deák, F., Kiss, I., Sparks, K., Argraves, W. S., Hampikian, G., and Goetinck, P. F. (1986). *Proc. Natl. Acad. Sci. U.S.A.* **83,** 3766–3770.

DeBoeck, H., Lories, V., David, G., Cassiman, J.-J., and Van den Berghe, H. (1987). *Biochem. J.* **247,** 765–771.

Doege, K., Sasaki, M., Horigan, E., Hassell, J. R., and Yamada, Y. (1987). *J. Biol. Chem.* **262,** 17757–17767.

Doolittle, R. F., Feng, D. F., and Johnson, M. S. (1984). *Nature (London)* **307,** 558–560.

Drickamer, K. (1988). *J. Biol. Chem.* **263,** 9557–9560.

Drickamer, K., Mamon, J. F., Binns, G., and Leung, J. O. (1984). *J. Biol. Chem.* **259,** 770–778.

Drickamer, K., Dordal, M. S., and Reynolds, L. (1986). *J. Biol. Chem.* **261,** 6878–6887.

Dziadek, M., Fujiwara, S., Paulsson, M., and Timpl, R. (1985). *EMBO J.* **4,** 950–912.

Esko, J. D., Stewart, T. E., and Taylor, W. H. (1985). *Proc. Natl. Acad. Sci. U.S.A.* **82,** 3197–3201.

Evered, D., and Whelan, J. (1986). *Ciba Found. Symp.* No. 124.

Fedarko, N. S., Ishihara, M., and Conrad, H. E. (1989). *J. Cell. Physiol.* **139,** 287–294.

Fisher, L. W., Termine, J. D., and Young, M. F. (1989). *J. Biol. Chem.* **264,** 4571–4576.

Fitch, J. M., Mentzer, A., Mayne, R., and Linsenmayer, T. F. (1988). *Dev. Biol.* **128,** 396–405.

Gallagher, J. T. (1989). *Curr. Opin. Cell Biol.* **1,** 1201–1218.

Goetinck, P. F. (1983). *In* "Cartilage" (B. K. Hall, ed.), Vol. III, pp. 165–189. Academic Press, New York.

Goetinck, P. F. (1985). *In* "Developmental Mechanisms: Normal and Abnormal" (J. W. Lash, ed.), pp. 137–147. Liss, New York.

Goetinck, P. F. (1988). *Pathol. Immunopathol. Res.* **7**, 73–75.

Goetinck, P. F., and Carlone, D. L. (1988). *Dev. Biol.* **127**, 179–186.

Goetinck, P. F., and Winterbottom, N. (1991). *In* "Biochemistry and Physiology of the Skin" (L. Goldstein, ed.), 2nd ed. Oxford Univ. Press, New York. In press.

Goetinck, P. F., Stirpe, N. S., Tsonis, P. A., and Carlone, D. (1987). *J. Cell Biol.* **105**, 2403–2408.

Goldstein, L. A., Zhou, D. F. H., Picker, L. J., Minty, C. N., Bargatze, R. F., Ding, J. F., and Butcher, E. C. (1989). *Cell* **56**, 1063–1072.

Gordon, M. Y., and Greaves, M. F. (1989). *Bone Marrow Transplant.* **4**, 335–338.

Gordon, M. Y., Riley, G. P., Wyatt, S. M., and Greaves, M. F. (1987). *Nature (London)* **326**, 403–405.

Gospodarowicz, D. (1990). *Curr. Top. Dev. Biol.* **24**, 57–93.

Gray, A., Dull, T. J., and Ullrich, A. (1983). *Nature (London)* **303**, 722–725.

Habuchi, H., Kimata, K., and Suzuki, S. (1986). *J. Biol. Chem.* **261**, 1031–1040.

Hagen, F. S., Gray, C. L., O'Hara, P., Grant, F. J., Saari, G. C., Woodbury, R. G., Hart, C., E., Insley, M., Kisiel, W., Kurachi, K., and Davie, E. W. (1986). *Proc. Natl. Acad. Sci. U.S.A.* **83**, 2412–2416.

Hardingham, T. E., Beardmore-Gray, M., Dunham, D. G., and Ratcliffe, A. (1986). *Ciba Found. Symp.* **124**, 30–46.

Hashimoto, C., Hudson, K. L., and Anderson, K. V. (1988). *Cell* **52**, 269–279.

Hassell, J. R., Leyshon, W. C., Ledbetter, S. R., Tyree, B., Suzuki, S., Kato, M., Kimata, K., and Kleinman, H. K. (1985). *J. Biol. Chem.* **260**, 8098–8105.

Hassell, J. R., Kimura, J. H., and Hascall, V. C. (1986). *Annu. Rev. Biochem.* **55**, 539–567.

Hayashi, K., Hayashi, M., Julkunen, M., Firestone, J. H., Trelsdad, R. L., and Bernfield, M. (1987). *J. Histochem. Cytochem.* **35**, 1079–1088.

Hedbom, E., and Heinegård, D. (1989). *J. Biol. Chem.* **264**, 6898–6905.

Heinegård, D., Franzen, A., Hedbom, E., and Sommarin, Y. (1986a). *Ciba Found. Symp.* **124**, 69–88.

Heinegård, D., Larsson, T., Sommarin, Y., Franzeis, A., Paulsson, M., and Hedbom, E. (1986b). *J. Biol. Chem.* **261**, 13866–13872.

Heremans, A., Cassiman, J.-J., Van den Berghe, H., and David, G. (1988). *J. Biol. Chem.* **263**, 4731–4739.

Heremans, A., Decock, B., Cassiman, J.-J., Van den Berghe, H., and David, G. (1990). *J. Biol. Chem.* **265**, 8716–8724.

Herskowitz, I. (1987). *Nature (London)* **329**, 219–222.

Hoffman, S., Crossin, K. L., and Edelman, G. M. (1988). *J. Cell Biol.* **106**, 519–532.

Huber, S., van der Rest, M., Bruckner, P., Rodriguez, E., Winterhalter, K. H., and Vaughan, L. (1986). *J. Biol. Chem.* **261**, 5965–5968.

Huber, S., Winterhalter, K. H., and Vaughan, L. (1988). *J. Biol. Chem.* **263**, 752–756.

Ishihara, M., and Conrad, H. E. (1989). *J. Cell. Physiol.* **138**, 467–476.

Jalkanen, M., Rapraeger, A., Saunders, S., and Bernfield, M. (1987). *J. Cell Biol.* **105**, 3087–3096.

Jalkanen, M., Mali, M., Härkönen, P., and Leppä, S. (1990). *J. Cell Biol.* **3**, 787a.

Jalkanen, S., Jalkanen, M., Bargatze, R., Tammi, M., and Butcher, E. C. (1988). *J. Immunol.* **141**, 1615–1623.

Kaesberg, P. R., Ershler, W. B., Esko, J. D., and Mosher, D. F. (1989). *J. Clin. Invest.* **83**, 994–1001.

Kataoka, T., Broek, D., and Wigler, M. (1985). *Cell* **43**, 493–505.

Kato, M., and Bernfield, M. (1990). *J. Cell Biol.* **111**, 263a.

Keating, A., and Gordon, M. Y. (1988). *Leukemia* **2**, 766–769.

Kiefer, M. C., Stephans, J. C., Crawford, K., Okino, K., and Barr, P. J. (1990). *Proc. Natl. Acad. Sci. U.S.A.* **87**, 6985–6989.

Kimata, K., Barrach, H. J., Brown, K. S., and Pennypacker, J. P. (1981). *J. Biol. Chem.* **256**, 6961–6968.

Kimata, K., Oike, Y., Tani, K., Shinomura, T., Yamagata, M., Uritani, M., and Suzuki, S. (1986). *J. Biol. Chem.* **261**, 13517–13525.

Kitamura, K. (1987). *Development* **100**, 501–512.

Kjellen, L., Pettersson, I., and Höök, M. (1981). *Proc. Natl. Acad. Sci. U.S.A.* **78**, 5371–5375.

Koda, J. E., and Bernfield, M. (1984). *J. Biol. Chem.* **259**, 11763–11770.

Koda, J. E., Rapraeger, A., and Bernfield, M. (1985). *J. Biol. Chem.* **260**, 8157–8162.

Konomi, H., Seyer, J. M., Ninomiya, Y., and Olsen, B. R. (1986). *J. Biol. Chem.* **261**, 6742–6746.

Kristensen, T., and Tack, B. F. (1986). *Proc. Natl. Acad. Sci. U.S.A.* **83**, 3963–3967.

Krueger, R. C., Jr., Fields, T. A., Hildreth, J., IV, and Schwartz, N. B. (1990a). *J. Biol. Chem.* **265**, 12075–12087.

Krueger, R. C., Jr., Fields, T. A., Hildreth, J., IV, and Schwartz, N. B. (1990b). *J. Biol. Chem.* **265**, 12088–12097.

Krusius, T., and Ruoslahti, E. (1986). *Proc. Natl. Acad. Sci. U.S.A.* **83**, 7683–7687.

Krusius, T., Gehlsen, K. R., and Ruoslahti, E. (1987). *J. Biol. Chem.* **262**, 13120–13125.

Landauer, W. (1965). *J. Hered.* **56**, 131–138.

Lasky, L. A., Singer, M. S., Yednock, T. A., Dowbenko, D., Fennie, C., Rodriguez, H., Nguyen, T., Stachel, S., and Rosen, S. D. (1989). *Cell* **56**, 1045–1055.

Laurie, G. W., Bing, J. T., Kleinman, H. K., Hassell, J. R., Aumailley, M., Martin, G. R., and Feldmann, R. J. (1986). *J. Mol. Biol.* **189**, 205–216.

LeBaron, R. G., Esko, J. D., Woods, A., Johansson, S., and Höök, M. (1988). *J. Cell Biol.* **106**, 945–952.

Lelong, B., Makino, H., Dalecki, T. M., and Kanwar, Y. S. (1988). *Dev. Biol.* **128**, 256–276.

Lever-Fischer, P. L., and Goetinck, P. F. (1988). *Arch. Biochem. Biophys.* **263**, 45–58.

Lopez, J. A., Chung, D. W., Fujikawa, K., and Hagen, F. S. (1987). *Proc. Natl. Acad. Sci. U.S.A.* **84**, 5615–5619.

Lories, V., David, G., Cassiman, J. J., and Van den Berghe, H. (1986). *Eur. J. Biochem.* **158**, 351–360.

Lories, V., De Boeck, H., David, G., Cassiman, J. J., and Van den Berghe, H. (1987). *J. Bio. Chem.* **262**, 854–859.

Lozier, J., Takahashi, N., and Putnam, F. W. (1984). *Proc. Natl. Acad. Sci. U.S.A.* **81**, 3640–3644.

Mali, M., Jaakkola, P., Arvilommi, A.-M., and Jalkanen, M. (1990). *J. Biol. Chem.* **265**, 6884–6889.

Mark, M. P., Baker, J. R., Kimata, K., and Ruch, J.-V., (1990). *Int. J. Dev. Biol.* **34**, 191–204.

Marynen, P., Zhang, J., Cassiman, J.-J., Van den Berghe, H., and David, G. (1989). *J. Biol. Chem.* **264**, 7017–7024.

Mayne, R. (1990). *Ann. N.Y. Acad. Sci.* **599**, 39–44.

Mendler, M., Eich-Bender, S. G., Vaughan, L., Winterhalter, K. H., and Bruckner, P. (1989). *J. Cell Biol.* **108**, 191–197.

Mörgelin, M., Paulsson, M., Malmström, A., and Heinegård, D. (1989). *J. Biol. Chem.* **264**, 12080–12090.

Neame, P. J., Christner, J. E., and Baker, J. R. (1986). *J. Biol. Chem.* **261**, 3519–3535.

Neame, P. J., Chois, H. U., and Rosenberg, L. C. (1989). *J. Biol. Chem.* **264**, 8653–8661.

Nishimura, I., Muragaki, Y., and Olsen, B. R. (1990). *J. Biol. Chem.* **264**, 20033–20041.

Noonan, D. M., Horigan, E. A., Ledbetter, S. R., Vogeli, G., Sasaki, M., Yamada, Y., and Hassell, J. R. (1988). *J. Biol. Chem.* **263**, 16379–16387.

O'Donnell, C. M., Kaczman-Daniel, K., Goetinck, P. F., and Vertel, B. M. (1988). *J. Biol. Chem.* **263**, 17749–17754.

Oldberg, Å., Antonsson, P., Lindblom, K., and Heinegård, D. (1989). *EMBO J.* **8**, 2601–2604.

Orkin, R. W., Pratt, R. M., and Martin, G. R. (1976). *Dev. Biol.* **50**, 82–94.

Palmoski, M. J., and Goetinck, P. F. (1972). *Proc. Natl. Acad. Sci. U.S.A.* **69**, 3385–3388.

Paulsson, M. (1987). *Collagen Relat. Res.* **7**, 443–461.

Paulsson, M., Yurchenco, P. D., Ruben, G. C., Engel, J., and Timpl, R. (1987). *J. Mol. Biol.* **197**, 297–313.

Pearson, C. A., Pearson, D., Shibahara, S., Hofsteenge, J., and Shiquet-Ehrismann, R. (1988). *EMBO J.* **7**, 2977–2981.

Perris, R., Krotoski, D., Lallier, T., Domingo, C., Sorrell, J. M. and Bronner-Fraser, M. (1991). *Development* **111**, 583–599.

Plaas, A. H. K., Neame, P. J., Nivens, C. M., and Reiss, L. (1990). *J. Biol. Chem.* **265**, 20634–20640.

Platt, J. L., Brown, D. M., Granlund, K., Oegema, T. R., and Klein, D. J. (1987). *Dev. Biol.* **123**, 293–306.

Pukac, L. A., Castellot, J. J., Wright, T. C. Caleb, B. L., and Karnovsky, M. J. (1990). *Cell Regul.* **1**, 435–443.

Ranscht, B. (1988). *J. Cell Biol.* **107**, 1561–1573.

Rapraeger, A. C., and Bernfield, M. (1983). *J. Biol. Chem.* **258**, 3632–3636.

Rapraeger, A. C., Jalkanen, M., Endo, E., Koda, J., and Bernfield, M. (1985). *J. Biol. Chem.* **260**, 11046–11052.

Rapraeger, A. C., Jalkanen, M., and Bernfield, M. (1986). *J. Cell Biol.* **103**, 2683–2696.

Rasmussen, S., and Rapraeger, A. (1988). *J. Cell Biol.* **107**, 1959.

Reinke, R., Krants, D. E., Yen, D., and Zipursky, S. L. (1988). *Cell* **52**, 291–301.

Roberts, R., Gallagher, J., Spooncer, E., Allen, T. D., Bloomfield, F., and Dexter, T. M. (1988). *Nature (London)* **332**, 376–378.

Rosenberg, L. C., Choi, H. U., Tang, L.-H., Johnson, T. L., Pal, S., Webber, C. R., Reines A., and Poole, A. R. (1985). *J. Biol. Chem.* **260**, 6304–6313.

Royal, P. D., Sparks, K. J., and Goetinck, P. F. (1980). *J. Biol. Chem.* **255**, 9870–9878.

Ruoslahti, E. (1988). *Annu. Rev. Cell Biol.* **4**, 229–255.

Ruoslahti, E. (1989). *J. Biol. Chem.* **264**, 13369–13372.

Sai, S., Tanaka, T., Kosher, R. A., and Tanzer, M. L. (1986). *Proc. Natl. Acad. Sci. U.S.A.* **83**, 5081–5085.

Saksela, O., and Rifkin, D. B. (1990). *J. Cell Biol.* **110**, 767–775.

Saksela, O., Moscatelli, D., Sommer, A., and Rifkin, D. B. (1988). *J. Cell. Biol.* **107**, 743–751.

Sanderson, R. D., and Bernfield, M. (1988). *Proc. Natl. Acad. Sci. U.S.A.* **85**, 9562–9566.

Sanderson, R. D., Lalor, P., and Bernfield, M. (1989). *Cell Regul.* **1**, 27–35.

Sandy, J. D., Flanner, C. R., Boynton, R. E., and Neame, P. J. (1990). *J. Biol. Chem.* **265**, 21108–21113.

Sant, A. J., Cullen, S. E., Giacoletto, K. S., and Schwartz, B. D. (1985). *J. Exp. Med.* **162**, 1916–1934.

Sasaki, M., and Yamada, Y. (1987). *J. Biol. Chem.* **262**, 17111–17117.

Sasaki, M., Kato, S., Kohno, K., Martin, G. R., and Yamada, Y. (1987). *Proc. Natl. Acad. Sci. U.S.A.* **84**, 935–939.

Saunders, S., and Bernfield, M. (1988). *J. Cell Biol.* **106**, 423–430.

Saunders, S., Jalkanen, M., O'Farrell, S., and Bernfield, M. (1989). *J. Cell Biol.* **108**, 1547–1556.

Schmidtchen, A., Carlstedt, I., Malmström, A., and Fransson, L.Å. (1990). *Biochem. J.* **265**, 289–300.

Schulz, T., Schaewable, W., Stanley, K., Weiss, E., and Dierich, M. (1986). *Eur. J. Immunol.* **16**, 1351–1355.

Schwartz, N. B., Belch, J., Henry, J., Hupert, J., and Sugahara, K. (1982). *Fed. Proc., Fed. Am Soc. Exp. Biol.* **41**, 852.

Scott, J., Urdea, M., Quiroga, M., Sanchiz-Pescador, R., Gond, N., Selby, M., Rutter, W., and Bell, G. I. (1983). *Science* **221**, 236–240.

Segarini, P. R., and Seyedin, S. M. (1988). *J. Biol. Chem.* **263**, 8366–8370.

Siegelman, M. H., van de Rihn, M., and Weissman, I. L. (1989). *Science* **243**, 1165–1172.

Sorrell, J. M., Mahmoodian, F., Schafer, I. A., Davis, B., and Caterson, B. (1990). *J. Histochem. Cytochem.* **38**, 393–402.

Spiro, R. C., Casteel, H. E., Laufer, D. M., Reisfeld, R. A., and Harper, J. R. (1989). *J. Biol. Chem.* **264**, 1779–1786.

Stacey, A., Bateman, J., Choi, T., Mascara, T., Cole, W., and Jaenisch, R. (1988). *Nature (London)* **332**, 131–136.

Stallcup, W. B., Dahlin, K., and Healy, P. (1990). *J. Cell Biol.* **111**, 3177–3188.

Stamenkovic, I., Amiot, M., Pesando, J. M., and Seed, B. (1989). *Cell* **56**, 1057–1062.

Stevens, R. L., and Austen, K. F. (1989). *Immunol. Today* **10**, 381–386.

Stevens, R. L., Avraham, S., Gartner, M. C., Bruns, G. A. P., Austen, K. F., and Weis, J. H. (1988). *J. Biol. Chem.* **263**, 7287–7291.

Stirpe, N. S., Argraves, W. S., and Goetinck, P. F. (1987). *Dev. Biol.* **124**, 77–81.

Svoboda, K. K., Nishimura, I., Sugrue, S. P., Ninomiya, Y., and Olsen, B. R. (1988). *Proc. Natl. Acad. Sci. U.S.A.* **85**, 7496–7500.

Takahashi, N., Takahashi, Y., and Putnam, F. W. (1985). *Proc. Natl. Acad. Sci. U.S.A.* **82**, 1906–1910.

Tan, S.-S., Crossin, K. L., Hoffman, S., and Edelman, G. M. (1987). *Proc. Natl. Acad. Sci. U.S.A.* **84**, 7977–7981.

Thesleff, I., Jalkanen, M., Vainio, S., and Bernfield, M. (1988). *Dev. Biol.* **129**, 565–572.

Toole, B. (1991). *In* "Cell Biology of the Extracellular Matrix" (E. D. Hay, ed.). In press.

Vainio, S., Jalkanen, M., Lehtonen, E., Bernfield, M., and Saxén, L. (1989). *Dev. Biol.* **134**, 382–391.

Van Vactor, D., Jr., Krantz, D. E., Reinke, R., and Zipursky, S. L. (1988). *Cell* **52**, 281–290.

Vlodavsky, I., Folkman, J., Sullivan, R., Fridman, R., Ishai-Michaeli, R., Susse, J., and Klagsburn, M. (1987). *Proc. Natl. Acad. Sci. U.S.A.* **84**, 2292–2296.

Vogel, K. G., and Trotter, J. A. (1987). *Collagen Relat. Res.* **7**, 105–114.

Wharton, K. A., Johansen, K. M., Xu, T., and Artavanis-Tsakonas, S. (1985). *Cell* **43**, 567–581.

Wight, T. N. (1989). *Arteriosclerosis* **9**, 1–20.

Williams, A. F. (1987). *Immunol. Today* **8**, 298–305.

Wolffe, E. J., Gause, W. C., Palfrey, C., Holland, S. M., Steinberg, A. D., and August, J. T. (1990). *J. Biol. Chem.* **265**, 341–347.

Woods, A., Couchman, J. R., Johansson, S., and Höök, M. (1986). *EMBO J.* **5**, 665–670.

Wright, T. C., Pukac, L. A., Castellot, J. J., Karnovsky, M. J., Levine, R. A., Kim-Park, H.-Y., and Campisi, J. (1989). *Proc. Natl. Acad. Sci. U.S.A.* **86**, 3199–3203.

Yada, T., Suzuki, S., Kobayashi, K. Kobayashi, K., Hoshino, T., Horie, K., and Kimata, K. (1990). *J. Biol. Chem.* **265**, 6992–6999.

Yamaguchi, Y., and Ruoslahti, E. (1988). *Nature (London)* **336**, 244–246.

Yamaguchi, Y., Mann, D. M., and Ruoslahti, E. (1990). *Nature (London)* **346**, 281–284.

Yanagishita, M., and Hascall, V. C. (1984a). *J. Biol. Chem.* **259**, 10260–10269.

Yanagishita, M., and Hascall, V. C. (1984b). *J. Biol. Chem.* **259**, 10270–10283.

Zimmerman, D. R., and Ruoslahti, E. (1989). *EMBO J.* **8**, 2975–2981.

6

Sequential Segregation and Fate of Developmentally Restricted Intermediate Cell Populations in the Neural Crest Lineage

James A. Weston
Institute of Neuroscience
University of Oregon
Eugene, Oregon 97403

The neural crest of vertebrate embryos has been usefully exploited to learn how differences in developmental ability are established in vertebrate embryonic cell lineages. Neural crest cells disperse along characteristic paths through embryonic interstitial spaces (see Weston *et al.*, 1984; Newgreen and Erickson, 1986; Erickson, 1986; Perris and Bronner-Fraser, 1989), where they encounter a variety of different environmental cues and ultimately produce a remarkable diversity of cellular phenotypes. These phenotypes include melanocytes; the neurons and glia of the sensory, autonomic, and enteric nervous systems; neurosecretory cells; dental papillae; structural components of the cardiac outflow tract; and skeletal and connective tissues of the cranial and facial derivatives of the branchial arches (see Le Douarin, 1982; Weston, 1982; Kirby *et al.*, 1983; Noden, 1986).

   The precise role of environmental cues in generating the diversity of crest phenotypes is unknown. This lack of understanding is due largely to the fact that we do not know the identity of the responsive crest-derived cells. Thus, the mechanism(s) that leads to expression of diverse cellular phenotypes within the crest lineage would clearly be different depending on whether all or only a subset of crest cells responds to specific environmental cues. Consequently, the interpretation of the behavior of a crest cell population in response to specific environmental cues depends on what assumptions are made about the composition of the crest cell population. In practice, we cannot easily distinguish whether local environmental cues effect changes in the developmental fates of crest cells within homogeneous developmentally labile (i.e., "pluripotent") populations, or whether they change the behavior of individual subpopulations that are already developmentally restricted and differentially responsive. Only when we understand clearly when and in what order developmental restrictions are imposed on crest-derived cells will these alternative mechanisms for phenotypic diversification be successfully distinguished.

To help elucidate these issues, I review the evidence that neural crest cells begin to diversify before they disperse, and that developmentally restricted intermediate subpopulations arise sequentially within the crest lineage. Then, I summarize results indicating that some of these developmentally distinct subpopulations respond differentially to specific developmental cues that they encounter on their migration pathways. Finally, I discuss how recent results with cultured crest cells can be reconciled with the early morphogenetic and differentiative behavior of crest cells *in vivo*, how developmental cues are normally presented to responsive crest-derived populations, and how differentially responsive crest populations might arise during development.

I. Subpopulations of Crest Cells with Partial Developmental Restrictions Are Present during Initial Dispersal of Neural Crest Populations

A variety of heterotopic grafting experiments have shown that the neural crest from every axial level has a wide range of developmental potentialities (see Le Douarin, 1982; Noden, 1984; Weston *et al.*, 1988). Moreover, when the developmental abilities of single cells have been analyzed *in vitro* (Cohen and Konigsberg, 1975; Sieber-Blum and Cohen, 1980; Baroffio *et al.*, 1988; Dupin *et al.*, 1990) or *in vivo* (Bronner-Fraser and Fraser, 1989), some crest-derived cells are able to give rise to diverse cellular phenotypes, so their progenitors were clearly not irreversibly restricted to individual fates. The presence of such pluripotent cells within the neural crest population has been used to support the idea that local environmental cues normally act on developmentally labile crest cells as they disperse and localize throughout the early embryo.

It is noteworthy, however, that premigratory and early-migrating neural crest cell populations also contain phenotypically distinct subpopulations, as first directly recognized by the application of cell type-specific monoclonal antibodies to premigratory and early-migrating crest cell populations (Ciment and Weston,

1981, 1982; Barald, 1982; Ziller *et al.*, 1983; Payette *et al.*, 1984; Girdlestone and Weston, 1985; Marusich *et al.*, 1986a; Barbu *et al.*, 1986; Maxwell *et al.*, 1988). Moreover, some of these phenotypically distinct subpopulations appear to be developmentally restricted, as suggested by grafting experiments which showed that cranial crest-derived cells expressing immunoreactivity characteristic of neuronal cells were unable to undergo melanogenesis in permissive locations *in vivo* (Ciment and Weston, 1985). Other grafting experiments have also revealed developmental restrictions among cranial neural crest-derived cells. Thus, only part of the rhombencephalic crest [the so-called "cardiac crest" (Kirby *et al.*, 1983)] contains cells that can produce the aorticopulmonary and conotruncal septa of the cardiac outflow tract (Kirby, 1989).

In fact, the cloning experiments mentioned above also show that individual cells with restricted developmental potential are present in populations of cultured crest cells. For example, although the conclusion that "trunk neural crest cells can be multipotent" (Bronner-Fraser and Fraser, 1989) was emphasized, the results from direct cell labeling experiments indicate that some clones *in vivo* produce only pigment derivatives, suggesting an early commitment by cloning progenitors to a nonneurogenic lineage. In addition, some small (i.e., two-cell) clones produced neurons in sensory ganglia, suggesting a neurogenic restriction. Similarly, there are reports that some crest-derived clonal progenitors *in vitro* produce small colonies of cells with neuronal traits (Baroffio *et al.*, 1988) or only nonneuronal (e.g., glial and pigment) derivatives (Dupin *et al.*, 1990). In light of these considerations, it is now clear that earlier cell culture experiments also provided suggestive, but unacknowledged, evidence that explanted crest populations were phenotypically and developmentally heterogeneous (see Maxwell, 1976; Loring *et al.*, 1981; Sieber-Blum and Sieber, 1981, 1984).

Indeed, although developmentally labile crest cells have long been thought to diversify in response to localized environmental cues *in vivo*, neuronal and glial derivatives both arise from crest cells that originate at the same time and place, disperse along the same medioventral pathway into the rostral sclerotome, and localize in the same embryonic sites. These facts suggest that some distinct neurogenic and nonneurogenic progenitors must exist *before* gangliogenesis *in vivo*, and may be present as part of an heterogeneous population at the earliest stages of crest cell dispersal. Although the presence of such neurogenic precursors, and their nonneurogenic counterparts, has not yet been directly demonstrated in premigratory crest populations, we are now able to infer their existence from a variety of recent results, summarized below.

II. Early Neural Crest Populations *in Vitro* Exhibit a Transient Ability to Generate New Neurons

Clusters of apparently undifferentiated neural crest cells accumulate on the surfaces of embryonic neural tubes when they are explanted onto nonadhesive culture substrata (Loring *et al.*, 1981; Glimelius and Weston, 1981b). Nascent crest cell clusters can give rise to cells with neuronal phenotype (i.e., MAb A2B5- and anti-neurofilament-immunoreactive, postmitotic cells with extended processes) if they are allowed to disperse promptly on appropriate culture substrata (Girdlestone and Weston, 1985; Vogel and Weston, 1988). The proportions of nondividing neuronal cells in the dispersed cell population increases initially, reaches a plateau, and then declines as they are "diluted" by proliferation of other crest-derived cells in the culture. When early-differentiating neuronal cells are selectively immunoablated in dispersed secondary cultures of nascent crest cell clusters, new cells with neuronal traits replace them. However, older crest cell cultures, in which more neurons have already differentiated, exhibit progressively diminished latent neurogenic ability (i.e., the ability to produce *new* neurons after ablation of existing ones) *in vitro* (Weston *et al.*, 1988; Vogel and Weston, 1988). The ability of cultures to produce neurons initially, and the latent neurogenic ability of the crest cell clusters also declines if dispersal of the nascent clusters is delayed (see below; Vogel and Weston, 1988). We have recently shown that this loss is irreversible, since neurogenic ability cannot be rescued even if crest-derived populations are returned to young embryos and allowed to disperse along normal paths *in vivo* (Vogel and Weston, J. A., in preparation).

The pattern of appearance of neurons in these cultures, the decline of neurogenic ability in older culture populations, and the apparently irreversible loss of neurogenic ability of crest-derived populations whose dispersal is delayed can be explained in at least two ways: first, the ability to produce new neurons might arise and disappear stochastically among multipotent crest-derived stem cells (see Tsuji and Nakahata, 1989). In this case the loss of neurogenic ability would occur when, for unknown reasons related to their developmental history (e.g., cell interactions; see Section VI below), the probability of recruiting new neurogenic cells from the stem cell population declines. Alternatively, new neurons might arise in early-migrating crest cell populations *only* from a limited subpopulation of covertly specified neurogenic progenitors (see Anderson, 1989; Hall and Watt, 1989). In this case, if such stem cells segregate early in a sequential process (Brown *et al.*, 1988), and recruitment of new precursors from less-restricted neural crest-derived cells is limited *in vitro*, then neurogenic ability of the population would diminish either by depletion of the putative neurogenic precursors as they differentiate into postmitotic neurons, or, as discussed in Section VII, by the developmentally regulated loss of such precursors.

Although we cannot discriminate between these alternatives at present, and such putative neurogenic precursors have not been unequivocally distinguished from other apparently undifferentiated crest cells *in vivo*, the latter hypothesis would clearly be favored by the detection of a distinct transient subpopulation of nonneuronal cells exclusively in crest-derived populations known to possess neurogenic ability. Since we know that nascent neural crest cell clusters have the ability to produce neurons *in vitro* and *in vivo*, and that older clusters, whose dispersal has been delayed, lack such neurogenic ability (see above; Vogel and Weston, 1988), we predicted that differential screening of hybridoma supernatants on such populations would detect monoclonal antibodies that recognized putative neurogenic precursors.

We have recently identified such a monoclonal antibody, 12E10, by this differential screening procedure. MAb 12E10 binds to a cytoplasmic epitope in a subpopulation of cells that lacks morphological evidence of neuronal differentiation in crest cell cultures known to possess neurogenic ability. No comparable, apparently nonneuronal, immunoreactive cell is present in crest-derived populations that lack the ability to produce new neurons (Marusich *et al.*, unpublished). Although this result does not prove that the immunoreactive cells are neurogenic precursors, it does suggest that differential screening may be successfully used to identify such markers. We have also discovered that sera from some patients with small-cell lung carcinoma contain an autoantibody [Anti-Hu (Graus *et al.*, 1986)], which recognizes apparently nonneuronal cells in cultures of crest-derived cells with neurogenic ability that are absent in cultures that lack neurogenic ability (Marusich and Weston, 1991). As neurogenesis proceeds in such cultures, the proportion of cells labeled both with Anti-Hu and an explicit neuronal marker, such as antineurofilament antibody, progressively increases. Conversely, the proportion of cells labeled *solely* with Anti-Hu declines in these cultures. We suggest, therefore, that Anti-Hu precociously identifies a subpopulation of crest-derived cells with neurogenic potential. The Anti-Hu antibody recognizes 35–42 kDa molecules in the cytoplasm and nuclei of immunoreactive cells. The intracellular location and pattern of immunoreactivity expressed by early embryonic cells *in vivo*, moreover, suggests that these molecules may play a regulatory role in this developmental process (Marusich and Weston, 1991).

III. Developmentally Restricted Subpopulations Probably Segregate Progressively, and in a Characteristic Sequence, from an Initially Pluripotent Crest Cell Population

A parsimonious interpretation of the objective evidence from heterotopic grafting and cell culture experiments is that developmentally restricted subpopulations segregate from pluripotent crest cells (Brown *et al.*, 1988; Anderson, 1989), and that segregation occurs sequentially (Fig. 1) (Weston, 1981, 1982). Thus, we know that the cranial crest cell population, which segregates early in development from the rostral neural folds, can give rise to every known crest derivative, including both ectomesenchymal and other crest derivatives, when grafted heterotopically into the trunk of an avian host embryo. In contrast, trunk crest appears to be unable to produce skeletal and connective tissue derivatives characteristic of cranial crest, even when transplanted into the cranial region of a host embryo. In addition, it has been recognized for some time that the cranial neural crest includes a subpopulation of cells, lacking from trunk crest populations, that produces fibronectin and exhibits a large flattened morphology *in vitro* (Greenberg and Pratt, 1977; Duband and Thiery, 1982; Rogers *et al.* 1990b; S. Rogers, personal communication). This phenotypically distinct subpopulation seems likely to be the ectomesenchymal component, which can also be recognized *in vivo* even before it gives rise to characteristic derivatives (see Nichols, 1981). We postulate, therefore, that ectomesenchyme (designated "em" in Fig. 1) segregates precociously from cranial neural folds (cnf). Another developmentally restricted subpopulation, which is uniquely able to give rise to the septal

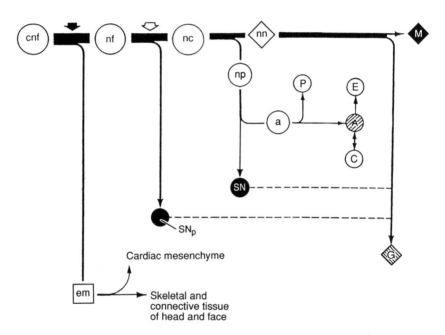

Fig. 1 Segregation of developmentally restricted subpopulations from the neural crest lineage. Circles, diamonds, and square represent subpopulation classes postulated to be present within the neural crest population at various times and embryonic locations (shapes and shadings correspond to conventions used in Fig. 2). Although developmental restrictions probably occur at various times and locations throughout early development, the horizontal axis suggests the sequence of such restrictions relative to the onset of dispersal by crest cells in the cranial (short solid arrow) and trunk (short open arrow) axial levels. Smaller arrowheads indicate terminal differentiations or modulations. Dashed lines indicate developmentally relevant cell interactions between crest-derived neurons and glial cell precursors. a, Autonomic neuronal precursors; A, adrenergic neurons; C, cholinergic neurons; cnf, cranial neural folds; E, enteric neurons; em, ectomesenchyme; G, Schwann sheath and other peripheral glia; M, melanocytes; nc, trunk neural crest (and cranial neural crest after fusion of the neural folds in the dorsal midline); nf, neural folds after the ectomesenchymal subpopulation has segregated; nn, nonneurogenic crest cells; np, neurogenic precursors; SN_p, *primary* sensory neurons; SN, other sensory neurons.

mesenchyme that divides the cardiac outflow tract, may also arise from this population of premigratory rostral crest cells (see above; Kirby, 1989).

A few cells with neuronal morphology have been observed among the crest population from all axial levels at the onset of cell dispersal. From their early appearance and morphology *in vivo* (Tennyson, 1965; Weston, 1982; Bronner-Fraser and Fraser, 1989) and *in vitro* (Girdlestone and Weston, 1985; Vogel and Weston, 1988), we suggest that they represent a limited subpopulation of primary sensory neurons (designated "SN_p" in Fig. 1) that segregates precociously from the crest lineage.

As discussed in the previous section, we have suggested that neurogenic ability of crest cell populations is correlated with the presence of a distinct subpopulation of neurogenic precursors (Ziller *et al.*, 1983; Girdlestone and Weston, 1985; Vogel and Weston, 1988; see also Boisseau and Simonneau, 1989), which subsequently give rise to cells with precocious neuronal traits (e.g., A2B5 immunoreactivity) *in vitro*. We have recently shown by a series of immunoablation experiments that a subpopulation derived solely from this early-differentiating neuronal population subsequently acquires TH immunoreactivity, and that this subpopulation represents a common bipotential precursor of both adrenergic neurons and pheochromocytes of the sympathoadrenal lineage (Vogel and Weston, 1990a,b). The conclusion that adrenergic neurons arise as a subpopulation of cells that previously express at least one more general neuronal trait is also implicit in the interesting observations by Sieber-Blum (1990) that adrenergic cells are never present as the sole neuronal component in neural crest clones. Accordingly, Fig. 1 posits that a subpopulation of neurogenic precursors (designated "np" in the figure) segregates from the early-migrating neural crest cell lineage and subsequently give rise to cells with early neuronal traits (see above).

As indicated in Fig. 1, we postulate that these early neuronal cells subsequently produce a variety of other neuronal subpopulations, including additional sensory neurons (designated "SN") (Marusich *et al.*, 1986a; Marusich and Weston, 1988; Sieber-Blum, 1989a,b), and precursors of the autonomic/enteric neuronal lineages ("a" in Fig. 1). Both of these neuron classes are known to contain cells with diverse combinations of neurotransmitter and neuromodulatory molecules. We suggest, therefore, that in response to specific environmental cues, the former will give rise to neurons with different sensory modalities (see Marusich *et al.*, 1986b; Weston *et al.*, 1988). We further suggest that the latter subpopulation can modulate transmitter phenotypes to produce the sympathoadrenal lineages (designated "A" and "P" in the figure; Doupe *et al.*, 1985; Anderson and Axel, 1986; Anderson, 1989; Vogel and Weston, 1990a,b) and other (e.g., cholinergic and peptidergic) neurons of the autonomic nervous system (designated "C"; Barald, 1982, 1988; Coulombe and Bronner-Fraser, 1989; Yamamori *et al.*, 1989; Nawa and Patterson, 1990; Nawa and Sah, 1990; Maxwell and Forbes, 1990), or the enteric nervous system (designated "E"; Rothman *et al.*, 1986; Baetge *et al.*, 1990).

Finally, as indicated in Fig. 1, we suggest that after segregation of neurogenic ability from the neural crest lineage, a nonneurogenic crest-derived subpopulation with dual developmental ability remains. Thus, since it appears that the development of glial and supportive cells of the peripheral nervous system requires the association of nerve cell bodies or fibers (Holton and Weston, 1982; Smith-Thomas *et al.*, 1990), and since some of these nonneuronal supportive cell precursors can produce melanin pigment if the association with neurons is disrupted or prevented (Nichols and Weston, 1977), we have postulated that a nonneurogenic crest-derived subpopulation (designated "nn" in Fig. 1) retains the ability to produce either glial (designated "G") or pigment cells (designated "M"), depending on whether they interact with peripheral nerve cell bodies or fibers (Nichols *et al.*, 1977; Holton and Weston, 1982; Weston *et al.*, 1988; see also Ciment, 1990) or encounter melanogenic cues (see Satoh and Ide, 1987; Derby, 1982; Morrison-Graham *et al.*, 1990a,b).

IV. Neural Crest-Derived Subpopulations Are Differentially Responsive to Growth Factor Cues in Their Environment

Various growth factors are known to be produced in a developmentally regulated way by embryonic tissues (see, e.g., Smith, 1989; Lyons and Hogan, 1990; Wilkinson *et al.*, 1988; Kalcheim and Neufeld, 1990; see also Nilsen-Hamilton, 1990). Many identified growth factors, in turn, are known to be localized on and/or potentiated by extracellular matrix (ECM) components present in embryonic interstitial spaces (Smith *et al.*, 1982; Campbell and Wicha, 1988; Dexter, 1989; Sanes, 1989; Panayotou *et al.*, 1989; Engel, 1989; Flaumenhaft *et al.*, 1989). It seems likely, therefore, that crest cells will encounter such "spatially buffered" developmental cues as they disperse along their interstitial migration pathways (see, e.g., Ratner *et al.*, 1988; Perris *et al.*, 1988 Ruoslahti and Yamaguchi, 1991; Nathan and Sporn, 1991).

Although much remains to be learned, it seems clear, as summarized in Table I, that different crest-derived cells exhibit distinct responses to such specific developmental (e.g., survival, proliferation, and differentiation) cues. For example, different subpopulations of neural crest-derived neurons appear to respond specifically to particular peptide neuronotrophic factors (e.g., NGF, NT3, BDNF, CNTF; reviewed by Davies, 1988; Barde, 1989). Some of these growth factors probably also affect the survival and/or differentiation of their crest cell precursors, as is the case for the effects of BDNF on the survival of sensory neuron precursors (Kalcheim *et al.*, 1987; Sieber-Blum, 1991) and CNTF on the survival of parasympathetic neurons of the ciliary ganglion (Manthorpe *et al.*, 1986). Other growth, differentiation, and survival factors appear to affect different crest-derived populations in cell type-specific ways (e.g., NGF, Bernd, 1988, 1989; Black *et al.*, 1990; IGF, Xue *et al.*, 1988; CNTF, Saadat *et al.*, 1989; EGF, Herschman *et al.*, 1983; FGF, Schubert *et al.*, 1987; Rydel and Greene,

Table I Crest-Derived Cells Respond Differentially to Peptide Growth Factor Activities[a]

| | Neural crest-derived cells | | | | | | |
| | Neurons | | | | Glia | Pigment | Ectomes[b] |
Growth factor	Cultured	Sensory	Cholinergic	Sympathoadrenal			
bFGF	S	S	S	M, D_n	M	M	N
NGF	B	D_n		D_n	B		
IGF	S	S, D		D			
BDNF		S	N	N			
CNTF			S	D_t			
EGF	M, D^m			S, D_t, D_n	N		
TGFβ	D_m				M		D_c
GGF	?	N	N	N	S, D		
PDGF	D_p			N	M	D_p	D_c

[a] B, Binding of ligand; D, differentiation; D_c, cartilage production; D_m, altered morphology and extracellular matrix production; D_n, neurite outgrowth; D_p, melanogenesis; D_t, increased transmitter production; M, proliferation; N, no effect observed or reported; S, enhanced survival.

[b] Cranial crest-derived connective tissue derivatives.

1987; Stemple *et al.*, 1988; Ferrari *et al.*, 1989; Kalcheim, 1989; PDGF, Weinmaster and Lemke, 1990; K. Morrison-Graham unpublished observations; and TGFβ, Rogers *et al.*, 1991). Likewise, analogs of retinoic acid *selectively* alter the development of subpopulations of cranial neural crest (ectomesenchyme) that contribute connective tissue to craniofacial structures (Webster *et al.*, 1986; Wedden, 1987; Wedden *et al.*, 1988), and glucocorticoids selectively affect the development of sympathoadrenal progenitors (Anderson and Axel, 1986; Vogel and Weston, 1990).

V. Differential Responses of Crest Cells to Environmental Cues Are Mediated by Specific Growth Factor Receptors

Several lines of evidence implicate growth factor receptors, characteristic of specific crest-derived subpopulations, in the selective responses to environmental cues. For example, a phorbol ester (TPA), alters the development of cultured neural crest cell subpopulations in a stage- and cell type-specific fashion (Glimelius and Weston, 1981a; Sieber-Blum and Sieber, 1981; Ciment *et al.*, 1986; Sears and Ciment, 1988). Since TPA is known to affect the activity of protein kinase C, which, in turn, is part of the signal transduction mechanism used by a number of cell surface receptors (Kikkawa and Nishizuka, 1986), its effects on the development of crest derivatives likely reflect the presence of specific cell surface receptor complexes on these crest-derived subpopulations.

Analysis of pleiotropic mouse mutations provides support for the idea that some growth factor receptors are expressed differentially in crest-derived subpopulations. Thus, two mutations in the mouse, *Steel* (*Sl*) and *Dominant spotting* (*W*), cause identical pleiotropic phenotypes involving migrating stem cell populations (e.g., melanocytes, primordial germ cells, and the hematopoietic system). Cells affected by the *Sl* mutation can be "rescued" when placed in a normal embryonic environment, whereas the effects of mutations at the *W* locus are cell autonomous. It has been suggested, therefore, that cell surface receptors, encoded by genetic determinants at the *W* locus, recognize developmental cues affected by mutations at the *Sl* locus (see Morrison-Graham and Weston, 1989). Indeed, the coding region of *W* has now been shown to contain sequences homologous to the oncogene c-*kit*, a protein kinase characteristic of receptors for growth factors such as TGF-β, PDGF, CSF-1, IGF (Chabot *et al.*, 1988; Geissler *et al.*, 1988; Nocka *et al.*, 1989).

Consistent with the inference that the *Sl* mutation somehow affects the ligand for a receptor encoded by c-*kit*, we have recently shown that the *Sl^d* mutation selectively alters the structure of the dermal interstitial matrix (Morrison-Graham *et al.*, 1990b) and the ability of cell-free ECM-associated material produced by cultured embryonic skin cells to promote the differentiation of crest-derived pigment cells (Morrison-Graham *et al.*, 1990a). It is important to note, however, that this *Sl* mutation appears to affect only *nonneurogenic* crest-derived cells and does not alter the ability of ECM to promote the differentiation of crest-derived autonomic neurons *in vitro*. These results are consistent with our postulate that melanocytes arise from a distinct nonneurogenic subpopulation of premigratory crest cells (see Fig. 1).

Remarkably, eight research reports (by 72 different authors, in various combinations) and an accompanying minireview (Witte, 1990) were recently published simultaneously. They reported the identification and structure of a gene product of the *Sl* locus. As predicted, this gene product appears to be a ligand of the c-*kit* protooncogene receptor encoded by the *W* locus and has growth factor activity on cells of the hematopoietic lineage. These cells, along with primordial germ cells and crest-derived pigment cells, develop abnormally in homozygotes of *W* and *Sl* mutant mice (see above; Morrison-Graham and Weston, 1989).

Sequences encoding this growth factor are partially deleted in mutant homozygotes. Although the nucleotide sequence within the *Sl* locus appears to include more than 6000 bp, the identified growth factor accounts for only about 10% of this length.

This and other results suggest that differential splicing events might generate gene products that encode a number of molecules with growth factor activities that regulate the development of other cell lineages affected by these pleiotropic mutations. One version of the c-*kit* ligand contains a transmembrane domain that is deleted in the Sl^d mutant (Flanagan *et al.*, 1991). Such a cell surface-associated molecule could account for the apparent short range of action of the *Sl*-gene product. It is also possible that the some of the identified sequences transcribed at the *Sl* locus encode macromolecular components of ECM that contain, or modulate, growth factor activity. The facts that *in situ* hybridization reveals localized expression of the *kit*-ligand in early embryos (Matsui *et al.*, 1990), and that the structure of the dermal interstitial matrix is altered in *Sl* embryos (see above; Morrison-Graham *et al.*, 1990b) are consistent with the short-range effects of the *Sl*-gene product.

Another mouse mutation, *Patch* (*Ph*), also perturbs the development of pigment cells, as well as other nonneurogenic crest derivatives (e.g., cranial ectomesenchyme and septal structures of the cardiac outflow tract). In contrast, the location and size of cranial, spinal, and enteric ganglia are not affected by the mutation (Morrison-Graham *et al.*, submitted). Significantly, it has recently been reported that *Ph* appears to be a deletion of at least some of the coding region for the PDGF receptor α subunit (Stephenson *et al.*, 1991). It is tempting to suggest, therefore, that *Ph* causes a defect in the expression of this growth factor receptor component, which is normally expressed in nonneurogenic crest-derived cells that require PDGF stimulation for survival or differentiation. In contrast, crest-derived neurogenic cells do not normally express the PDGFα receptor subunit, and therefore would be insensible to its deletion in the mutant. It is noteworthy that we have recently found by *in situ* hybridization studies that abundant mRNA for the α-subunit of the PDGF receptor is expressed in nonneurogenic, but not in neuronal tissues of normal mouse embryos (G. Schatteman, personal communication). The report that the expression of a functional PDGF receptor seems to be regulated cell-type-specifically in crest-derived, nonneurogenic (Schwann sheath) cells (Weinmaster and Lemke, 1990) is also consistent with this conclusion.

It is also of interest that expression studies by *in situ* hybridization to embryonic mouse tissue sections have revealed the presence of the c-*kit* gene product specifically in those tissues affected by the *W* mutation (i.e., erythropoietic cells in blood islands and embryonic liver, primordial germ cells in the genital ridges and in oocytes of the adult ovary, and in putative pigment cells within hair follicles; Orr-Urtreger *et al.*, 1990). These authors also report, however, that c-*kit* proto-oncogene transcripts appear in branchial arches, nervous tissue, and embryonic gut that are apparently unaffected by the alleles of the mutation examined. This apparent paradox might be explained by the fact that glial cell precursors and related nonneurogenic neural crest-derived cells are known to be present in these tissues, and may be the source of the detected signal. Alternatively, neuronal cells may normally express c-*kit*, but the adverse affects of the *W* mutation might be mitigated by the presence of complementary growth factor support, as suggested above.

Finally, consistent with the notion that characteristic growth factor receptors are expressed differentially in specific crest-derived cells, a member of the protein tyrosine kinase receptor family, the *trk* protooncogene, has recently been reported to be expressed specifically in developing murine sensory ganglia (Martin-Zanca *et al.*, 1990), and appears to code for a high-affinity NGF receptor molecule (Kaplan *et al.*, 1991a,b).

Taken together, these recent results make it tempting to speculate that different growth factor receptors are expressed in neurogenic and nonneurogenic subpopulations of the crest lineage. How such selective expression is regulated, of course, remains a crucial issue to be elucidated (see Section VIII). Nevertheless, such selective developmental expression of receptor complexes would at once provide a mechanism for the segregation of such developmentally distinct subpopulations, and a useful marker for their presence in the early embryo.

VI. Early Developmental Fates of Neural Crest Subpopulations Are Affected by Dispersal and Cell Association

It is noteworthy, as mentioned above, that crest-derived neurons and nonneuronal cells coalesce in the rostral sclerotome of each somite to form spinal ganglia, whereas the crest-derived cells that disperse dorsolaterally into the embryonic skin undergo melanogenesis and never normally give rise to neuronal derivatives. Moreover, we know that when nascent spinal ganglia are experimentally dispersed *in vitro*, some of the nonneuronal cells in the ganglia undergo melanogenesis, which they would never normally do (Cowell and Weston, 1970; Nichols and Weston, 1977; see also Ciment *et al.*, 1986). These observations suggest that dispersal of crest cells promotes melanogenesis, whereas cell association resulting from the aggregation of crest-derived cells leads to neuronal differentiation (see Weston, 1970).

Paradoxically, however, we have also learned that when nascent clusters of premigratory neural crest cells are maintained in culture, the proportion of cells expressing neuronal traits increases only when the clusters are allowed to disperse promptly (Girdlestone and Weston, 1985; Vogel and Weston, 1988). If dispersal is delayed, not only do new neurons fail to differentiate, but latent neurogenic ability of the population is irreversibly lost and melanogenesis is promoted (see Section II; Vogel and Weston, 1988; K. Vogel and J. A. Weston, unpublished observations). Thus, timely dispersal of crest cells appears to be required for neuronal differentiation *in vitro*, and delay or lack of dispersal of early crest cell populations promotes melanogenesis (Girdlestone and Weston, 1985; Rogers *et al.*, 1990a).

To reconcile these apparently discrepant conclusions, we postulate (1) that survival of the putative neurogenic precursors, which we have suggested arise as a subset of the initial premigratory neural crest cell population (see above; Weston *et al.*, 1988), requires timely encounters with specific growth or survival factors, and (2) that these encounters normally occur *only* when crest cells disperse on appropriate matrix substrata with which growth or survival factors are known to associate.

The fate of putative neurogenic precursors that fail to encounter suitable trophic factors is unknown. One, but certainly not the only, possibility is that developmentally regulated cell death (i.e., apoptosis) eliminates such neurogenic precursors from populations that fail to encounter growth or survival factors in a timely way (see Umanski, 1982; Snow, 1987; Wyllie, 1987; Martin *et al.*, 1988). This prediction would explain the irreversible loss of neurogenic ability that has been observed *in vitro* and, as discussed below (Section VII), also suggests a novel mechanism for regulating the ability of embryonic tissues to respond to developmental stimuli *in vivo*. It further emphasizes that apoptosis may be a much more prevalent and pervasive phenomenon in early development than has been suspected previously (see Snow, 1987).

VII. *In Vitro* Results Can Be Reconciled with Neural Crest Cell Behavior *in Vivo*

The hypothesis that putative neurogenic precursors require timely encounters with growth or survival factors can reconcile some puzzling observations about neural crest cell behavior *in vivo*—namely, that neuronal differentiation and gangliogenesis occur *only* among crest cells that follow the ventral migration pathways, and that neurogenesis *never* normally occurs among crest cells that migrate dorsolaterad into the embryonic ectoderm. Thus, we know that when trunk neural crest cells first segregate from the neural tube in avian and murine embryos, they enter a cell-free ECM-rich "staging area" bounded by the neural tube, the overlying ectodermal epithelium, and the somite (Pratt *et al.*, 1975; Weston *et al.*, 1978; Erickson and Weston, 1983; Erickson *et al.*, 1989) (see Fig. 2). Based on arguments summarized above, we postulate that the premigratory crest population in this staging area is already heterogeneous and contains at least two subpopulations—neurogenic and nonneurogenic precursors (represented in Fig. 2 by open circles and open diamonds; see also Fig. 1)—and probably also some pluripotent crest cells that continue to segregate at these early stages from the epithelial neural tube.

Crest cells transiently reside close to each other in the staging area, then leave the area at well-defined times and locations. Some crest cells depart immediately between neighboring somites (Thiery *et al.*, 1982) or into the sclerotome as it and the dermomyotome ("D/M" in Fig. 2) form from the rostral epithelial somite (Rickmann *et al.*, Bronner-Fraser, 1986; Loring and Erickson, 1987). We propose that gangliogenesis results when differentiating neuronal derivatives on the ventral crest cell migratory path (indicated by solid circles in Fig. 2) associate specifically with nonneurogenic cells [presumably by the acquisition of appropriate cell surface adhesion mechanisms (see Weston, 1970; Thiery *et al.*, 1985; Rutishauser and Jessell, 1988)]. The nonneurogenic crest-derived cells that are present in nascent ganglia then undergo glial cell differentiation in response to interactions with neurons (indicated by shaded diamonds in Fig. 2) (Holton and Weston, 1982; Smith-Thomas *et al.*, 1990). As noted above, if such associations are experimentally prevented or disrupted, these nonneurogenic crest-derived cells can still undergo melanogenesis (Nichols *et al.*, 1977; Ciment *et al.*, 1986).

Although crest cells begin to disperse immediately into the rostral half-somite, it is important to note that many of the cells in the staging area adjacent to the caudal portion of each somite remain clustered there until a new migratory pathway opens up between the dermomyotome and the overlying ectodermal epithelium (Loring and Erickson, 1987; Serbedzija *et al.*, 1989). In mouse and avian embryos, at least, this dorsolateral pathway appears approximately 1 day after the onset of dispersal of crest cells on the ventral migration pathway (see Derby, 1978; Loring and Erickson, 1987; Teillet *et al.*, 1987; Serbedzija *et al.*, 1989). Therefore, compared to crest cells that disperse into the rostral sclerotome of each segment, the cells that eventually migrate on the dorsolateral pathway remain clustered in the staging area for an extended period before they disperse.

We have shown that when nascent clusters of premigratory crest cells are placed in secondary culture, the proportion of cells expressing neuronal traits increases only if the clusters are allowed to disperse. If dispersal is delayed by as

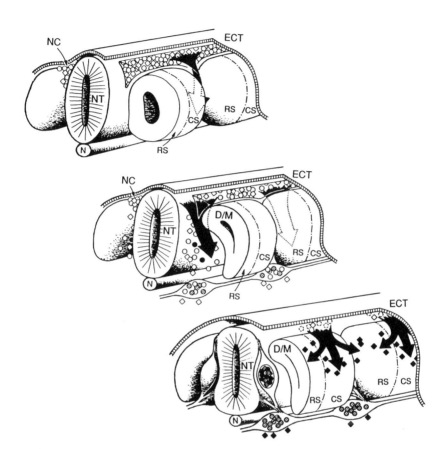

Fig. 2 Stages of trunk crest cell dispersal and fate of neurogenic precursors and nonneurogenic crest-derived cells. (Top) Two distinct crest subpopulations in the migration "staging area" first disperse between adjacent somites. (Center) Crest cells in the staging area subsequently disperse into rostral sclerotome; crest cells adjacent to caudal half-somites remain clustered in the staging area. Neurogenic precursors whose dispersal is delayed begin to undergo apoptosis. (Bottom) The nonneurogenic crest-derived cells, which remain in the staging area adjacent to the caudal somite, finally disperse when a dorsolateral migration pathway between the dermomyotome and the overlying epithelium becomes available. CS, Caudal somite; D/M, dermomyotome; ECT, ectoderm; N, notochord; NC, neural crest; NT, neural tube; RS, rostral somite. Open circles, Putative neurogenic precursors; solid circles, differentiated sensory neurons; hatched circles, differentiated sympathoadrenal cells; broken circles, neurogenic precursors undergoing developmental cell death; open diamonds, nonneurogenic crest cells; solid diamonds; melanocytes; shaded diamonds, glial cells. (Illustrion by of George Gessert.)

little as 8 hours, new neurons fail to differentiate, neurogenic ability of the population progressively diminishes, and the proportion of cells in the cultures undergoing melanogenesis increases (Vogel and Weston, 1988). We have suggested that crest-derived neurogenic precursors that fail to disperse lack access to developmental cues needed for their survival (see above; Martin *et al.*, 1988). We propose, therefore, that the delay of dispersal of crest cells in the staging area adjacent to the posterior somite *in vivo* results in the same loss of neurogenic ability, with a similar time course, as in clusters of neural crest cells *in vitro*. It seems reasonable to suggest, moreover, that the loss of neurogenic ability *in vivo* is the result of the disappearance of the putative neurogenic precursor subpopulation in the premigratory crest population (signified by the broken circles in the center and bottom panels of Fig. 2). Such a loss of neurogenic precursors can account for the intriguing fact that the crest cells which disperse under the skin on the lateral pathway never normally make neurons. Furthermore, in the absence of neurons, the remaining nonneurogenic neural crest-derived cells on this pathway undergo melanogenesis by default (Holton and Weston, 1982; Smith-Thomas *et al.*, 1990) (see Fig. 1). In this regard, it is especially interesting to note that some premigratory crest cells adjacent to the caudal portion of each somite initially *do* have neurogenic ability. Thus, when caudal somite halves were replaced by grafted rostral somite halves, crest cells were able to migrate ventrally over a broader front, proliferate, and contribute additional neurons to enlarged spinal ganglia (Kalcheim and Teillet, 1989; Goldstein *et al.*, 1990).

Finally, although the details differ, it has now been shown that a similar pattern of migration and differentiation exists in the embryo of the zebrafish *Brachydanio rerio*. Thus, crest cells segregate from the embryonic neural keel in a rostrocaudal sequence and disperse ventrad in interstitial spaces between the neural keel and the somite and laterad under the ectoderm (Wood *et al.*, 1991). Direct Di-I-marking of neural crest cells in living zebrafish embryos has revealed two spatially and temporally distinct migrating populations. One, an early-migrating population lateral to the embryonic neural keel, migrates ventrally into the somite and gives rise to both neurons in peripheral ganglia and nonneuronal (e.g., glial and pigment cell) derivatives. The second, mediodorsal, population undergoes a delayed migration laterally under the skin and appears to lack neurogenic ability (Bobrowicz and Eisen, 1989; J. Eisen personal communications).

VIII. Autonomous Cellular Processes Could Generate Diverse Neural Crest-Derived Subpopulations

The general inference from recent studies of neural crest cell development is that some differentiative events occur very early, and perhaps cell autonomously, to establish neurogenic and nonneurogenic lineages from pluripotent crest cells. We have argued, moreover, that neural crest cells in these lineages undergo further diversification by a sequence of developmental restrictions to produce subpopulations of cells with different developmental abilities. Within each partially restricted, developmentally intermediate subpopulation, local environmental stimuli, including localized growth/survival factor activity or interactions with other crest-derived subpopulations, could presumably elicit expression of one or more of the phenotypes that remain in its repertoire. Conversely, in the absence of appropriate local cues, some intermediate cell types might fail to thrive or, if they survive, might remain developmentally quiescent. The developmental repertoire of such quiescent cells could be preserved, or be further segregated by subsequent developmental events into more highly restricted intermediate populations. The time of appearance, location, and developmental responses of such intermediate cell types obviously require further attention.

Specifically, two issues must soon be addressed. First, we must determine how distinct subsets of cells, presumably with different growth/trophic factor receptors and trophic factor requirements (see above), arise from pluripotent (i.e., uniformly responsive or previously unresponsive) cells. This issue, in turn, suggests that we must also establish the relationship between cell pluripotentiality and the presence and/or activity of such growth/trophic factor receptors in early embryonic cell populations.

We know that growth factor receptors can be down-regulated by their ligands and those of other receptors [i.e., heterologous down-regulation (see Lazarovici et al., 1987; Bryckaert et al., 1988; Ouchi et al., 1988)]. Conversely, we have seen that when cells become responsive to growth factors, they sometimes become dependent on them for survival. Moreover, one growth factor can cause responsive cells to alter the production of another growth factor receptor (Gronwald et al., 1989) or to become dependent on other factors, as when fibroblast growth factor promotes nerve growth factor dependence among responsive pheochromocytes (Stemple et al., 1988; Rydel and Greene, 1987). If various growth/survival factor activities were localized by matrix components on crest migratory pathways, therefore, particular sequences of exposure to such factors might be orchestrated during crest cell dispersion. It is possible, therefore, that pluripotent crest cells initially possess a diverse assortment of growth factor receptors on their surfaces, and that the process of heterologous regulation in response to encountered growth factor activity generates a series of subpopulations, each with different growth factor sensitivities specified by their characteristic patterns of functional surface receptors. Such a process suggests how population heterogeneity might arise progressively in early embryonic cell populations, as well as the way that phenotypic expression might be selectively promoted in particular embryonic locations.

Acknowledgments

I am grateful to David Anderson, Ira Black, Michael Marusich, Kathleen Morrison-Graham, Kristine Vogel, and Andrew Wood for their critical comments and helpful suggestions, to Wendy Hodsdon for technical assistance, and to George Gessert for his expert graphics.

References

Anderson, D. J. (1989). *Neuron* **3**, 1–12.
Anderson, D. J., and Axel, R. (1986). *Cell* **42**, 649–662.
Baetge, G., Pintar, J. E., and Gershon, M. D. (1990). *Dev. Biol.* **141**, 353–380.
Barald, K. F. (1982). *In* "Neuronal Development" (N. C. Spitzer, ed.), pp. 101–119. Plenum, New York.
Barald, K. F. (1988). *J. Neurosci. Res.* **21**, 107–118.
Barbu, M., Ziller, C., Rong, P. M., and Le Douarin, N. M. (1986). *J. Neurosci.* **6**, 2215–2225.
Barde, Y.-A. (1989). *Neuron* **2**, 1525–1534.
Baroffio, A., Dupin, E., and Le Douarin, N. M. (1988). *Proc. Natl. Acad. Sci. U.S.A.* **85**, 5325–5329.
Bernd, P. (1988). *J. Neurosci.* **8**, 3549–3555.
Bernd, P. (1989). *Int. J. Dev. Neurosci.* **7**, 449–463.
Black, I. B., DiCicco-Bloom, E., and Dreyfus, C. F. (1990). *Curr. Top. Dev. Biol.* **24**, 161–192.
Bobrowicz, G., and Eisen, J. (1989). *J. Cell Biol.* **109**, 62a.
Boisseau, S., and Simmonneau, M. (1989). *Development* **106**, 665–674.
Bronner-Fraser, M. (1986). *Dev. Biol.* **115**, 44–55.
Bronner-Fraser, M., and Fraser, S. E. (1989). *Neuron* **3**, 755–766.
Brown, G., Bunce, C. M., Lord, J. M., and McConnell, F. M. (1988). *Differentiation (Berlin)* **39**, 83–89.
Bryckaert, M. C., Lindroth, M., Loenn, A., Tobelem, G., and Wasteson, A. (1988). *Exp. Cell Res.* **179**, 311–321.
Campbell, A. D., and Wicha, M. S. (1988). *J. Lab. Clin. Med.* **112**, 140–146.
Chabot, B., Stephenson, D. A., Chapman, V. M., Besmer, P., and Bernstein A. (1988). *Nature (London)* **335**, 88–89.
Ciment, G. (1990). *Comments Dev. Neurobiol.* **1**, in press.
Ciment, G., and Weston, J. A. (1981). *Cold Spring Harbor Rep. Neurosci.* **2**, 73–89.
Ciment, G., and Weston, J. A. (1982). *Dev. Biol.* **93**, 355–367.
Ciment, G., and Weston, J. A. (1985). *Dev. Biol.* **111**, 73–83.
Ciment, G., Glimelius, B., Nelson, D. M., and Weston, J. A. (1986). *Dev. Biol.* **118**, 392–398.
Cohen, A. M., and Konigsberg, I. R. (1975). *Dev. Biol.* **46**, 262–280.
Coulombe, J. N., and Bronner-Fraser, M. (1986). *Nature (London)* **324**, 569–572.
Cowell, L., and Weston, J. A. (1970). *Dev. Biol.* **22**, 670–697.
Davies, A. M. (1988). *Trends Genet.* **4**, 139–143.
Derby, M. A. (1978). *Dev. Biol.* **66**, 321–336.
Derby, M. A. (1982). *Cell Tissue Res.* **225**, 379–386.
Dexter, T. M. (1989). *Br. Med. Bull.* **45**, 337–349.
Doupe, A. J., Landis, S. C., and Patterson, P. H. (1985). *J. Neurosci.* **5**, 2119–2142.
Duband, J.-L., and Thiery, J.-P. (1982). *Dev. Biol.* **93**, 308–323.
Dupin, E., Baroffio, A., Dulac, C., Cameron-Curry, P., and Le Douarin, N. M. (1990). *Proc. Natl. Acad. Sci. U.S.A.* **87**, 1119–1123.

Engel, J. (1989). *FEBS Lett.* **251,** 1–7.

Erickson, C. A. (1986). *In* "Developmental Biology" (L. W. Browder, ed.), pp. 481–543. Plenum, New York.

Erickson, C. A., and Weston, J. A. (1983). *J. Embryol. Exp. Morphol.* **74,** 97–118.

Erickson, C. A., Loring, J. F., and Lester, S. M. (1989). *Dev. Biol.* **134,** 112–118.

Ferrari, G., Minozzi, M.-C., Toffano, G., Leon, A., and Skaper, S. D. (1989). *Dev. Biol.* **133,** 140–147.

Flanagan, J. G., Chan, D. C., and Leder, P. (1991). *Cell* **64,** 1025–1035.

Flaumenhaft, R., Moscatelli, D., Saksela, O., and Rifkin, D. B. (1989). *J. Cell. Physiol.* **140,** 75–81.

Geissler, E. N., Ryan, M. A., and Housman, D. E. (1988). *Cell* **55,** 185–192.

Girdlestone, J., and Weston, J. A. (1985). *Dev. Biol.* **109,** 274–287.

Glimelius, B., and Weston, J. A. (1981a). *Dev. Biol.* **82,** 95–101.

Glimelius, B., and Weston, J. A. (1981b). *Cell Differ.* **10,** 57–67.

Goldstein, R. S., Teillet, M.-A., and Kalcheim, C. (1990). *Proc. Natl. Acad. Sci. U.S.A.* **87,** 4476–4480.

Graus, F., Elkon, K. B., Cordon-Cardo, C., and Posner, J. B. (1986). *Am. J. Med.* **80,** 45–52.

Greenberg, J. H., and Pratt, R. M. (1977). *Cell Differ.* **6,** 119–132.

Hall, P. A., and Watt, F. M. (1989). *Development* **106,** 619–633.

Herschman, H. R., Goodman, R., Chandler, C., Simpson, D., Crawley, D., Cole, R., and de Vellis, J. (1983). *Birth Defects, Orig. Artic. Ser.* **19,** 79–94.

Holton, B., and Weston, J. A. (1982). *Dev. Biol.* **89,** 64–81.

Kalcheim, C. (1989). *Dev. Biol.* **134,** 1–10.

Kalcheim, C., and Neufeld, G. (1990). *Development* **109,** 203–215.

Kalcheim, C., and Teillet, M.-A. (1989). *Development* **106,** 85–93.

Kalcheim, C., Barde, Y.-A., Thoenen, H., and Le Douarin, N. M. (1987). *EMBO J.* **6,** 2871–2873.

Kaplan, D. R., Hempstead, B. L., Martin-Zance, D., Chao, M. V., and Parada, L. F. (1991a). *Science* **252,** 554–558.

Kaplan, D. R., Martin-Zance, D., and Parada, L. F. (1991b). *Nature (London)* **350,** 158–160.

Kikkawa, U., and Nishizuka, Y. (1986). *Annu. Rev. Cell Biol.* **2,** 149–178.

Kirby, M. L. (1989). *Dev. Biol.* **134,** 402–412.

Kirby, M. L., Gale, T. F., and Stewart, D. E. (1983). *Science* **220,** 1059-1061.

Lazarovici, P., Dickens, G., Kuzuya, H., and Guroff, G. (1987). *J. Cell Biol.* **104,** 1611–1621.

Le Douarin, N. M. (1982). "The Neural Crest." Cambridge Univ. Press, Cambridge, England.

Loring, J. F., and Erickson, C. A. (1987). *Dev. Biol.* **121,** 220–236.

Loring, J. F., Glimelius, B., Erickson, C., and Weston, J. A. (1981). *Dev. Biol.* **82,** 86–94.

Lyons, K. M., and Hogan, B. L. M. (1990). *In* "Genetics of Pattern Formation and Growth Control" (A. Mahowald, ed.), pp. 137–156. Wiley–Liss, New York.

Manthorpe, M., Skaper, S. D., Williams, L. R., and Varon, S. (1986). *Brain Res.* **367,** 282–286.

Martin, D. P., Schmidt, R. E., DiStefano, P. S., Lowry, O. H., Carter, J. G., and Johnson, E. M. (1988). *J. Cell Biol.* **106,** 829–844.

Martin-Zanca, D., Barbacid, M., and Parada, L. F. (1990). *Genes Dev.* **4,** 683–694.

Marusich, M. F., and Weston, J. A. (1988). *J. Neurosci. Res.* **21,** 480–486.

Marusich, M. F., Pourmehr, K., and Weston, J. A. (1986a). *Dev. Biol.* **118,** 494–504.

Marusich, M. F., Pourmehr, K., and Weston, J. A. (1986b). *Dev. Biol.* **118,** 505–510.

Marusich, M. F., and Weston, J. A. (1991). Submitted for publication.

Matsui, Y., Zsebo, K. M., and Hogan, B. L. M. (1990). *Nature (London)* **347,** 667–669.

Maxwell, G. D. (1976). *Dev. Biol.* **49,** 66–79.

Maxwell, G. D., and Forbes, M. E. (1990). *J. Neurosci. Res.* **25,** 172–179.

Maxwell, G. D., Forbes, M. E., and Christie, D. S. (1988). *Neuron* **1**, 557–568.

Morrison-Graham, K., and Weston, J. A. (1989). *Trends Genet.* **5**, 116–121.

Morrison-Graham, K., West-Johnsrud, L., and Weston, J. A. (1990a). *Dev. Biol.* **139**, 299–307.

Morrison-Graham, K., Bork, T., and Weston, J. A. (1990b). *Dev. Biol.* **139**, 308–313.

Nathan, C., and Sporn, M. (1991). *J. Cell Biol.* **113**, 981–986.

Nawa, H., and Patterson, P. H. (1990). *Neuron* **4**, 269–277.

Nawa, H., and Sah, D. W. Y. (1990). *Neuron* **4**, 279–287.

Newgreen, D. F., and Erickson, C. A. (1986). *Int. Rev. Cytol.* **103**, 89–145.

Nichols, D. H. (1981). *J. Embryol. Exp. Morphol.* **64**, 105–120.

Nichols, D. H., and Weston, J. A. (1977). *Dev. Biol.* **60**, 217–225.

Nichols, D. H., Kaplan, R., and Weston, J. A. (1977). *Dev. Biol.* **60**, 226–237.

Nilsen-Hamilton, M., ed. (1990). *Curr. Top. Dev. Biol.* **24.**

Nocka, K., Majumder, S., Chabot, B., Ray, P., Cervone, M., Bernstein, A., and Besmer, P. (1989). *Genes Dev.* **3**, 816–826.

Noden, D. M. (1984). *Anat. Rec.* **208**, 1–13.

Noden, D. M. (1986). *J. Craniofacial Genet. Dev. Biol., Suppl.* **2**, 15–31.

Orr-Urtreger, A., Avivi, A., Zimmer, Y., Givol, D., Yarden, Y., and Lonai, P. (1990). *Development* **109**, 911–923.

Ouchi, Y., Hirosumi, J., Watanabe, M., Hattori, A., Nakamura, T., and Orimo, H. (1988). *Biochem. Biophys. Res. Commun.* **157**, 301–307.

Panayotou, G., End, P., Aumailley, M., Timpl, R., and Engel, J. (1989). *Cell* **56**, 93–101.

Payette, R. F., Bennett, G. S., and Gershon, M. D. (1984). *Dev. Biol.* **105**, 273–287.

Perris, R., and Bronner-Fraser, M. (1989). *Comments Dev. Neurobiol.* **1**, 61–83.

Perris, R., von Boxberg, Y., and Lofberg, J. (1988). *Science* **241**, 86–89.

Pratt, R., Larson, M., and Johnston, M. (1975). *Dev. Biol.* **67**, 444–464.

Ratner, N., Hong, D., Lieberman, M. A., Bunge, R. P., and Glaser, L. (1988). *Proc. Natl. Acad. Sci. U.S.A.* **85**, 6992–6996.

Rickman, M., Fawcett, J. W., and Keynes, R. J. (1985). *J. Embryol. Exp. Morphol.* **90**, 437–455.

Rogers, S. L., Bernard, L., and Weston, J. A. (1990a). *Dev. Biol.* **141**, 173–182.

Rogers, S. L., Gegick, P. J., Alexander, S. M., and McGuire, P. G. (1991). *Devel. Biol.* (in press).

Rothman, T. P., Sherman, D., Cochard, P., and Gershon, M. D. (1986). *Dev. Biol.* **116**, 357–380.

Ruoslahti, E., and Yamaguchi, Y. (1991). *Cell* **64**, 867–869.

Rutishauser, U., and Jessell, T. M. (1988). *Physiol. Rev.* **68**, 819–857.

Rydel, R. E., and Greene, L. A. (1987). *J. Neurosci.* **7**, 3639–3653.

Saadat, S., Sendtner, M., and Rohrer, H. (1989). *J. Cell Biol.* **108**, 1807–1816.

Sanes, J. R. (1989). *Annu. Rev. Neurosci.* **12**, 521–546.

Satoh, M., and Ide, H. (1987). *Dev. Biol.* **119**, 579–586.

Schubert, D., Ling, N., and Baird, A. (1987). *J. Cell Biol.* **104**, 635–643.

Sears, R., and Ciment, G. (1988). *Dev. Biol.* **130**, 133.

Serbedjiza, G., Bronner-Fraser, M., and Fraser, S. (1989). *Development* **106**, 809–816.

Sieber-Blum, M. (1989a). *Science* **243**, 1608–1611.

Sieber-Blum, M. (1989b). *Dev. Biol.* **134**, 362–375.

Sieber-Blum, M. (1990). *Comments Dev. Neurobiol.* **1**, 225–251.

Sieber-Blum, M. (1991). *Neuron* **6**, 1–20.

Sieber-Blum, M., and Cohen, A. M. (1980). *Dev. Biol.* **79**, 170–180.

Sieber-Blum, M., and Sieber, F. (1981). *Differentiation (Berlin)* **20**, 117–123.

Sieber-Blum, M., and Sieber, F. (1984). *Dev. Brain Res.* **14**, 241–246.

Smith, J. C. (1989). *Development* **105**, 667–677.

Smith, J. C., Singh, J. P., Lillquist, J. S., Goon, D. S., and Stiles, C. D. (1982). *Nature (London)* **296**, 154–156.

Smith-Thomas, L. C., Johnson, A. R., and Fawcett, J. W. (1990). *Development* **109**, 925–944.

Snow, M. H. L. (1987). *In* "Perspectives on Mammalian Cell Death" (C. S. Potten, ed.), pp. 202–228. Oxford Univ. Press, New York.

Stemple, D. L., Mahanthappa, N. K., and Anderson, D. J. (1988). *Neuron* **1**, 517–525.

Stephenson, D. A., Mercola, M., Anderson, E., Wang, C., Stiles, C. D., Bowen-Pope, D., and Chapman, V. M. (1990). *Proc. Natl. Acad. Sci. U.S.A.* **88**, 6–10.

Teillett, M.-A., Kalcheim, C., and Le Douarin, N. M. (1987). *Dev. Biol.* **120**, 329–347.

Tennyson, V. (1965). *J. Comp. Neurol.* **124**, 267–317.

Thiery, J.-P., Duband, J.-L., and Delouvee, A. (1982). *Dev. Biol.* **93**, 324–343.

Thiery, J.-P., Duband, J.-L., and Tucker, G. C. (1985). *Annu. Rev. Cell Biol.* **1**, 91–113.

Tsuji, K., and Nakahata, T. (1989). *J. Cell. Physiol.* **139**, 647–653.

Umanski, S. R. (1982). *J. Theor. Biol.* **97**, 591–602.

Vogel, K., and Weston, J. A. (1988). *Neuron* **1**, 569–577.

Vogel, K., and Weston, J. A. (1990a). *Dev. Biol.* **139**, 1–12.

Vogel, K., and Weston, J. A. (1990b). *Dev. Biol.* **139**, 13–23.

Webster, B., Johnston, M., Lammer, E., and Sulik, K. (1986). *J. Craniofacial Genet. Dev. Biol.* **6**, 211–222.

Wedden, S. E. (1987). *Development* **99**, 341–351.

Wedden, S. E., Ralphs, J. R., and Tickle, C. (1988). *Development* **103**, 31–40.

Weinmaster, G., and Lemke, G. (1990). *EMBO J.* **9**, 915–920.

Weston, J. A. (1970). *Adv. Morphol.* **8**, 41–114.

Weston, J. A. (1981). *Adv. Neurol.* **29**, 77–95.

Weston, J. A. (1982). *In* "Cell Behaviour" (R. Bellairs, A. Curtis, and G. Dunn, eds.), pp. 429–470. Cambridge Univ. Press, Cambridge, England.

Weston, J. A., Derby, M. A., and Pintar, J. E. (1978). *Zoon* **6**, 103–113.

Weston, J. A., Ciment, G., and Girdlestone, J. (1984). *In* "The Role of Extracellular Matrix in Development" (R. Trelstad, ed.), pp. 433–460, Liss, New York.

Weston, J. A., Vogel, K. S., and Marusich, M. F. (1988). *In* "From Message to Mind" (S. S. Easter, K. F. Barald, and B. M. Carlson, eds.), pp. 224–237. Sinauer, Sunderland, Massachusetts.

Wilkinson, D. G., Peters, G., Dickson, C., and McMahon, A. P. (1988). *EMBO J.* **7**, 691–695.

Witte, W. N. (1990). *Cell* **63**, 5–6.

Wood, A., Hodsdon, W., Raible, P., Weston, J., and Eisen, J. (1991). Manuscript in preparation.

Wyllie, A. (1987). *Arch. Toxicol., Suppl.* **11**, 3–10.

Xue, Z.-G., Le Douarin, N., and Smith, J. (1988). *Cell Differ. Dev.* **25**, 1–10.

Yamamori, T., Fukada, K., Aebersold, R., Korsching, S., Fann, M., and Patterson, P. H. (1989). *Science* **246**, 1412–1416.

Ziller, C., Dupin, E., Brazeau, P., Paulin, D., and Le Douarin, N. (1983). *Cell* **32**, 627–638.

7

Development of Mouse Hematopoietic Lineages

Shelly Heimfeld and Irving L. Weissman
Department of Pathology and the Howard Hughes Medical Institute
Stanford Medical Center
Stanford, California 94305

I. Introduction

Differentiation, the process through which cellular diversity is created, is crucial to the function of higher organisms. However, very little is understood about this central theme of developmental biology. How do multipotent cells choose which pathway they will follow? Furthermore, how does the organism regulate differentiation to insure that appropriate amounts and types of mature cells are generated? To answer these questions, well-defined cellular systems are required in which the mechanisms of determination and regulation are accessible to experimental manipulation. The hematopoietic (i.e., blood-forming) system, because it represents one of the better-characterized cell populations, has been an important model for studying basic questions about the processes of commitment, restriction, and differentiation.

A wealth of information about hematopoietic function at the cellular level has been accumulated over the last 30 years (for a review see Till and McCulloch, 1980). The mature blood cells have well-characterized morphologies and functional properties which make their classification straightforward. Erythrocytes are responsible for oxygen and carbon dioxide transport; megakaryocytes generate the platelets necessary for blood clotting; T and B cells contribute to immune surveillance and responsiveness; and macrophages and granulocytes aid in the disposal of invading microorganisms and damaged tissue cells. Most blood cells have a limited life span of a few days to weeks. To maintain steady-state levels, these mature cellular elements must be continuously produced. In adult vertebrates the bone marrow is the primary site of hematopoiesis, containing the precursor cells which ultimately give rise to all the hematopoietic lineages. Of critical importance, these cells normally exist in loose association within the bone marrow microenvironment. Thus, they can be easily obtained in suspension, labeled with specific markers, and separated into distinct subsets. These fractions can then be assayed in experimental systems *in vitro* and *in vivo* to determine their unique developmental capacities.

The earliest progenitors have been termed the stem cells. These are defined by their capacity for self-renewal and their ability to differentiate into multiple cell types. Self-renewal can be roughly defined as proliferation without loss of growth or differentiation potential. This property of self-renewal is the distinguishing characteristic of stem cells. Unfortunately, because it requires analysis of the progeny of individual stem cells, it is also one of the more difficult parameters to measure experimentally. It is generally believed that stem cells first give rise to more restricted precursor cells, which in turn generate unipotent progenitors through an unknown series of differentiation steps. These lineage-committed cells then mature into the various specialized end cells (see Fig. 1).

In this review we focus on the earliest stages of hematopoiesis: the pluripotent stem cells and committed progenitor cells. We primarily detail results generated within our laboratory, especially as regard specific enrichment protocols for these primitive precursor cells. However, it seems clear that, while the particular methodologies may have differed, similar data and conclusions have been reached by many other workers in the field. In Section II the isolation of pluripotent stem cells and several unique classes of progenitor cells is described. These precursor subsets have been characterized as to their proliferative and developmental potentials *in vivo*. On the basis of these findings, a model of lineage restriction has been constructed. This model may provide clues as to the pathways that pluripotent stem cells follow in the process of commitment, and suggests possible mechanisms which could influence that decision. In Section III the regulatory properties that stem cells exhibit when placed into irradiated animals are discussed. The results suggest that both global control and local microenvironment influence stem cell proliferation and differentiation. In Section IV the *in vitro* responsiveness of these precursors to bone marrow stromal

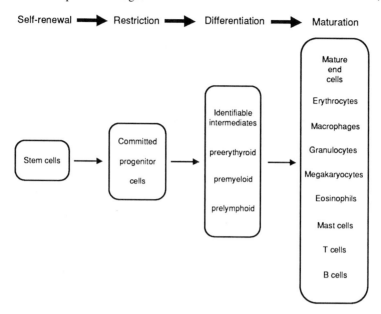

Fig. 1 Simple model of hematopoietic development. Stem cells are the rarest and most primitive cell type, retaining self-renewal and multipotent differentiation potential. Stem cells give rise to a series of committed progenitor cells, which lose the capacity for unlimited proliferation. These progenitors generally also have restricted abilities to differentiate into the various lineages. Progenitors generate intermediate precursors, which are further restricted in their differentiation and proliferation potential. These can begin to show morphological indications as to the types of progeny cells they will produce. The largest compartment consists of the mature end cells, in which the final stages of differentiation occur.

cells and defined growth factors is examined, which, again, offers clues to possible mechanisms of regulation.

II. Isolation and Characterization of Stem and Progenitor Cells

A. Introduction

Given the low frequency of precursors in bone marrow, it becomes clear that two elements are essential for experimental analysis of the early stages of hematopoiesis. The first requirement is a reproducible procedure for the separation of these progenitor cells from the rest of the marrow. The second is a set of assay systems which can measure the progeny of individual precursors in a *quantitative* fashion. Several assays are needed because, as detailed below, not all precursors may be detected in any one system. Furthermore, in many assays stem cell activity is indistinguishable from committed progenitor cell responses. In addition quantitation is critical to assess both the level of enrichment and the potential heterogeneity of the isolated population.

B. Purification of Precursor Cells

A variety of methodologies have been developed to isolate progenitor cells (for reviews see Spangrude, 1989; Visser and van Bekkum, 1990). The precursors described here were obtained using monoclonal antibody staining and multi-parameter fluorescence-activated cell sorting (Muller-Sieburg *et al.*, 1986; Spangrude *et al.*, 1988; Heimfeld *et al.*, 1991a). Particular antigens were selected because of their initial characterization as lineage-specific markers. An example depicting staining of adult bone marrow with three such markers is shown in Fig. 2.

Thy-1 is found at a high level on all mature mouse T cells (Reif and Allen, 1964). There is an additional rare set of cells in bone marrow which express a 10- to 20-fold lower level of Thy-1 (designated "Thy^{lo}" in Fig. 2A). Most hematopoietic progenitor activity falls within this 1% of bone marrow. Other markers, such as B220 (B), are expressed on immature pre-B and mature B cells (Coffman and Weissman, 1983) (Fig. 2B). Mac-1 (M) marks cells of the granulocyte/macrophage lineages (Springer *et al.*, 1979) (Fig. 2C). Using these and additional markers (see Table I for a listing and the abbreviations used), the Thy^{lo} cells are subdivided into five fractions.

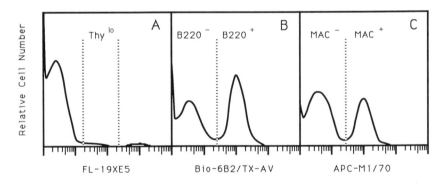

Fig. 2 Three-color stain of mouse bone marrow for the isolation of Thy^{lo} progenitor cells. (A) Fluorescein isothiocyanate-stained anti-Thy-1. The brightest cells are mature T cells. The dashed lines indicate the settings used to gate on the Thy^{lo} progenitor fraction. (B) Texas Red stained anti-B220. The bright cells contain mature B cells and immature pre-B progenitors, 35–50% of the bone marrow. (C) Allophycocyanin-stained anti-Mac-1. The bright cells are macrophages, granulocytes, and their precursors, representing 25–35% of the total cells.

Table I Differentiation of Thy^{lo} Progenitor Cells *in Vivo*[a]

Cell type	% of Bone marrow	CFU-S[b]	Day 12/Day 8	CFU-T[c]	Reconstitution *in Vivo*[d]		
					T cells	B cells	Myeloid cells
Bone marrow	100	+	1.0	+	+	+	+
Thy^{lo},B+,M−	0.6	−	ND	−	−	++++	−
Thy^{lo},B−,M+	0.4	+++	0.6	−	−	+/−	++++
Thy^{lo},B+,M+	0.1	+++	1.3	++	++	+++	+++
Thy^{lo},L−,S−	0.15	+++	0.7	−	−	+/−	+++
Thy^{lo},L−,S+	0.05	+++++	7.9	+++++	++++	+++++	+++++

[a] B, B220; M, Mac-1; L, lineage markers B220, Mac-1, Gr-1, CD4, and CD8; S, Sca-1.

[b] Colony-forming unit–spleen (CFU-S) values are given as the relative enrichment for spleen colony activity as compared to unseparated bone marrow. The ratio of late-forming day 12 to early day 8 CFU-S is also listed.

[c] Colony-forming unit–thymus (CFU-T) were assayed following intrathymic injection into irradiated congenic hosts. Results are indicated as the relative enrichment for T cell progenitors.

[d] Reconstitution ability was determined by intravenous injection of 10^2–10^4 sorted cells into lethally irradiated congenic animals along with 10^5 syngeneic bone marrow cells to insure survival. Repopulation was measured by two-color fluorescence-activated cell sorting analysis of peripheral blood, staining for donor type versus individual lineage markers for B, T, and myeloid cells at 4–8 weeks postirradiation. Data are given as the relative percentage of donor cells found for each of the indicated lineages. (See text for further explanations.)

C. Analysis of Differentiation *in Vivo*

Several assays have been used to define the developmental potential of these Thy^{lo} fractions. Following irradiation of mice the injection of bone marrow results in hematopoietic activity in the spleen, in the form of micro- and macroscopic colonies. The properties of these colony-forming units (CFU-S) have been well documented (Siminovitch *et al.*, 1963; Till and McCulloch, 1980). Particular to the work reported here, several points should be emphasized. First, there is a direct linear relationship between the number of cells injected and the number of colonies found. Thus, the assay is quantitative, although it is clear that only a fraction of the CFU-S actually seed the spleen. Second, CFU-S undergo active proliferation and then differentiation to the myeloid and/or erythroid lineages. No lymphoid differentiation is apparent in these colonies (Till and McCulloch, 1961). Therefore, certain types of restricted progenitors may not be detected in this assay. Third, there is a correlation between the extent of new CFU-S progenitors (i.e., self-renewal) within individual colonies and the time after injection, the later-appearing day 12 CFU-S having much greater stem cell activity (Siminivotch *et al.*, 1963; Magli *et al.*, 1982).

All of the Thy^{lo} fractions are enriched for CFU-S activity, with the significant exception of those cells which coexpress B_{220} but not Mac-1 (Thy^{lo}, B^+, M^-; see Table I). This suggests that each subset contains myeloerythroid progenitor cells. A relative measure of self-renewal capacity can be estimated by calculating the ratio of early to late colonies. The Thy^{lo}, L^-, S^+ cells (see Table I, footnote *a*, for abbreviations) give the best response: one colony per 10 cells injected. They also form predominantly day 12 colonies (Table I). Taking into consideration the proportion of injected cells which actually seed the spleen [0.1–0.2 (Till and McCulloch, 1972)], this yields a value of one colony per one or two sorted cells. This implies that Thy^{lo}, L^-, S^+ cells are a virtually pure population of primitive myeloerythroid stem cells (Spangrude *et al.*, 1988).

Unlike the spleen, the thymus supports the proliferation and subsequent maturation of T cell precursors. Following irradiation direct intrathymic injection of progenitors leads to reconstitution of the thymocyte pool. Limiting-dilution analysis is used to determine the frequency of pre-T cells in the Thy^{lo} fractions, using a congenic marker system to distinguish the donor cells (Spangrude *et al.*, 1988; Heimfeld *et al.*, 1991a). Only two populations give any significant T cell reconstitution: the Thy^{lo}, B^+, M^+ and Thy^{lo}, L^-, S^+ fractions (Table I). Again, taking into account the technical limits of this assay, the data suggest that virtually every Thy^{lo}, L^-, S^+ cell can generate T cells. Together with the CFU-S data, this implies that each individual cell in the Thy^{lo}, L^-, S^+ population is multipotent (i.e., capable of both myeloerythroid and lymphoid development) (see Section III).

A more complete measure of developmental potential of the Thy^{lo} fractions is obtained by intravenous injection into irradiated mice—again, using a congenic marker system to detect donor progeny. Syngeneic marrow is coinjected to insure long-term survival of the host (see below). Periodically after injection, peripheral blood is taken from the reconstituted animals and analyzed for lineage-specific markers and donor versus host cells. Data from a series of such experiments are summarized in the last three columns of Table I. The results indicate that Thy^{lo},B^+,M^- cells are committed to the B cell lineage, while Thy^{lo},B^-,M^+ cells are restricted to myeloid differentiation. The Thy^{lo},B^+,M^+ and Thy^{lo},L^-,S^+ populations are multipotent, in that both fractions can differentiate into cells of the B, T, and myeloid lineages. However, since these assays are not quantitative, it is unclear whether individual cells in these fractions are multipotent. Furthermore, an evaluation for other lineages such as erythroid, platelets, and mast cells has not been done. Thus, whether any of the Thy^{lo} fractions can form these other cell types *in vivo* has not been determined, although some information has been obtained from *in vitro* analysis (see Section IV).

Self-renewal capacity among the Thy^{lo} progenitors can be assayed in two ways. The first involves staining the bone marrow of reconstituted mice for donor cells that still express the progenitor cell phenotype (i.e., cells that are still Thy^{lo}). The only fraction that gives rise to new Thy^{lo} cells is the Thy^{lo},L^-,S^+ subset, implying that these cells are the ultimate precursors for the other progenitor cell classes. As a more stringent test bone marrow from reconstituted mice is transferred to a second set of irradiated animals. Again, only Thy^{lo},L^-,S^+ cells generate donor cells in these secondary hosts. This strongly indicates that this fraction contains the true self-renewing stem cell. Again, these self-renewal assays are not quantitative. Therefore, potential heterogeneity of the Thy^{lo},L^-,S^+ cells as regards self-renewal capacity remains an open question.

As a final test of proliferative and differentiative capacity, no syngeneic marrow is included in the initial injection. Only the Thy^{lo},L^-,S^+ fraction is capable of protecting mice from irradiation. Furthermore, 30 cells are sufficient to rescue 50% of the animals, while 80–100 cells save every animal (Spangrude *et al.*, 1988). This represents nearly a 1000-fold enrichment over unseparated bone marrow and strongly indicates that the Thy^{lo},L^-,S^+ cells are a very highly enriched, perhaps pure, population of pluripotent stem cells.

Using alternative methods of enriching for bone marrow progenitors, others have obtained fractions in which self-renewal capacity is distinct from the bulk of the day 12 CFU-S response. Additional evidence also suggests the existence of cells which are considered pre-CFU-S stem cells (Bertoncello *et al.*, 1985; Mulder and Visser, 1987; Ploemacher and Brons, 1988). In a similar fashion Spangrude and Johnson (1990) have shown that the Thy^{lo},L^-,S^+ cells can be further fractionated on the basis of staining with the mitochondrial-selective dye rhodamine-123. While the specific arguments are beyond the scope of this review, these data imply that a hierarchy exists within the stem cell population, representing a continuum in self-renewal potential.

D. Developmental Lineage Scheme

Putting the experimental findings together, we have proposed the lineage scheme outlined in Fig. 3. The most primitive stem cells are Thy^{lo}, L^-, S^+. These are the only cells which can self-renew: They are multipotent, and they give rise to all other progenitor cell classes following reconstitution of irradiated animals. A first step in stem cell commitment probably involves a loss of self-renewal capacity. This may occur prior to lineage restriction, generating the Thy^{lo}, B^+, M^+ cells. These cells have little, if any, self-renewal capacity. Thy^{lo}, B^+, M^+ cells appear to be multipotent; however, their low frequencies of

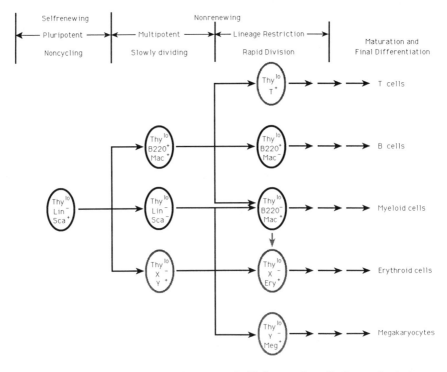

Fig. 3 Developmental lineage relationships among the Thy^{lo} progenitor cells. Progression is shown from the earliest precursor stem cell compartment (the Thy^{lo}, L^-, S^+ cells shown on the left) through the next stage(s) of Thy^{lo}, B^+, M^+ and/or Thy^{lo}, L^-, S^-. This is where self-renewal capacity is lost and some restrictions in developmental potential may become apparent. This is followed by further commitment to a single lineage and then terminal differentiation. The cells indicated by lighter shading represent proposed Thy^{lo} phenotypes not yet defined with the particular set of lineage markers used. The capacity of certain cell types to contribute to the erythroid lineage has not been fully determined, thus the lighter shading of the arrow between the Thy^{lo}, B^-, M^+ and the erythroid progenitor. (See text for further explanations.)

response in the various assays raise the possibility that the population is heterogeneous, containing a mix of restricted progenitors (Heimfeld et al., 1991a).

It seems reasonable that Thy^{lo}, B^+, M^+ cells serve as precursors for the B cell-restricted (Thy^{lo}, B^+, M^-) and myeloid-restricted (Thy^{lo}, B^-, M^+) progenitors. If the Thy^{lo}, B^+, M^+ phenotype is a mandatory stage, this leads to an interesting model of developmental choice. In the initial process of commitment, pluripotent stem cells begin expressing many lineage-specific markers. Such cells, which include the Thy^{lo}, B^+, M^+ class, would remain truly multipotent. In response to intrinsic and/or environmental cues, these cells lose expression of some lineage markers and retain others as they become restricted to a single pathway of differentiation. This attractive model focuses attention on lineage markers as potential growth or differentiation factor receptors. External signals might interact with one or more of these putative receptor species to trigger development along a particular pathway.

This model is consistent with results from other investigators. Heterogeneity in the types of cells which can give rise to CFU-S has been found (Worton et al., 1969; Monette et al., 1974). In addition, evidence for various types of lineage-committed precursors has also been observed (Abramson et al., 1977; Paige, et al., 1981; Mulder et al., 1985; Muller-Sieburg et al., 1986). However, the relationships of these precursors to each other have rarely been analyzed. In B cell development there is a subset of mature cells which expresses CD5, a T cell marker, and the myeloid marker Mac-1 (Hayakawa et al., 1985). Other experimental systems also lend support to this model. T cells have been subdivided into two groups by the expression of either CD4 or CD8 antigen. This expression is correlated with the functional properties of the mature cells. During thymocyte maturation, initially negative T cell precursors become CD4 and CD8 double positive before progressing to the single-positive mature cells (for a review see Schwartz, 1989). Certain tumor cell lines coexpress markers indicative of several lineages, potentially indicating transformation of an early precursor. The specific case of the HAFTL cell line appears to represent a common B/myeloid progenitor that expresses both B220 and Mac-1 (Davidson et al., 1988).

It is interesting to note that only two lineage markers, B220 for B cells and Mac-1 for myeloid cells, are reported here. The model predicts that additional markers exist that would define restricted precursors for the other hematopoietic lineages, such as T cells, erythrocytes, or megakaryocytes. Such progenitors are indicated by the lighter shading in Fig. 3. Each precursor cell would presumably still be Thy^{lo} and potentially also $Sca-1^+$. The Sca-1 antigen, known to be expressed at a high level on the multipotent stem cell (Spangrude et al., 1988), is present on some of the other Thy^{lo} progenitors (unpublished observations).

Alternatively, several differentiation pathways from stem cell to restricted progenitors could exist, including those such as the Thy^{lo}, L^-, S^- cell, which may bypass the Thy^{lo}, B^+, M^+ stage. The decision as to which pathway is used may be stochastic (Till *et al.*, 1964; Ogawa *et al.*, 1983) or under environmental control. Direct experiments with single isolated cells observed over short time intervals will be required to work out these lineage relationships specifically, and to define the role these lineage-specific antigens play in regulating growth and commitment. Given the difficulties of such experiments in animal models, it seems likely that *in vitro* systems will be necessary to better characterize these first steps in hematopoietic development.

III. Clonal Analysis of Stem Cell Differentiation *in Vivo*

A. Introduction

As described in Section II, a powerful tool for analysis of hematopoietic development is the repopulation of irradiated animals. Several aspects of this reconstitution are not well understood. To what extent do individual stem cells contribute to the repopulation? Over what time span is this contribution maintained? At any one time how many stem cells are actively generating progeny? To address these questions, the developmental potential of individual Thy^{lo},L^-,S^+ stem cells has been assessed. Two methods of analysis have been used. One is a limiting-dilution approach in which there is a high probability that the donor progeny are derived from a single stem cell. In some cases a single Thy^{lo},L^-,S^+ stem cell was isolated for this reconstitution. In all experiments a minimum number of purified host stem cells (i.e., 100) are coinjected to insure survival. The other type of assay involves mixing genetically distinct stem cells in varying proportions. Thus, a competitive repopulation system is created in which the resultant number of mature donor T, B, and myeloid cells can be measured. The data are then analyzed statistically to determine the frequency of responding stem cells and the total number of stem cell clones contributing to the repopulation.

B. Analysis of Reconstituted Animals

Limiting-dilution experiments indicate that one of 13 injected Thy^{lo},L^-,S^+ stem cells gives rise to donor progeny in irradiated animals by 4–8 weeks (Smith *et al.*, 1991). This value probably represents a minimum estimate, given the following technical limitations: (1) the level of detection for donor progeny, (2) the efficiency of seeding into an appropriate microenvironment, and (3) the probability that any individual stem cell will become activated. Since the donor stem cells are injected along with an excess of host stem cells, the possibility exists that regulatory mechanisms may operate to maintain some stem cells in a quiescent state (discussed in more detail below). Thus, it is likely that a higher percentage of the Thy^{lo},L^-,S^+ cells can contribute to this reconstitution.

By statistical calculations 77% of those mice in which five or fewer marked cells were injected represent cases in which only a single stem cell generated the mature donor progeny. Data on the percentage of donor cells and the lineage composition of these putative clones are summarized in Table II. Donor cells of all four lineages analyzed (T cells, B cells, granulocytes, and macrophages) were found in the vast majority of such animals. The only single-lineage clones observed were in animals in which the level of donor reconstitution was very small. It is possible that these missing lineages fall below the threshold limit of detection (i.e., 1%). Such experiments have also been extended to animals in which a single Thy^{lo}, L^-, S^+ stem cell was injected. The results were similar to the reconstitution observed with five cells (Table II), supporting the idea that these donor cells represent the progeny of a single stem cell. Again, the predomi-

Table II Clonal Stem Cell Differentiation *in Vivo*

Mouse #	Lineage[a]	% of Donor cells[b]	Last time point GM detected (weeks)[c]
Five-cell mice			
1	T, B, GM	1	6
2	B	2	—
3	B	2	—
4	GM	2	4
5	B, GM	3	6
6	T, GM	3	4
7	T, B, GM	8	11
8	T, B, GM	10	11
9	T, B, GM	11	38
10	T, B, GM	29	12
11	T, B, GM	29	6
12	T, B, GM	65	9
Single-cell mice			
1	T, B	1	—
2	B, GM	1	5
3	B, GM	1	5
4	T, B, GM	5	7
5	T, B, GM	11	6
6	T, B, GM	26	6
7	T, B, GM	57	d

[a] T, T cells; B, B cells; GM, granulocytes and macrophages.

[b] Data are reported as the maximum percentage found at any time point during the analysis.

[c] The last analysis point at which donor-positive GM cells were still detectable in the peripheral blood. (See text for an explanation.)

[d] Animal was sacrificed at 8 weeks and bone marrow was transferred to secondary hosts. (See text for further details.)

nant result was multiple-lineage repopulation (Smith *et al.*, 1991). These results imply that when individual stem cells commit to differentiation, they do not immediately undergo lineage restriction, but, rather, generate progenitors that mature into many different cell types.

If one assumes that every stem cell contributes equally to the mature progeny pool, one prediction would be that the frequency of donor cells in the periphery is related to the ratio of donor to host stem cells injected into the reconstituted animals. For example, mixing 25 marked stem cells along with 100 host stem cells should give approximately 20% donor cells, while a 50:50 ratio should yield equal numbers of both donor and host cells. The experimental findings do not match this prediction. As indicated in Table II, individual animals showed 1– 60% donor cells even though only one or five marked stem cells were injected with 100 host stem cells. Similar variability has also been obtained for other ratios of donor to host stem cells (Smith *et al.*, 1991). Thus, it appears that the total number of progeny any individual stem cell generates can be highly variable and may be independent of the competing stem cell pool.

The period that individual stem cells generate mature progeny in these reconstituted animals has also been assessed. Such an analysis is complicated by the variable life spans of the cells types. T and B lymphoid cells may survive for several weeks to months, while granulocytes and macrophages circulate for less than 24 hours before leaving the bloodstream (Boggs and Winkelstein, 1983). Thus, the persistence of myeloid cells in the blood has been used as the most sensitive measure of continuous production from stem and progenitor cells. The results indicate that individual stem cell contributions to the myeloid lineages are highly variable over time (Table II). Some clones contain donor-positive granulocytes and macrophages for longer than 9 months, while others cease production after only a few weeks. Without exception the smallest clones stop generating myeloid cells before 9 weeks. In addition some larger clones also exhibit short-term reconstitution. Thus, it appears that loss of myeloid differentiation is not correlated to overall size of the clone.

Self-renewal of the donor stem cells is measured by transferring bone marrow from reconstituted mice to new irradiated animals. In approximately one-third of the cases, new donor reconstitution was found in these secondary hosts, implying that donor stem cell numbers had increased. A direct demonstration of the extent of this self-renewal capacity is seen from the single-cell mouse #7. First, separate analysis of all eight major limb bones indicated the presence of equal amounts of donor cells, indicating wide dispersion of the clone within this animal. Second, donor cells isolated from the bone marrow were able to rescue and reconstitute several irradiated recipients. Calculations indicate that a minimum of 1000 new stem cells must have been generated to account for this activity. Third, donor myeloid cells were detected in the secondary hosts for longer than 1 year (Smith *et al.*, 1991). Together, these observations indicate that most, if not all, of the Thy^{lo},L^-,S^+ stem cells are multipotent, although only a subset may undergo self-renewal.

C. Regulation *in Vivo*

Other investigators have used retroviral markers (Lemishka *et al.*, 1986; Jordan and Lemishka, 1990; Keller and Snodgrass, 1990) or enzyme differences (Micklem *et al.*, 1987; Harrison *et al.*, 1988) to analyze the clonal progeny of individual stem cells. Similar to the results reported here, they have also shown that individual clones vary in size and life span. Their data indicate that the number of repopulating clones is small, on the order of three to 12 stem cells. Statistical calculations indicate that the mean number of clones (marked or unmarked) contributing to repopulation with the sorted Thy^{lo},L^-,S^+ cells is 8. Such oligoclonal reconstitution has been interpreted as the activation of only a subset of the available stem cells, while holding the remainder in reserve.

The question arises as to whether this number of active clones is relatively fixed, or increases in proportion to the total stem cell pool. To address this possibility, the following experiment was done. Groups of irradiated mice were injected with sorted Thy^{lo},L^-,S^+ cells in which the number of marked stem cells was held constant at 25 cells, while the number of host stem cells was 100, 300, or 1000. If the number of contributing clones is fixed, then the frequency of donor-positive animals should be lower as the number of unmarked competitors increases. Alternatively, if there is a proportional increase in the number of active clones, then frequencies should remain constant. The results indicate that the number of contributing clones is not fixed, but increases with total stem cell numbers. The mean number of active stem cells is 10 for the 125 group, 25 at 325, and 79 at 1025 (Smith *et al.*, 1991). How the hematopoietic system regulates to specify these numbers remains unknown. Perhaps the process is stochastic, such that each stem cell has an intrinsic probability of contributing to hematopoiesis (Till *et al.*, 1964; Ogawa *et al.*, 1983).

In summary, these reconstitution experiments reveal several aspects of Thy^{lo},L^-,S^+ stem cell repopulation. The contribution that an individual cell makes to the mature progeny is highly variable, both in total amount and over time. Whether this variability reflects intrinsic differences in the developmental potential of individual stem cells or is the result of specific regulatory mechanisms remains to be determined. In the process of commitment, stem cells generate precursors that contribute to many hematopoietic lineages. There does not appear to be a direct step to single-lineage restriction. Some stem cells can undergo self-renewal as well as generate mature progeny, while other appear to commit totally to differentiation. Again, the reasons for these differences in response are unknown. It is clear that *in vivo* experiments reveal a highly complex set of interactions and responses which can sometimes be difficult to interpret. Thus, we have begun to turn to *in vitro* assays, as outlined in Section IV, which will hopefully allow a more comprehensive dissection of the hematopoietic system.

IV. Analysis of Stem Cell Development *in Vitro*

A. Introduction

Blended within the hierarchy of hematopoietic progenitors outlined in Section II are sets of control mechanisms which influence these precursors to modulate the output of differentiated cells. This regulatory machinery can be viewed as an intricate network that permits communication of hematopoietic cells among themselves, with various bone marrow stromal elements, and with the extracellular matrix. It is these layers of communication which form the positive and negative feedback loops that give the hematopoietic system its homeostatic and renewal properties.

Given this complexity, elucidation of specific regulatory elements requires a level of experimental manipulation that is difficult to achieve *in vivo*. As an alternative *in vitro* culture systems have been developed which allow the proliferation and differentiation of early hematopoietic cells in a more controlled environment. These systems can be classified into two distinct categories: (1) long-term bone marrow cultures in which a mix of accessory cells supports the growth of the precursor populations or (2) factor-dependent culture in which the progenitors grow in media supplemented with various growth factors. In this section the response of purified Thy^{lo} progenitor cells in both kinds of culture systems is described.

B. Analysis of Growth in Bone Marrow Cultures

Two types of bone marrows cultures, Whitlock–Witte and Dexter, have been developed. Both share the characteristic that proliferation and differentiation occur only when bone marrow-adherent cells are present. In their absence the progenitor cells rapidly die. However, the outcomes from these two culture conditions are very different. Whitlock–Witte cultures primarily support pre-B cell proliferation. There is some short-term myeloid development (i.e., <3 weeks) and no T cell differentiation (Whitlock *et al.*, 1984). In contrast Dexter cultures promote the growth of myeloid and erythroid cells. No T or B cell lymphopoiesis is detectable (Dexter *et al.*, 1977). Dexter cultures have the additional property of maintaining early progenitor cells (i.e., CFU-S) for several months, while CFU-S disappear in the first few days of Whitlock–Witte cultures.

In the initial establishment of these long-term cultures, all classes of immature and mature cells are present. This makes it difficult to determine how many and what type of precursor cells are contributing to the proliferation response. To reduce this problem, several modifications have been made to the standard cultures. For Whitlock–Witte cultures cloned lines have been developed which maintain the capacity to support progenitor cells (Whitlock et al., 1987). In Dexter cultures preestablished adherent layers are irradiated to restrict endogenous hematopoietic activity. Sorted Thy^{lo} cells are then added to these depleted cultures, and the extent and type of response are measured.

In Whitlock–Witte cultures the Thy^{lo} subsets show restricted differentiation patterns (Heimfeld et al., 1991a) (Table III) similar to those found in the in vivo reconstitution experiments (see Table I). Thy^{lo},L$^-$,S$^+$ stem cells give rise to both B cells and myeloid cells. Furthermore, this is the only fraction which continues to grow in these cultures for longer than 3 weeks. However, CFU-S capacity and the ability to reconstitute irradiated animals are lost rapidly within the first 1–2 weeks, implying that no self-renewal or even maintenance of stem cells occurs in these cultures. These data suggest that stem cells require a specific set of environmental interactions and conditions in order to undergo self-renewal, as opposed to differentiation, divisions.

Self-renewal was analyzed in more detail in the Dexter cultures. Bone marrow cells seeded onto irradiated Dexter cultures form colonies of actively proliferating cells. Most of the cells in the colonies are maturing granulocytes and macrophages. These colonies have the interesting property that many of them are short-lived, disappearing within 4 weeks (Ploemacher et al., 1989; Weilbaecher et al., 1991). Seeding the Dexter cultures with the Thy^{lo} subsets reveals that

Table III Differentiation of Thy^{lo} Progenitor Cells in Vitro[a]

Cell type	Whitlock–Witte culture[b]		Dexter culture[c]		
	B cells	Myeloid cells	Early	Middle	Late
Bone marrow	+	+	+	+	+
Thy^{lo},B$^+$,M$^-$	+	−	−	−	−
Thy^{lo},B$^-$,M$^+$	−	+	+	+	−
Thy^{lo},B$^+$,M$^+$	+	+	+	+	−
Thy^{lo},L$^-$,S$^-$	−	+	+	+	−
Thy^{lo},L$^-$,S$^+$	+	+	+	+	+

[a] B, B220, M, Mac-1; L, lineage markers B220, Mac-1, Gr-1, CD4, and CD-8; S, Sca-1.

[b] Growth was in coculture with cloned stromal lines under conditions favoring long-term lymphopoiesis. The ability of the sorted population to generate pre-B cells or macrophages is indicated.

[c] Growth was in coculture with established preirradiated mixed stromal cells under conditions favoring myelopoiesis. The capacities of the sorted fractions to give rise to early (1–2 weeks)-, middle (2–3 weeks)-, and late (3–4 weeks)-appearing colonies are indicated. (See text for further explanations.)

these transient colonies are primarily derived from the committed progenitor cells (Table III). Only the Thy^{lo},L$^-$,S$^+$ cells are capable of generating colonies maintained for longer periods. Additional assays indicate that, after 2 weeks of culture, only colonies derived from this fraction still contain CFU-S (Weilbaecher et al., 1991). However, the total CFU-S recovered after 2 weeks are much fewer than the number of CFU-S originally seeded into the culture. Thus, whether stem cells have self-renewed or whether some stem cells have simply been maintained in a quiescent state remains unknown. Single-cell analyses will be necessary to answer this question directly.

The stem cells' unique ability for continued proliferation *in vitro* for longer than 4 weeks has an important consequence. *In vitro* assays represent the only methodology available for analysis using human hematopoietic cells. The corresponding *in vivo* experiments cannot be done (for a possible alternative see McCune et al., 1988). Dexter cultures have been established from human bone marrow (Mergenthaler and Dormer, 1990). It should be possible to use these cultures for enriching and isolating the human equivalent of the Thy^{lo},L$^-$,S$^+$ stem cell (Sutherland et al., 1990). The effect of certain drug treatments on the stem cell population prior to bone marrow transplantation could also be tested. Finally, the ability to distinguish the most primitive stem cells from more committed precursors should make it possible to identify conditions or factors that influence these earliest stages in hematopoietic development. This should help define how self-renewal versus differentiation is regulated in normal animals and how the process can be uncoupled during malignant transformation.

C. Analysis of Growth with Defined Growth Factors

Isolated progenitors can be grown in clonal culture in either liquid or semisolid media. Such proliferation is dependent on a set of glycoproteins collectively termed growth factors. Many of these factors have now been cloned and purified to homogeneity (Table IV). Specific details as to cellular sources for these factors, the amounts of factors found in different tissues, and factor modulation in response to changing demands have been reviewed elsewhere (e.g., Metcalf, 1989). Unique cell surface receptors have been found for many of these factors. Most cells can simultaneously express receptors for more than one factor, and therefore can proliferate in response to more than one factor. This may partially explain why, with the possible exception of erythropoietin, the activity of these factors is not restricted to a single lineage.

Of critical significance, most growth factors do not function simply as stimuli for proliferation. *In vitro*, each has at least three other distinct actions: increased survival, of both the precursors and the mature cells; induction of cellular differentiation and maturation; and stimulation of the functional activity of the mature cells. It is the latter property which has raised some confusion as to the precise

Table IV Hematopoietic Growth Factors[a]

Factor	Abbreviation	Other synonyms
Erythropoietin	Epo	—
Macrophage colony-stimulating factor	M-CSF	CSF-1
Granulocyte colony-stimulating factor	G-CSF	Pluripoietin, CSF-β
Granulocyte/macrophage colony-stimulating factor	GM-CSF	Pluripoietin-α
Interleukin 1	IL-1	Hemopoietin 1
Interleukin 2	IL-2	T cell growth factor
Interleukin 3	IL-3	Multi-CSF, HCGF
Interleukin 4	IL-4	B cell growth factor
Interleukin 6	IL-6	BSF-2, β$_2$-interferon

[a] The factors listed here represent only a partial catalog of previously characterized cytokines shown to exert some influence on hematopoiesis in culture.

role that these factors may play in regulating hematopoiesis *in vivo*. These factors are clearly involved in stimulating and modulating effector cells of the immune system. Thus, high local or circulating levels of factors in the body probably represent the outcome of peripheral immune reactions, rather than regulation of hematopoietic precursor cells.

Nevertheless, these factors can exert a powerful control on the proliferation of progenitor cells *in vitro*. As in the Dexter cultures differentiation in response to these growth factors is primarily in the myeloid and erythroid pathways. Having defined a hierarchy of hematopoietic potential *in vivo* (Fig. 3), it is of interest to assess the growth factor requirements of these different progenitors. Two specific fractions are described here: the Thy^{lo},L$^-$,S$^+$ stem cells, since they represent the most primitive cell population, and the Thy^{lo},L$^-$,S$^-$ subset, which has restricted myeloerythropoietic activity and no lymphopoietic or self-renewal capacity (see Section II).

D. Regulation *in Vitro*

In methycellulose cultures progenitor cells grow as discrete clonal colonies. The number of colonies is easily quantitated, and individual colonies can be picked from the cultures for subsequent analysis. Thy^{lo},L$^-$,S$^-$ progenitor cells show a substantial response to interleukin 3 (IL-3) alone, one in 10 cells giving rise to a colony after 1 week in culture. In contrast only one in 100 Thy^{lo},L$^-$,S$^+$ stem cells grow in IL-3 alone (Fig. 4). If factor addition is delayed for 1–2 days, no colony formation is observed from either fraction. This implies that the purified cells are absolutely factor dependent not only for growth, but also for viability. The results indicate that IL-3 is the most active cytokine and can promote the growth of a committed myeloid progenitor. However, IL-3 is itself insufficient to support the proliferation of the more primitive stem cells (Heimfeld *et al.*, 1991b).

Combinations of factors are required to maximize colony formation (McNeice *et al.*, 1988). Sca⁻ cells showed little proliferation in response to IL-1 or IL-6, but significant numbers of colonies formed with IL-3. However, combinations of IL-1 plus IL-3 or IL-3 plus IL-6 augmented the frequency of response by a factor of 2 (Fig. 4A). Thus, there is a strong synergistic effect: Simultaneous factor addition results in much greater colony formation than the sum of single factors. Such synergy is even more apparent in the stem cell fraction, in which colony formation in the presence of IL-3 is poor, but addition of other factors enhances proliferation in a stepwise fashion, such that when five or six factors are added together, greater than one of two sorted cells form a colony (Heimfeld *et al.*, 1991b) (Fig. 4B). The molecular basis for this incremental increase in colony

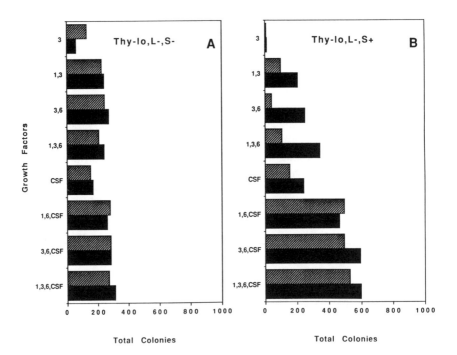

Fig. 4 Response of Thy^lo cells to defined growth factor combinations. A total of 1000 sorted (A) Thy^lo,L⁻,S⁻ or (B) Thy^lo,L⁻,S⁺ cells were plated in methycellulose in the presence of factor combinations indicated on the x axis. On the y axis are the total numbers of colonies (i.e., >50 cells) detected. 1, 3, 6, Interleukin 1 plus interleukin 3 plus interleukin 6; CSF, the three colony-stimulating factors (granulocyte/macrophage, granulocyte, or macrophage) used together. Hatched bars indicate the number of colonies found at 1 week; solid bars, colonies found at 2 weeks.

formation is unknown, although it is intriguing to speculate that it may reflect intrinsic differences in growth factor receptor numbers per cell or the activation state of the cells.

The diversity of cell types within individual colonies, and differences in colony size and morphology, have been used as indicators of the type of progenitor cell that gave rise to the colony. Colonies that contained granulocytes, erythrocytes, macrophages, and megakaryocytes were assumed to have arisen from a more primitive cell than a colony consisting of only granulocytes and macrophages (McNeice et al., 1986; Metcalf, 1989). Comparison of the Thy^{lo},L^-,S^+ and Thy^{lo},L^-,S^- fractions reveals no such differences in the diversity of cell types generated, nor much difference in the sizes of the colonies formed. Under optimum conditions both fractions generate equivalent ratios of single- and mixed-lineage colonies of all types, and all colonies tend to be large in size. Thus, these cytokine assays do not appear to allow a clean distinction among the early progenitor cell populations. It seems more likely that colony diversity and size reflect stochastic and environmental control mechanisms (Ogawa et al., 1983), rather than intrinsic differences in proliferation and differentiation potential.

In addition to the factor requirements, another difference between the Thy^{lo},L^-S^+ stem cells and the Thy^{lo},L^-,S^- progenitor cells is the rate at which the cells respond to the growth factors. The Thy^{lo},L^-,S^- fraction respond quickly in these assays, showing maximum colony formation by week 1 of culture. However, some Thy^{lo},L^-S^+ cells generate additional new colonies, which appear only by 2–3 weeks. This suggests that a fraction of the stem cells can remain quiescent for several days to weeks before beginning active proliferation. This ability to remain quiescent appears to be a property unique to stem cells. Whether the subset of Thy^{lo},L^-,S^+ cells which remains quiescent is functionally different from the rest of the stem cell population is currently being investigated.

These differences in factor requirements and growth kinetics for Thy^{lo},L^-,S^- and Thy^{lo},L^-,S^+ cells suggest a potential mechanism for regulation. The more mature progenitors require fewer positive stimuli for proliferation than do the stem cells. In response to a minor hematopoietic depletion, release of one or a few growth factors activates these restricted precursors, resulting in rapid reconstitution of the appropriate cell types, while the stem cell pool is only minimally affected. If demand is much greater, release of additional factors triggers some stem cells to proliferate and differentiate—again, yielding a rapid recovery. The diversity of factors (and perhaps the amounts) released would regulate the number of stem cells activated, and thus influence the kinetics of hematopoietic recovery. It remains to be determined whether such a regulatory hierarchy exists in vivo. However, we view the present work as an important first step in establishing clonal assay systems which will ultimately lead to a better understanding of the signals that control the earliest stages of hematopoiesis.

V. Conclusion

In this review we have outlined our understanding of the earliest stages of progenitor cells involved in hematopoiesis, as well as the stromal cells and growth factors that may interact with them to produce the terminally differentiated blood cells. In each of the sections, the experimental analyses have emphasized responses at the cellular level. These responses have yielded particular insights into possible mechanisms which influence blood cell formation. Given the availability of purified populations of cells and growth factors, it should now be possible to begin an analysis of the molecular events involved in the self-renewal, proliferation, and differentiation processes. Future aspects for study in the hematopoietic system will focus on describing these regulatory mechanisms which operate to maintain homeostasis, and determining which control the generation of diversity from the pluripotent stem cells.

Acknowledgments

We thank Christa Muller-Sieburg, Donna Rennick, Laurie Smith, Gerald Spangrude, Kathy Weilbaecher, and Cheryl Whitlock for their contributions of data. S.H. is a Fellow of the Leukemia Society. This work was supported by U.S. Public Health Service grant Al-09022, National Institutes of Health award OIG-42551, a grant from the Weingart Foundation (to I.L.W.), and Stanford Bone Marrow Transplantation Program Project Grant 1P01 CA 49605 (to S.H. and I.L.W.).

Dedication

We dedicate this review to Cheryl Whitlock, who lost her battle with acute myelogenous leukemia on January 21, 1990. Cheryl's important contributions to the field of experimental hematology will always be remembered, as will the memory of her enthusiasm and interest in science and life.

References

Abramson, S., Miller, R. G., and Phillips, R. A. (1977). *J. Exp. Med.* **145**, 1567.

Bertoncello, I., Hodgson, G. S., and Bradley, T. R. (1985). *Exp. Hematol. (Copenhagen)* **13**, 999.

Boggs, D. R., and Winkelstein, A. (1983). *In* "White Cell Manual," 4th ed. Davis, Philadelphia, Pennsylvania.

Coffman, R. L., and Weissman, I. L. (1983). *J. Mol. Cell. Immunol.* **1**, 31.

Davidson, W. F., Pierce, J. H., Rudikoff, S., and Morse, H. C., III (1988). *J. Exp. Med.* **168**, 389.

Dexter, T. M., Testa, N. G., and Lajtha, L. G. (1977). *J. Cell. Physiol.* **91**, 335.

Harrison, D. E., Astle, C. M., and Lerner, C. (1988). *Proc. Natl. Acad. Sci. U.S.A.* **85**, 822.

Hayakawa, K., Hardy, R. R., Herzenberg, L. A., and Herzenberg, L. A. (1985). *J. Exp. Med.* **161**, 1554.

Heimfeld, S., Spangrude, G. J., Smith, L. G., and Weissman, I. L. (1991a). *J. Exp. Med.* (in press).

Heimfeld, S., Hudak, S., Weissman, I. L., and Rennick, D. (1991b). *Proc. Natl. Acad. Sci. U.S.A.* (in press).

Jordan, C. T.., and Lemischka, I. R. (1990). *Genes Dev.* **4**, 220.

Keller, G., and Snodgrass, R. (1990). *J. Exp. Med.* **171**, 1407.

Lemishka, I. R., Raulet, D. H., and Mulligan, R. C. (1986). *Cell* **45**, 917.

Magli, M. C., Iscove, N. N., and Odartchenko, N. (1982). *Nature (London)* **295**, 527.

McCune, J. M., Namikawa, R., Kaneshima, H., Schultz, L. D., Lieberman, M., and Weissman, I. L. (1988). *Science* **241**, 1632.

McNeice, I. K., Bradley, T. R., Kreigler, A. B., and Hodgson, G. S. (1986). *Exp. Hematol.* **14**, 856.

McNeice, I. K., Stewart, F. M., Deacon, D. M., and Quesenberry, P. J. (1988). *Exp. Hematol.* **16**, 383.

Mergenthaler, H. G., and Dormer, P. (1990). *Blut* **60**, 228.

Metcalf, D. (1989). *Nature (London)* **339**, 27.

Micklem, H. S., Lennon, J. E., Ansell, J. D., and Gray, R. A. (1987). *Exp. Hematol.* **15**, 241.

Monette, F. C., Gilio, M. J., and Chalifoux, P. (1974). *Cell Tissue Kinet.* **7**, 443.

Mulder, A. H., and Visser, J. W. M. (1987). *Exp. Hematol.* **15**, 99.

Mulder, A. H., Visser, J. W. M., and van den Engh, G. J. (1985). *Exp. Hematol.* **13**, 768.

Muller-Sieburg, C. E., Whitlock, C. A., and Weissman, I. L. (1986). *Cell* **44**, 653.

Ogawa, M., Porter, P. N., and Nakahata, T. (1983). *Blood* **61**, 823.

Paige, C. J., Kincade, P. W., Moore, M. A. S., and Lee, G. (1981). *J. Exp. Med.* **153**, 154.

Ploemacher, R. E., and Brons, N. H. C. (1988). *J. Cell. Physiol.* **136**, 531.

Ploemacher, R. E., van der Sluis, J. P., Voerman, J. S., and Brons, N. H. (1989). *Blood* **74**, 2755.

Reif, A. E., and Allen, J. M. V. (1964). *J. Exp. Med.* **120**, 413.

Schwarz, R. H. (1989). *Cell* **57**, 1073.

Siminovitch, L. McCulloch, E. A., and Till, J. E. (1963). *J. Cell. Comp. Physiol.* **62**, 327.

Smith, L. G., Weissman, I. L., and Heimfeld, S. (1991). *Proc. Natl. Acad. Sci. U.S.A.* **88**, 2788.

Spangrude, G. J. (1989). *Immunol. Today* **10**, 344.

Spangrude, G. J., and Johnson, G. R. (1990). *Proc. Natl. Acad. Sci. U.S.A.* **87**, 7433.

Spangrude, G. J., Heimfeld, S., and Weissman, I. L. (1988). *Science* **241**, 58.

Springer, T. Galfre, G., Secher, D. S., and Milstein, C. (1979). *Eur. J. Immunol.* **9**, 301.

Sutherland, H. J., Landsdorp, P. M., Henkelman, D. H., Eaves, A. C., and Eaves, C. J. (1990). *Proc. Natl. Acad. Sci. U.S.A.* **87**, 3584.

Till, J. E., and McCulloch, E. A. (1961). *Radiat. Res.* **14**, 213.

Till, J. E., and McCulloch, E. A. (1972). *Ser. Haematol.* **2**, 15.

Till, J. E., and McCulloch, E. A. (1980). *Biochim. Biophys. Acta* **605**, 431.

Till, J. E., McCulloch, E. A., and Siminovitch, L. (1964). *Proc. Natl. Acad. Sci. U.S.A.* **51**, 26.

Visser, J. V. M., and van Bekkum, D. W. (1990). *Exp. Hematol.* **18**, 248.

Weilbaecher, K. N., Weissman, I. L., Blume, K. G., and Heimfeld, S. (1991). *Blood* **78**, 1.

Whitlock, C. A., Robertson, D., and Witte, O. N. (1984). *J. Immunol. Methods* **67**, 353.

Whitlock, C. A., Tidmarsh, G. F., Muller-Sieburg, C. E., and Weissman, I. L. (1987). *Cell* **48**, 1009.

Worton, R. G., McCulloch, E. A., and Till, J. E. (1969). *J. Exp. Med.* **130**, 91.

8

Control of Cell Lineage and Cell Fate during Nematode Development

Paul W. Sternberg
Howard Hughes Medical Institute
Division of Biology
California Institute of Technology
Pasadena, California 91125

I. Introduction

The striking invariance of nematode development has inspired and intrigued developmental biologists for 100 years (e.g., Boveri, 1892; zur Strassen, 1892; Pai, 1928). We now know that this invariant development is the result of both intrinsic and extrinsic controls over cell fate. Highly reproducible cell interac-

Current Topics in Developmental Biology, Vol. 25

tions occur since most cells do not migrate, and are thus always subject to signals from the same neighbors. Some of the very features that make the nematode *Caenorhabditis elegans* an attractive organism with which to study development—its small cell number and essentially invariant development—make one wonder how relevant studies of this nematode will be to animals whose development is not invariant: To what extent will conclusions based on studies with *C. elegans* apply to organisms with a large number of cells and variable development? One can answer that nematode development is not wholly invariant. One can also answer this question of relevance by arguing that molecular mechanisms are conserved even if developmental phenomena are not, and what one learns about a particular gene product in one organism can be extended to other organisms. This "model system" argument is certainly meritorious, and the success of yeast molecular genetics in unraveling cell biological problems might well be repeated by *C. elegans* molecular genetics for problems specific to metazoans. Moreover, since nematodes diverged from their coelomate relatives prior to the arthropod–chordate split, nematodes afford useful molecular biological comparisons for genes conserved between, for example, insects and mammals. *Caenorhabditis elegans* will provide such a comparison, given the intensive molecular biological studies driven by the genome-mapping project (Coulson *et al.*, 1986, 1988; reviewed by Robertson, 1990).

A more interesting answer to the question of relevance is that the unique characteristics of each species can be exploited to learn about development and evolution. Most cell fates in nematodes are specified autonomously, and nematodes thus lie toward one end of a continuum of organisms whose development ranges from mostly conditional to mostly autonomous (see the review by Davidson, 1990). Invariant cell interactions are experimentally useful: The experimenter knows what a cell will do before the cell becomes specified. As for understanding autonomous specification of cell fate, the original attraction of nematodes still exists: Asymmetric cell divisions, in which two daughter cells differ in their fates, presumably due to the asymmetric distribution of some factors at the cell division, can be studied in a variety of cells, from the first cleavage of the zygote to late in sexual maturation. Having a complete description of cell lineage and cell fates allows a discussion of basic questions concerning the origin of symmetry and asymmetry during development and evolution. The simple problem of how fates are specified in groups of oligopotent cells is beginning to be understood, and the interplay of inductive and lateral signaling can be studied in the context of vulval induction, during which tripotent cells are specified by the combined action of at least two signaling systems. Rather than review comprehensively recent molecular genetic analyses of nematode development, I focus instead on the developmental and comparative studies that define key issues in nematode development. I summarize the evidence for intrinsic and extrinsic controls of cell fates, describe studies of the mechanisms of cell fate specification, and consider the evolution of fate-specifying mechanisms.

II. General Features of Nematode Development

Free-living soil nematodes develop during a relatively short period of embryo-genesis, followed by a more extended period of postembryonic development. During postembryonic development growth-associated increases in cell number and sexual differentiation occur. Typically, nematodes undergo four larval molts (L1, L2, L3, and L4), at which they shed their external cuticle.

A. Lineage and Fate; Autonomy and Nonautonomy

Direct observations by Nomarski differential interference microscopy of cell lineage in nematodes revealed a striking correlation of the lineage history of a cell and its fate (Sulston and Horvitz, 1977; Kimble and Hirsh, 1979; Sulston *et al.*, 1980, 1983; Sternberg and Horvitz, 1981, 1982). Thus, each cell division can be thought of as involving a determinative decision that specifies cell type or the extent of cell division (i.e., the number of rounds of mitosis a precursor cell undergoes). The fate of each daughter cell—what type of differentiated cell it becomes or the lineage it generates—might be specified autonomously or non-autonomously. Experimental results so far indicate that many cell fate decisions appear to be autonomous, while some clearly are nonautonomous. There are excellent candidates for autonomously specified fates (e.g., the E lineage which generates intestinal cells). For many sublineages autonomy (or local non-autonomy) would appear to be the mode of specification based on cell ablation experiments. Other homologous cells have the same, although limited, set of potentials.

The embryonic E lineage is one of a few cases in which a structure is generated clonally: The E blastomere generates the whole intestine and it generates only intestine (Sulston *et al.*, 1983). Laufer *et al.* (1980) and Edgar and McGhee (1986) demonstrated the autonomy of the P1 blastomere for gut-specific markers: the appearance of gut granules and gut esterase expression, respectively. The results of a cleavage block experiment (Whittaker, 1973), in which cleavage is arrested with cytochalasin D, indicate that, at successive points in time, the P1, EMS, and E blastomeres have the potential to express gut markers (Fig. 1). In addition, by squeezing two-cell embryos, half-embryos are obtained, with either the P1 or the AB blastomere remaining. The descendants of P1, but not AB, can express gut esterase. Thus, the descendants of P1 do not require the descendants of AB in order to express the esterase. Evidence for cytoplasmic determination has been provided by Schierenberg and Wood (1985), who extruded the P1 nucleus and then fused by laser-microbeam irradiation the P1 and AB blastomeres. An enucleated P1 blastomere does not express gut granules (another intestinal marker), but after fusion the P1 cytoplasm is able to stimulate the AB nucleus to express gut granules. Additional studies of early blastomere fate

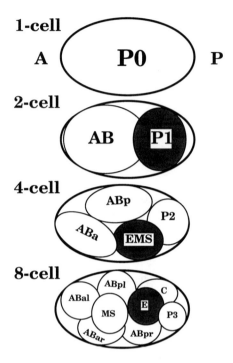

Fig. 1 Potentials of blastomeres to express gut esterase after cleavage arrest. Schematic positions of blastomeres are shown at the one-, two- four- and eight-cell stages. The 8-cell embryo is shown ventral side up; all others are shown left side up. Shading indicates that a blastomere can express gut esterase after cleavage arrest at the given stage. A, Anterior; P, posterior. Data are from Edgar and McGhee (1986).

determination have been reviewed by Strome (1989). The genetic locus *ges-1*, encoding the esterase, has been identified (McGhee and Cottrell, 1986) and its molecular cloning will provide an opportunity to study the regulation of this lineage-specific gene.

Similar results demonstrating the potentials of blastomeres have been obtained by Cowan and McIntosh (1985) for muscle and hypodermal markers. Arrested P1, C, MS, and P2, but not P0, AB, EMS, E, and AB, blastomeres can express a muscle-specific marker. Arrested P0, P1, AB, P2, ABa, and ABp, but not EMS, blastomeres can express a hypodermal-specific marker. The exclusivity of expression of these two markers and gut granules suggests that regulatory factors positively and negatively regulate lineage-specific genes. For example, a cleavage-arrested EMS blastomere expresses the intestinal marker, but not the muscle marker.

Priess and Thomson (1987) demonstrated the existence of cell interactions early during embryogenesis, prior to the 28-cell stage. I describe these elegant experiments in the simplest form. ABa generates the anterior pharyngeal muscles. The EMS blastomere generates posterior pharyngeal muscles. If P1 is extruded from a two-cell embryo, or EMS is extruded from a four-cell embryo, ABa fails to generate pharyngeal muscle. If ABa is extruded, ABp makes pharyngeal muscle. EMS generates pharyngeal muscle in the absence of P1. Thus, the ability for some cells (the EMS progeny) to make pharyngeal muscle is autonomous, while for other cells (the ABa progeny) it is dependent on an inductive interaction. If the positions of ABa and ABp are reversed by manipulation, then a normal pharynx is still formed, indicating that the fates of these blastomeres or their descendants have been altered, since in the intact embryo ABa and ABp make distinct (although overlapping) sets of progeny cells. The conclusion from these experiments is that ABa becomes different from ABp due to an inductive signal from EMS. The signal could occur as early as the four-cell stage, but could also occur later, among the descendants of EMS and ABa. Since ablation of cells at the 28-cell stage does not alter the production of pharyngeal muscle, the cell interactions must take place prior to this stage.

A possible component of this EMS–ABa cell interaction mechanism is encoded by the *glp-1* locus, which is necessary for the production of pharyngeal muscle cells by ABa (Priess *et al.*, 1987). Molecular evidence supports this hypothesis: The *glp-1* locus encodes a transmembrane protein of the lin-12/Notch family that is likely to act in intercelluar communication (Austin and Kimble, 1987, 1989; Yochem and Greenwald, 1989; Maine and Kimble, 1989).

Certain cells during nematode development have the potential to follow a number of developmental pathways, yet choose only one. Sets of such multipotent cells are known as "equivalence groups" because the member cells are thought to be equivalent in their developmental potential (Kimble *et al.*, 1979). The simplest examples of equivalence groups comprise two member cells, each bipotent. For example, during development of the *C. elegans* male tail, the B ectoblast generates two bipotent cells derived from equivalent positions in lineages on the left and right sides of the developing male. These homologous cells, B.alaa and B.araa, move to the midline and adopt either of two positional configurations; these configurations are equally likely to occur (Sulston and Horvitz, 1977). The sister of B.alaa and the sister of B.araa are morphologically identical and generate identical sets of progeny cells. Thus, B.alaa and B.araa are expected to be similar in their developmental fate. The lineage generated by each cell depends on its position. The cell that adopts the anterior position, Bα, generates two proctodeal cells and two neuronal supporting cells. The cell that adopts the posterior position, Bβ, generates two neurons and four supporting cells (Sulston *et al.*, 1980). If only one of the α/β cells is present (because the other cell has been ablated), the remaining cell always becomes an α (Sulston and White, 1980); thus, the α fate is called the "primary" fate; the β fate is called the "secondary" fate. Such hierarchies of cell fates are characteristic of equivalence groups and reflect the nature of the underlying cell–cell interactions.

Another example of two homologous bipotent cells is provided by the gonadogenesis of the *C. elegans* hermaphrodite, during which two cells each have the potential to become either an anchor cell (AC) or a ventral uterine precursor (VU) cell (Kimble and Hirsh, 1979). In a given hermaphrodite only one cell becomes an AC, while the other becomes a VU cell; the bipotent cells are referred to as "AC/VU cells" constituting the "AC/VU equivalence group." Both AC and VU cells are homologs, and their equivalent potentials support the correlation of lineage and fate. These cells are constrained to either of two fates by their ancestry. Specific examples of equivalence groups are discussed in more detail in Section V.

In studies of cell fate specification, it is always easier to prove nonautonomy than autonomy; nonetheless, there are a number of well-characterized examples in which it appears that cell fates are specified autonomously. For example, ablation of derivatives of the MS blastomere at its four- or eight-cell stage failed to reveal any alterations in the fates of the remaining cells (Sulston *et al.*, 1983). These results are based on the failure to see a change in cell fate after ablation of specific cells. The caveats to these ablation experiments are spelled out explicitly by Sulston and White (1980) and are summarized by Sulston (1988). Briefly, one caveat is that the debris left after microbeam irradiation might retain the capacity to "signal." A second caveat is that it is difficult to kill one of two sister cells immediately after cytokinesis; thus, signaling that occurs immediately following cell division is difficult to demonstrate. In practice, it is exceedingly difficult to distinguish very local nonautonomy (e.g., signaling between sister cells) from completely autonomous development.

Even though the general features of a cell lineage may be autonomous to the precursor of that lineage, later divisions may not be autonomous. Kimble (1981) examined the lineages generated by isolated sheath–spermathecal (SS) precursors and found that the lineages generated by the isolated SS cell were different from those in the intact gonad. Many features of the SS lineage were conserved in these isolated lineages. For example, the initial division is unequal in size and asymmetric in fate, generating a small sheath precursor and a large spermathecal precursor. The variability in these lineages is due to reversals in polarity and the occurrence of extra cell divisions. These observations suggest that cell interactions are important in specifying the polarity and extent of cell divisions.

B. Sublineages and Modular Programming

The occurrence of multiply utilized stereotypical patterns of cell divisions generating identical sets of progeny cells—a "sublineage"—suggests the existence of an underlying developmental program that specifies the pattern of cell divisions and the fates of the progeny cells (Sulston and Horvitz, 1977; Chalfie *et al.*,

A

young L1 larva

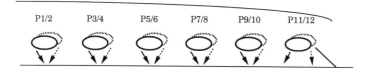

mid-L1 larva

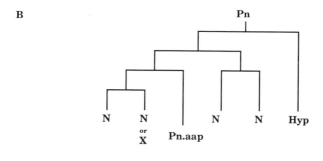

B

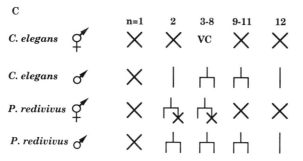

C

		n=1	2	3-8	9-11	12
C. elegans	♀	X	X	VC	X	X
C. elegans	♂	X	|	⊓	⊓	|
P. redivivus	♀	X	⊓X	⊓X	X	X
P. redivivus	♂	X	⊓	⊓	⊓	|

Fig. 2 The Pn sublineages. (A) During the L1 stage, bilaterally symmetric pairs of ectoblasts, the Pn/Pn+1 cells migrate into the ventral cord and intercalate to form a line of 12 cells, the Pn cells. (B) General Pn sublineage. N, Neuron; X, a cell that dies; Hyp, a cell that fuses with the hypodermal syncytium, is a vulval precursor cell, or divides to generate one hypodermal cell and a cell that dies. (C) Position-, sex, and species-specific variation in Pn.aap fates. An X indicates that the Pn.aap cell dies. A line indicates differentiation as a neuronal or supporting cell; a branch indicates a cell division. Data are from Sulston and Horvitz (1977), Sternberg and Horvitz (1982), and Sulston *et al.* (1980).

1981; Sternberg and Horvitz, 1982). In general sublineages are only a few cell divisions in length.

The L1 ventral cord lineages (Pn) are an excellent example of a set of related sublineages. The 12 Pn cells move from sublateral positions into the ventral cord to form a line of 12 precursor cells (Fig. 2A). All 12 Pn lineages in both sexes of *C. elegans* and *Panagrellus redivivus* follow the same basic pattern (Fig. 2B), but position-, sex-, and species-specific variations in the fates of some progeny occur (Fig. 2C). For example, the Pn.aap cell generated by P1 dies in both sexes of both species (Fig. 2C), while P(9–11).aap cells die in hermaphrodites and females, but divide in the L3 stage in males of both species. The P2.aap fate is unique to each sex and species: P2.aap dies in *C. elegans* hermaphrodites, differentiates in *C. elegans* males, divides to generate one surviving cell and a cell that dies in *P. redivivus* females, and divides to generate two surviving progeny in *P. redivivus* males. Homologous (i.e., lineally equivalent) cells from similar sublineages are in most cases analogous in fate or are members of equivalence groups. The exceptions suggest the existence of genes specifying these differences. In some cases such genes have been identified. For example, P(1–10).aaap differentiates as a VB motoneuron in *C. elegans*, while P(11–12).aaap dies (Sulston and Horvitz, 1977). In a *mab-5* mutant P(11–12).aaap do not die (Kenyon, 1986). Thus, *mab-5*, which is necessary for anteroposterior spatial patterning, is responsible for this position-specific difference in the Pn sublineages. *mab-5* is known to be cell autonomous in its action, suggesting that it acts within cells to interpret their position (Kenyon, 1986). *mab-5* encodes a homeodomain-containing protein, the expression of whose mRNA is localized to the region around P11 and P12 (Costa *et al.*, 1988). This positional expression is consistent with a role in specifying position-specific cell fates.

A comparison of the *P. redivivus* and *C. elegans* postembryonic lateral ectoblast (Vn) lineages provides an excellent example of modular programming using sublineages as modules. The Vn lineages have sex-, time-, and species-specific variations (Fig. 3): During L1 the sublineage is a single cell division generating a

Fig. 3 Modular programming in the V lineages. Five sublineages that are used in a modular fashion are shown at the top of the figure. (A) Simple seam cell sublineage. A seam cell divides to generate an anterior daughter (indicated by a solid circle) that fuses with the hypodermal syncytium. (B) *P. redivivus* sublineage. A seam cell generates two seam cells (indicated by arrowheads) and four hypodermal nuclei by the lineage shown (C) *P. redivivus* sublineage. A seam cell generates two seam cells and two hypodermal nuclei by the lineage shown (R) A ray or papillae sublineage. st, Structural cell; A, RnA neuron; B, RnB neuron, (PD) Postdeirid sublineage. N, neuron; so, socket cell; sh, sheath cell. (*C. elegans*) Position- and sex-specific utilization of modular sublineages in *C. elegans* V lineages. The utilization of each sublineage is shown in the context of the entire V lineages in the hermaphrodite and the male. Note that in the L2 stage the duplication of the seam cell can be considered a separate module or part of more complicated modules than those proposed in the top panel. (*P. redivivus*) Position- and sex-specific utilization of modular sublineages in *P. redivivus* V lineages. Data are from Sulston and Horvitz (1977), Sulston *et al.* (1980), and Sternberg and Horvitz (1982).

Modular Sublineages

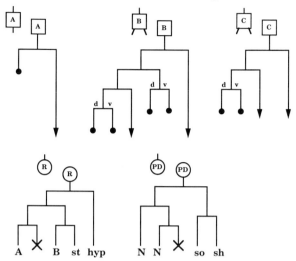

C. elegans

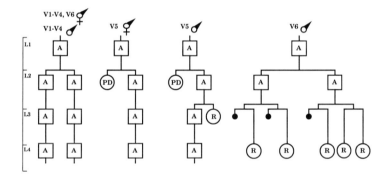

P. redivivus

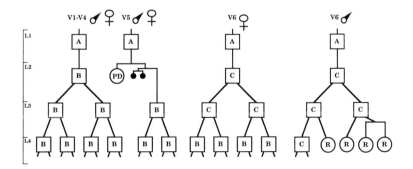

syncytial hypodermal nucleus and a seam cell. During L2 the sublineages include the generation of a postdeirid. In the L4 male the Rn sublineage occurs. Ray sublineages are only present in the male, and only produced by V5, V6, and T in *C. elegans* and V6 and T in *P. redivivus*. Furthermore, sublineages can be nested. The seam cell produced by one Vn sublineage itself generates another sublineage (Fig. 3). The lateral hypodermal sublineages are used repeatedly within the same lineage. For example, in the *P. redivivus* female V4 lineage the sublineage shown in Fig. 4A is used seven times. Seam cells choose between alternative sublineages, depending on their position and sex.

An important implication of the sublineage hypothesis is that genes that act to control cell lineage do so by controlling either the utilization of a sublineage or some of the characteristics of that sublineage. Extensive analysis of the Vn lineages has been carried out. Spatial control of postdeirid sublineages involves the *lin-22* gene (Fixsen *et al.* 1985). Spatial control of ray sublineages depends on *lin-22*, *mab-5*, and *pal-1* (Waring and Kenyon, 1990). Temporal control of sublineage utilization depends on the "heterochronic" gene pathway, involving *lin-4*, *lin-14*, *lin-28*, and *lin-29* (Ambros and Horvitz, 1984, 1987; Ambros, 1989; Liu and Ambros, 1989; Ruvkun *et al.*, 1989; Ruvkun and Giusto, 1989).

A second implication of the sublineage hypothesis is that genes that control the execution of one example of a sublineage also act to control other examples of that sublineage. This is borne out in several cases. For example, *lin-11* mutations affect both the 2° VPC sublineages, and in a genetic background that results in six 2° VPC sublineages *lin-11* acts in each case (Ferguson *et al.*, 1987). An *unc-86* mutation alters both the postdeirid sublineages (Chalfie *et al.*, 1981), and in a *lin-22* mutant background alters all 10 postdeirid sublineages (Horvitz *et al.*, 1983).

C. Variability, Proliferation, and Evolution

Most of the observed cell lineages in *C. elegans* are invariant. Most of the cell lineages in *P. redivivus* are also invariant, but differ from those of *C. elegans*. How does one invariant cell lineage change during evolution to another? Some lineages are variable. Is this variability due to a lack of fine tuning, reflecting a lineage in the process of evolution? Or is it due to a necessary consequence of extensive proliferation, for example, because precision does not increase as the number of cell cycles increases?

There are a few cases of variability in *C. elegans*. In the *C. elegans* ventral hypodermis, P3.p either divides or does not before it fuses with the large hypodermal syncytium hyp7 (Sulston and Horvitz, 1977). In several other free-living soil nematode species P3.p either fuses or divides one or two rounds, while in at least one *Pellioditis* species P3.p always fuses with the syncytium but P4.p does not, indicating that the fate of P3.p can be invariant (P. W. Sternberg, L. Carta,

A

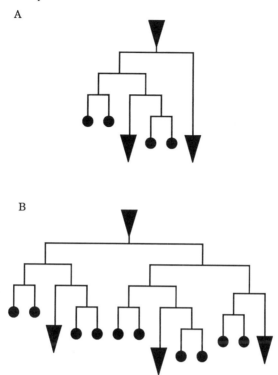

B

Fig. 4 Variability in the *P. redivivus* lateral hypodermal lineages. (A) L2, L3, and L4 pattern. Arrowheads indicate seam cells, solid circles indicate cells that fuse with the hypodermal syncytium. (B) A variant lineage. Data are from Sternberg and Horvitz (1982).

and P. Kayne, unpublished observations). Thus, the *C. elegans* program is imprecise because the fate of P3.p can be invariant in some species. Exactly what selective advantage, if any, is conferred by invariance is not clear. Ablation of P3.p in *C. elegans* has no adverse effects on viability (Sulston and White, 1980), and *P. redivivus*, which is larger than *C. elegans*, has fewer ventral hypodermal nuclei (Sternberg and Horvitz, 1982).

Some variability occurs as a function of temperature. In *C. elegans* hermaphrodites of the standard laboratory strain N2, a 2° vulval precursor cell (VPC) sometimes generates eight nuclei at 25°C rather than the seven normally generated at 20°C (Sternberg and Horvitz, 1986). In another free-living nematode, WS1–4, a duplication of the seam cell (e.g., as the L2 V1–V4 lineages in *C. elegans;* Fig. 2) occurs in the L3 stages at 20°C, but in the L4 stage at 10°C (Ambros and Fixsen, 1987).

Another form of variability is correlated with increased size of a nematode. Adult nematodes can range from less than 1 mm to over 4 m [e.g., *Placentonema gigantissimus* (Gubanov, 1951)], a range of almost 10^4! It is not known, in general, whether larger nematodes have constant cell number. However, in at least some larger nematode species particular lineages proliferate; these proliferative lineages can be variable. I refer to such variability in which only the number of divisions (as opposed to the fates of progeny cells) is variable, as "proliferative variability." For example, in the development of the lateral hypodermis of *C. elegans*, at each larval molt the seam cells undergo one or two rounds of cell division, depending on the molt (Fig. 3). In a slightly larger nematode, *P. redivivus*, which is roughly twice as long as *C. elegans*, the seam cells produce a sublineage that generates four syncytial hypodermal nuclei and two seam cells. However, these lineages generated by a seam cell often do not match the canonical pattern (Sternberg and Horvitz, 1982) (Fig. 4). Some of these abnormal sublineages are reminiscent of Vn lineages after ablation of their neighbors in which proliferation occurs (Sulston and White, 1980).

The postembryonic intestinal lineages provide a second example of proliferative variability and also suggest a conservation of cellular DNA content, rather than nuclear number or ploidy. In *C. elegans* 10–14 of the 20 intestinal nuclei present at hatching divide during the first larval stage; these nuclei then undergo endoreduplication, resulting in cells with two tetraploid nuclei. In *P. redivivus* 16–18 intestinal nuclei are present at hatching; these divide during the first larval stage to generate tetranucleate cells (Sternberg and Horvitz, 1982). Thus, in both species intestinal cells become at least 8C by the end of the L1 stage, but differ in the number and ploidy of nuclei (Hedgecock and White, 1985). In other nematode taxa considerable more cellular or nuclear divisions occur in the intestine. For example, in the Strongylina, some intestinal cells contain 10–500 nuclei; Chromadorids have on the order of 10^4 intestinal cells (reviewed by de Coninck, 1965).

III. Asymmetric Cell Divisions

The general problem of how a cell divides to generate daughter cells with distinct fates remains unsolved. In *C. elegans* progress has been made recently by the identification of genes necessary for asymmetric cell divisions.

A. Founder Cell Lineage

The first cleavage of the *C. elegans* zygote is the best example of an asymmetric cell division. Early *C. elegans* embryogenesis has been reviewed by Wood (1988), Strome (1989), and Kemphues (1989), so here I just summarize the most pertinent findings and hypotheses. At most one embryonic axis, the anteroposterior axis, is specified prior to fertilization. Dorsal–ventral and left–right axes are plastic (Priess and Thomson, 1987). Fertilization takes place at the uterine–proximal (presumed posterior) end of the oocyte. The anteroposterior axis could be established prior to fertilization, but there is no direct evidence for an axis (see Strome, 1989, for a review). However, the existence of asymmetry in oocytes—the oocyte nucleus is located at the distal (presumed anterior) end of the oocyte—suggests that there is a preformed anteroposterior axis. Regardless of whether an anteroposterior axis is established prior to or after fertilization, some of the asymmetries in the zygote must be responsible for the different fates of the AB and P1 blastomeres.

The extensive reorganization during the first cell cycle of the zygote establishes the asymmetry of the first cleavage. During the first cell cycle extensive cytoplasmic reorganization occurs, such that actin moves to the anterior end of the zygote and P granules (associated with the germ line) move posteriorly. The most striking example of cytoplasmic localization is provided by the P granules, which are segregated to P1, P2, P3, P4, and then Z2 and Z3 (reviewed by Strome, 1989). The first mitotic spindle forms in the center of the zygote and moves posteriorly, such that the first cleavage is unequal. The anterior blastomere, AB, inherits 58% of the cytoplasm; the posterior blastomere, P1, inherits the remaining 42% (E. Schierenberg, cited by Schierenberg, 1984). At each unequal cell division the larger daughter typically divides earlier and generates more progeny than its smaller sister during embryogenesis. [This correlation also holds true during postembryonic development, and for other organisms, such as the sea urchin (Cameron et al., 1987), leech (Weisblat et al., 1984), and yeast (Hartwell and Unger, 1977).] The early timing of nematode cleavages is species specific (discussed by Roman and Hirschmann, 1969; E. Schierenberg, personal communication): In particular, the relative timing of AB versus P1 divisions can change. However, cell cycle time is not altered by changes in nuclear:cytoplasmic volume ratios caused by cytoplasmic extrusion and blastomere fusion (Schierenberg and Wood, 1985). Moreover, experimentally altered cleavage planes often do not alter the rate of subsequent cleavage (Hill and Strome, 1990). Thus, it is likely that *specific* cytoplasmic factors control cell cycle timing. One can speculate that such factors might act to modify a default cell cycle time based on nuclear:cytoplasmic ratio.

Molecular genetic analysis of the founder cell lineages holds great promise. The *par* genes, defined by mutations which result in defective partitioning of components at the first cleavage, might be required for the organization of cytoplasmic components during the first cell cycle (Kemphues et al., 1988). Additional maternally acting genes involved in early embryonic development have been defined (Mains et al., 1990; Schnabel and Schnabel, 1989). At least one sperm-supplied product (i.e., a paternally acting gene) is required for early development (Hill et al., 1989). Further analysis of these genes is expected to unravel the complexities of the early cleavages.

B. Postembryonic Cell Lineage Mutants

Mutations that disrupt asymmetric cell divisions and result in the production of two sister cells with the same fates are excellent candidates for genes that define the molecular mechanisms of asymmetric cell division. Two such cell lineage genes, *unc-86* and *lin-11*, encode apparent transcription factors (Finney *et al.*, 1988; Freyd *et al.*, 1990). Consider an asymmetric cell division (Fig. 5) in which a cell A divides to produce a daughter with fate B and another daughter with fate C. *unc-86* is necessary for one daughter cell to be different from its mother: In the simple example in Fig. 5, C would act like its mother, A, and generate another cell B and an A. *lin-11* is necessary for the two sisters to be different: A would generate two B cells (or two C cells). Freyd *et al.* (1990) hypothesize that the LIM domain, a putative metal binding domain of *lin-11*, might be involved in localization or segregation at cell division of the lin-11 protein. This hypothesis is intriguing because another protein, mec-3, similar to lin-11 in its homeodomain and LIM domain, is also necessary for cell type specification during certain cell lineages (Way and Chalfie, 1988, 1989). In particular, mec-3 is necessary for the specification of the two Q.paa touch receptor neurons, which are generated from the two Q neuroblasts. Each of two Q neuroblasts (QL on the left and QR on the right) generate three neurons (one of which is Q.paa) and two cells that undergo programmed cell death. Since, in a *mec-3* mutant, the Q.paa cells are indistinguishable from their sisters, Chalfie and co-workers have suggested that mec-3 is necessary for differences between sister cells at an asymmetric cell division (Way and Chalfie, 1988), much like lin-11. Thus, since *lin-11* and *mec-3* are similar in their homeodomains and LIM motifs, Freyd *et al.* (1990) have suggested that they might play analogous roles in asymmetric cell divisions.

These cloned genes provide excellent markers for the cell type, and a starting point from which to go forward and backward to elucidate the mechanism. However, they do not, in and of themselves, offer a solution to the problem. A transcription factor necessary for the C fate might have a role in setting up the conditions for the asymmetric cell division, be an activator of the C fate, or be a negative regulator of the B fate. However, once the cells that express the transcription factor are known, these hypotheses can be distinguished. Finney and Ruvkun (1990) have determined the cells that express unc-86 protein: unc-86

Fig. 5 Asymmetric cell division. Cell A divides and generates a daughter cell with fates B and C.

protein accumulates in the nuclei of the affected daughter cells; thus, *unc-86* is necessary to promote the C state and inhibit the A fate. Clearly, other genes that interact with a transcription factor are involved in specification of an asymmetric cell division. For example, while the cells that express *lin-11* are not yet known, two other genes, *lin-17* and *lin-18*, have been identified because of their effects on the 2° VPC lineage (Ferguson and Horvitz, 1985; Ferguson *et al.*, 1987). *lin-17* affects other asymmetric cell divisions and, for at least some, acts at or prior to cell division: The mutations affect cell size as well as fate (Sternberg and Horvitz, 1988). Since other asymmetric cell divisions affected by *lin-17* mutations are not unequal in size, *lin-17* is most likely not controlling asymmetries in fate by controlling inequality in size. *lin-18* mutations also affect the 2° VPC lineage by reversing polarity or abolishing asymmetry. Understanding the interactions of *lin-17* and *lin-18* with *lin-11* might provide a handle on this particular asymmetric cell division.

IV. Symmetry and Asymmetry

Nematodes are, in general, bilaterally symmetric, although there are some bilateral asymmetries. In addition there are two-, three, four, and sixfold symmetries that arise during development (Sulston *et al.*, 1983; Kimble and Hirsh, 1979; Sulston and Horvitz, 1977). Morphogenesis involves the creation or breakage of symmetry. Knowledge of the cell lineage allows an examination of these processes. The cell lineage diagram, while excellent for depicting the time of cell divisions and ancestral relationships, eliminates any indication of the geometry of the embryo, which is central to understanding symmetries, cell interactions, and morphogenesis.

A. Creation and Breakage of Symmetry

Sulston *et al.* (1983) have described in detail the origins of symmetries in the *C. elegans* embryo. Some bilateral symmetry arises from left–right cells generating identical sublineages. Other aspects of bilateral symmetry arise by analogous cells being generated by distinct lineages on the two sides of the developing animal (see Section IV,D).

The creation of threefold symmetry is accomplished in either of two ways. In the first, two bilaterally symmetric homologous cells are joined by a third cell recruited from elsewhere (Fig. 6A). For example, the three marginal cells of the pharynx (mc3 cells) are the homologs MSaaapapa and MSpaapapa and the cell ABalpappapp (Sulston *et al.*, 1983). The homolog of ABalpappapp is ABarapapapp, which is an I5 pharyngeal interneuron. A second way in which threefold symmetry is created by the diversion of one of four cells and the subsequent generation of identical sublineages by each of the three cells. This process is exemplified by the vas deferens (VD) development in *C. elegans* and *P. redivivus* males (Kimble and Hirsh, 1979; Sternberg and Horvitz, 1981). The linker cell (LC) fate is one of two alternative fates of the two members of the LC/VD equivalence group; the other fate is a precursor cell (see Section V,B). The sister of each potential LC is a VD. Thus, as shown in Fig. 6B, one of four

A

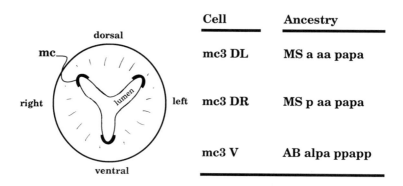

B

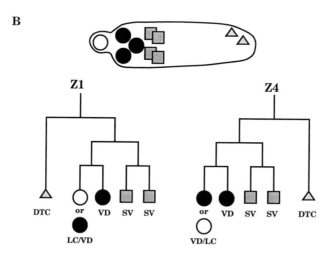

Fig. 6 Origins of threefold symmetry. (A) Threefold symmetry of the pharynx arises in part from recruitment of a third cell to join two homologs. Two of the three mc3 marginal cells are homologs: MS(a/p)aapapa. The third cell is ABalpappapp. Data are from Sulston *et al.* (1983). (B) Threefold symmetry in the male somatic gonad arises from the removal of one of four cells. Four vas deferens precursors (VD) and a presumed vas deferens precursor cell (LC/VD) are generated. One of the presumed LC/VD cells is diverted to become the linker cell (LC), thus leaving three VD cells. DTC, Distal tip cell; SV, seminal vesicle. Data are from Kimble and Hirsh (1979) and Kimble (1981).

cells is diverted to create the threefold symmetry of the developing VD. In *P. redivivus* an analogous process occurs, but the three non-LC cells are ED blast cells, which generate ejaculatory duct cells. The threefold symmetry of the VD might be argued to be less important than the production of a unique LC, which is necessary for morphogenesis of the gonad and for connecting the VD and ED to the cloaca (Hirsh *et al.*, 1976; Kimble, 1981).

B. Bilateral Asymmetry

The "deep and neglected problem" of bilateral asymmetry (see Brown and Wolpert, 1990, for a review) extends to the nematodes. Bilateral asymmetries in nematodes include the following. The M mesoblast is located on the right side of many, if not all, free-living nematodes (Sulston and Horvitz, 1977; Sternberg and Horvitz, 1982; P. W. Sternberg, unpublished observations). The Q neuroblast migrates anteriorly on the right side and posteriorly on the left side. The gonad lies typically anterior on the right and posterior on the left; the embryonic coelomocytes are located anterior of the gonad primordium on the right side of the animal. The gonad primordium is on the left side of the larvae. The ventral

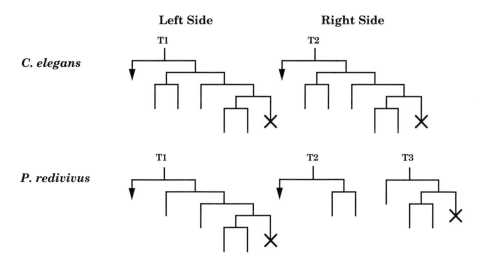

Fig. 7   Bilateral asymmetry in the T lineages. In *C. elegans* the T blast cells (T1 on the left and T2 on the right) undergo identical patterns of cell division, generating identical sets of progeny cells. The posterior daughters, T1.p and T2.p, are neuroblasts. On the left side of each larva, in *P. redivivus* T1.p generates almost the same lineage as T1.p in *C. elegans*. However, on the right side of each larva, the T2.p lineage is truncated, and another cell, T3, apparently generates the remaining cells. Since the fate of the *P. redivivus* cells is not precisely known, we can only speculate that the functions of the cells in the two species are analogous. Arrowheads indicate that additional cell divisions occur; the patterns are the same in both species. Data are from Sulston and Horvitz (1977), Sternberg and Horvitz (1982), and Sulston *et al.* (1983).

nerve cord lies on the left side of the ventral hypodermal ridge, while the dorsal nerve cord lies on the right side of the dorsal hypodermal ridge. Individual nematodes with reversed bilateral asymmetry have been reported in some strains at low penetrance, suggesting genetic control (Sternberg and Horvitz, 1982; J. E. Sulston, personal communication; W. B. Wood, personal communication).

Wood (1991) has recently demonstrated that the bilateral asymmetry of *C. elegans* arises from cell interactions early during embryogenesis. In normal 6-cell embryos, the blastomeres ABal and ABpl lie on the left side more anterior than their counterparts on the right side, ABar and ABpr, respectively. In general, ABal and ABpl generate cells on the left side of the embryo, while ABar and ABpr generate cells on the right side of the embryo. By manipulating the spindles of ABa and ABp, Wood was able to alter the relative positions of ABal and ABpl with respect to ABar and ABpr; such embryos developed into healthy animals with reversed bilateral asymmetry. These observations indicate that ABal is equivalent in developmental potential to ABar, that ABpl is equivalent in potential to ABpr, and that cell interactions establish the differences in the fates of these blastomeres or their progeny. Wood points out that since the cells at the 8-cell stage (see Fig. 1) have distinct contacts with each other and with other cells in the embryo, such differences in cell contacts might be responsible for establishing the asymmetric fates of the equivalent blastomeres or their descendants. For example, ABpr but not ABpl contacts P3, while ABar but not ABal contacts ABpr, raising the possibility that contact with an autonomously-specified blastomere such as P3 might induce "rightsidedness" in AB descendants.

The postembryonic tail ectoblast (T) lineages provide an example of interspecific differences in bilateral symmetry. In *C. elegans* bilaterally symmetric homologs T1 and T2 (on the left and right sides of the animal, respectively) each generate stereotyped lineages producing four hypodermal nuclei, seven neural cells, and one cell that dies (Sulston and Horvitz, 1977). In *P. redivivus* T1.a and T2.a, like their *C. elegans* counterparts, generate four hypodermal cells and one neural cell (a neuron or supporting cell). However, while T1.p generates a lineage very similar to its *C. elegans* counterpart (see Fig. 7), T2.p generate only two neural cells. An asymmetric blast cell, T3, generates three neural cells and a cell that dies (Sternberg and Horvitz, 1982). In *P. redivivus* Caappa becomes T3 in *P. redivivus*, but PVR, the asymmetric interneuron, in *C. elegans* (Sulston *et al.*, 1983). In *C. elegans* Cpappa, the homolog of Capappa, is the asymmetric hypodermal cell hyp11. Thus, in *C. elegans* only Caappa and Cpappa are asymmetric, while T1 and T2 are bilaterally symmetric; in *P. redivivus* both Caappa/Cpappa and T1/T2 are asymmetric.

C. Development and Evolution of Asymmetry

One never knows whether symmetry is being created or destroyed during evolution, but in the case of the asymmetry in the gonad development of *P. redivivus*, it is likely that the symmetry is being destroyed. This inference is based on a comparison of gonad symmetry in various taxa. In contrast to *C. elegans*, which has a two-armed, or didelphic, gonad, each with an ovary and a spermatheca, but with a common uterus, the *P. redivivus* female has a one-armed, or mono-delphic, gonad, which is equivalent in its overall structure to one arm of the *C. elegans* gonad and a short postvulval sac (Hechler, 1970). Three factors conspire to produce the asymmetry of the *P. redivivus* female gonad (Sternberg and Horvitz, 1981): the programmed death of the presumptive distal tip cell (DTC), Z4.ppp, the late division of Z4, and the difference in proliferation of PR and PL as opposed to their anterior homologs AL and AR. One major difference between the gonads of the *C. elegans* hermaphrodite and the *P. redivivus* female is in the number of DTCs; the *C. elegans* hermaphrodite has two DTCs and the *P. redivivus* female has only one DTC located anterior to the vulva. In the *P. redivivus* female the presumed posterior distal tip cell, Z4.pp, dies with the morphology typical of programmed cell death (Sulston and Horvitz, 1977; Robertson and Thomson, 1982). The loss of this regulatory cell can account for the lack of a posterior ovary. However, death of Z4.pp and survival of its anterior homolog Z1.aa is not the earliest sign of anteroposterior asymmetry in the development of the *P. redivivus* female gonad. Z1 divides considerably earlier than does Z4. This difference in timing is sex specific: In *P. redivivus* males Z1 and Z4 undergo identical patterns of cell divisions with identical timing during the early (i.e., L2) lineages, although some fates differ. A later difference observed is in the lineages produced by the anterior ovary cells. AR and AL, versus their posterior homologs, PR and PL (Fig. 8) (these cells are considered homologous to the SS precursors in the *C. elegans* hermaphrodite gonad (Kimble and Hirsh, 1979; Kimble, 1981). AR and AL generate 16 sheath cells, eight oviduct cells, six "constriction" cells, and 12 spermathecal cells. PR and PL each generate eight postvulval sac cells and one or two cells that die. The death of PR.pa and PR.pp, or of PL.pa and PL.pp, is the only known case of sister cells dying in nematodes. The postvulval sac is considered to be vestigial, derived evolutionarily from presumed ovary. As discussed in Section III,C such variability might reflect a lineage in the process of evolution. In another genus with one-armed gonads, *Pratylenchus*, cells in the developing postvulval sac also degenerate, and various species have different length postvulval sacs (Roman and Hirschmann, 1969), suggesting evolutionary divergence in the length of the postvulval sac.

D. Phase Shifts

The fates of certain lineally equivalent cells are not identical, but rather are identical to the sister (or cousin) of their homolog (Fig. 9A). Phase shifts, or altered segregation, occurs in several lineages, during embryogenesis (see Fig.

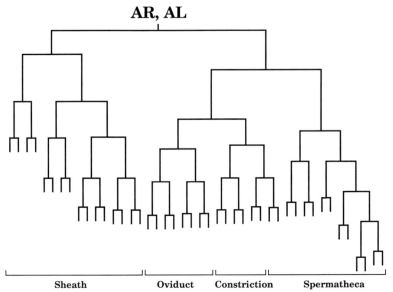

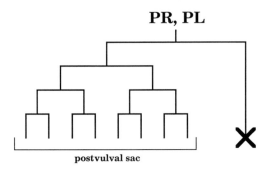

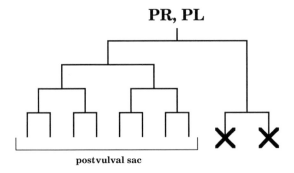

20 in Sulston *et al.*, 1983) and the male sex mesoderm development (Sulston *et al.*, 1980; Sulston and White, 1980).

The fates of certain homologous cells generated by myoblasts on the left and right sides of the developing *C. elegans* male are not identical (Sulston *et al.*, 1980). When differences are present, the right homolog has the fate associated with the more anterior left homolog. For example, SM2.pap on the right is the same cell type as SM2.paa on the left. In *P. redivivus* the cell fates are not characterized, except that both SM2L.pp and SM2R.pp become coelomocytes, while in *C. elegans* only SM2L.pp becomes a coelomocyte (Fig. 9B), raising the possibility that the fates are in phase in *P. redivivus*.

Some of the differences in the male somatic gonad lineages of *C. elegans* and *P. redivivus* are due to an apparent phase shift. In *P. redivivus* the DS blast cell ("distal structures") is larger than the ED cell; in *C. elegans* the seminal vesicle (SV) cell is smaller than the VD cell. The gross anatomy of the male gonad can be described as having the following structures from the proximal end (at the cloaca) to the distal end (mitotic germ line): proximal, ED, VD, SV, distal. In *C. elegans* the VD cell generates cells of the ED, VD, and SV, while the SV cell generates only cells of the SV. In *P. redivivus* the ED cell generates only cells of the ED, while the DS cell generates cells of the ED, VD, and SV. Note that the autonomy of the terminal cell fates has not been tested, and thus the apparent phase shift could be due to cell interactions.

Phase shifts might represent a fascinating difference in the programming of cell fates, or they might represent the vestiges of cell–cell interactions in the evolutionary past. Sulston and colleagues have proposed that cells are recruited piecemeal to form symmetric structures, depending on where they happen to be generated. Implicit in this view is the notion that *C. elegans* evolved from an ancestor where the fates of these cells were specified by cell interactions. Several mechanisms for phase shifts have been proposed (Sulston and White, 1980; Sternberg and Horvitz, 1982; Hedgecock, 1985; see the latter for a review): altered segregation of determinants, reversed order of binary-state switches set at each cell division, and cell interactions occurring after the divisions.

E. Cell Migrations and Polarity Reversals

There are relatively few cell migrations during nematode development. In some cases a cell that migrates in one species is correctly positioned at its birth in

---

Fig. 8 Comparison of the *P. redivivus* female AL/AR and PL/PR lineages. AL and AR are homologous to PL and PR. (A) Two of the anterior somatic gonad lineages, AL and AR, generate cells of the sheath (which covers the germ line), the oviduct, a constriction between the oviduct and the spermatheca, and the spermatheca. B. The posterior homologs, PL and PR, generate fewer cells, which form the postvulval sac (a sheathlike structure). PL.p and PR.p either die or generate two daughters, both of which die. Data are from Sternberg and Horvitz (1981).

A

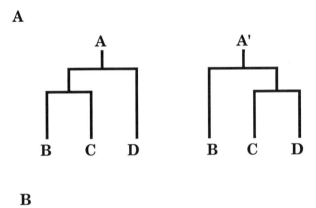

B

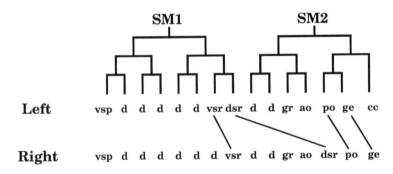

Fig. 9 (A) Generalized phase shift. Cell A generates cells B, C, and D by the lineage shown. Cell A′, a homolog of A, or A in a different species, generates cells B, C, and D by a different lineage. (B) Phase shifts in fates of left and right sex mesoblast (SM) lineages in the *C. elegans* male cell types. vsp, Ventral spicule protractor muscle; d, diagonal muscle; vsr, ventral spicule retractor; dsr, dorsal spicule retractor muscle; gr, gubernacular retractor; ao, anterior oblique muscle; po, posterior oblique muscle; ge, gubernacular erector muscle; cc, coelomocyte. [Adapted from Sulston *et al.* (1980).]

Fig. 10 Cell migration and polarity reversal. (A) The founder cell lineage of the early embryo in the nematode *Bradynema rigidum*. The germ-line precursor, P4, is generated at the posterior pole and migrates anterior of the D blastomere prior to gastrulation. In the *C. elegans* embryo, P4 is generated anterior to D, the correct position for its subsequent gastrulation. The polarity of the P3 division with respect to anteroposterior axis is thus reversed. (The polarity of the P2 division is slightly different in the two species, but the axis is mostly dorsal–ventral.) Data are from Deppe *et al.* (1978) and zur Strassen (1959). (B) During formation of the male gonadal somatic primordia, in *C. elegans*, the distal tip cell (DTC) Z1.a is formed at the anterior end and migrates posteriorly. In *P. redivivus* a potential DTC, Z1.pp, is formed close to the correct position. LC, Linker cell; VD, vas deferens precursor cell; sv, SV, seminal vesicle precursor cell; DS, distal structures precursor cell; ED, ejaculatory duct precursor cell. Data are from Kimble and Hirsh (1979) and Sternberg and Horvitz (1981).

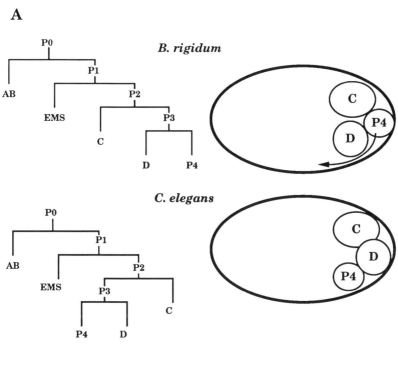

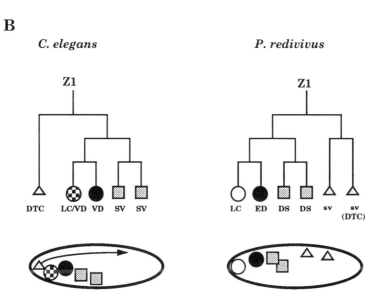

another species. For example, in *Bradynema rigidum* P4 is generated at the posterior end of the embryo and migrates anterior to D. During gastrulation P4 follows the E cells (zur Strassen, 1959; discussed in English by Schierenberg, 1987). In *C. elegans* P4 is formed anterior to D (Deppe *et al.*, 1978). The migration in *Bradynema* apparently has been replaced by a polarity reversal in the founder cell lineage (Fig. 10A). A second example is provided by the development of the gonad in *C. elegans* and *P. redivivus* males. In *C. elegans* Z1.a, one of two DTCs, is formed at the anterior end of the developing gonad and migrates posteriorly to the presumed distal end (Kimble and Hirsh, 1979). In *P. redivivus* Z1.pp, which can become the DTC if Z4.pp is destroyed, is formed in a more posterior position (Sternberg and Horvitz, 1981) (Figure 10B). In both of these examples, a polarity reversal in one species obviates the necessity for the migration. Since we do not know the direction of evolution, we can only speculate that the polarity reversal is of a more highly evolved character.

V. Indeterminacy and the Flexibility of Cell Fate

Equivalence groups, small groups of oligopotent cells whose fates are specified by cell interactions, are an important feature of fate specification in many organisms: in the leech, fly, grasshopper, ascidians, as well as in at least four species of nematodes (e.g., Sulston and White, 1980; Kimble, 1981; Sternberg and Horvitz, 1981, 1982; Doe and Goodman, 1985; Shankland, 1987; Simpson, 1990; P. W. Sternberg, P. Kayne, and L. Carta, unpublished observations). Equivalence groups were first described and have been best characterized in nematodes. Additional examples have been described more recently. For example, in the ascidian embryo (*Halocynthia roretzi*) two pigment cells, the ocellus and the otolith melanocytes, form an equivalence group (Nishida and Satoh, 1989). Two bilaterally positioned cells are bipotent, since either can become the ocellus or the otolith melanocyte. Differentiation as the ocellus melanocyte is the primary fate. If these two cells remain separate (due to a cytochalasin block), both adopt the primary fate (i.e., ocellus melanocyte).

A. AC/VU Decision

The specification in *C. elegans* of Z1.ppp and Z4.aaa to become either the AC or VU is one of the simplest cell fate decisions in an equivalence group. Kimble and Hirsh (1979) showed that the fates of the somatic gonadal cells Z1.ppp and Z4.aaa are determined at random. Kimble (1981) demonstrated that the AC fate is primary. Hedgecock *et al.* (1990) observed that, in *unc-6* mutants, two anchor cells could form in gonad primordia with abnormal cell positions, apparently because presumed AC/VU cells must be in contact for lateral signaling. This observation is not likely to be a consequence of the particular mutation used, since, in *lin-17* gonad primordia, two anchor cells can also form, presumably because they are not in contact (Sternberg and Horvitz, 1988). Kimble (1978) observed that, at successive stages of development, Z1 and Z4, Z1.p and Z4.a, and Z1.pp and Z4.aa are in contact, suggesting that Z1.ppp and Z4.aaa are in contact as well. Thus, the presumed AC/VU cells are likely to be in contact, and this contact (or at least close proximity) is required for the intercellular signaling.

Genetic studies of the *lin-12* locus indicate that this locus specifies the VU versus AC type (Greenwald *et al.*, 1983). A high level of *lin-12* activity specifies one cell fate, while a low level of *lin-12* activity specifies the alternative cell fate. High *lin-12* activity is sufficient to specify the VU fate among the two cells in the equivalence group (Seydoux and Greenwald, 1989). Ablation of all somatic gonad cells except Z1.ppp or Z4.aaa in a wild-type animal results in an AC (Kimble, 1981). Ablation of all somatic gonad cells except Z1.ppp or Z4.aaa in a *lin-12(d)* animal results in a VU cell (Seydoux and Greenwald, 1988), indicating that if *lin-12* is acting only in the gonad with respect to AC/VU specification, then *lin-12* must act in the cell that expresses it. Clearly, *lin-12* does not act alone, and other genes that may act in concert with *lin-12*, or in the *lin-12* pathway, are expected to be identified by mutations that suppress or enhance the phenotypes of *lin-12* mutations.

lin-12 is a member of a family of genes that includes *gly-1* of *C. elegans* and *Notch* of *Drosophila* and has members in vertebrates (Coffman *et al.*, 1990, cited by Greenwald and Seydoux, 1990). In particular these proteins each have a putative transmembrane domain and extracellular cysteine-rich repeats. These observations have led Greenwald and co-workers to suggest that *lin-12* may be an extracellular protein mediating cell–cell interactions, possibly as a ligand or a receptor involved in establishing or interpreting positional information (see Greenwald, 1989, for a review). In addition, *lin-12* is quite similar in overall and Yochem *et al.*, 1988, structure to the *Drosophila Notch* product (Wharton *et al.*, 1985; Kidd *et al.*, 1986). The *Notch* product is believed to be necessary for lateral inhibition during insect early neurogenesis (reviewed by Campos-Ortega, 1990; Simpson, 1990). Mosaic analyses indicate that both gene products are required cell autonomously (Seydoux and Greenwald, 1989; Hoppe and Green-span, 1990).

Molecular genetic analysis of two members of this family highlight the importance of a cross-species approach. Reduction-of-function mutations in *Notch* occur in individual epidermal growth factor (EGF)-like repeats (Hartley *et al.*, 1987), indicating that the individual properties of these repeats might be important for the function of this gene. Gain-of-function mutations have been most extensively characterized in the *lin-12* locus (Greenwald *et al.*, 1983). Most of these gain-of-function mutations analyzed are in the protein coding region (Greenwald and Seydoux, 1990). Thus, *lin-12(d)* mutations most likely result in constitutively active or more stable protein, as opposed to an overexpressed protein. Some of the genes defined by suppressor mutations might encode a ligand for *lin-12*, and convey information from the cell surface to the nucleus to specify the 2° VU fate and inhibit the 1° AC fate.

Two different classes of mechanism might account for a fate hierarchy in a two-cell equivalence group. In one mechanism the position of each cell determines its fate. Two cells might compete for access to a signal supplied by another cell(s), with a random element supplied by the relative positions of the two cells. The 1° cell would then passively prevent the secondary cell from receiving the signal to be 1°. In the absence of the presumed 1° cell, the remaining cell would receive the signal to be 1°. A second class of mechanism might involve solely interactions between the two cells, each cell initially being poised to follow either developmental alternative of adopting the 1° or 2° cell fate. This initial unstable state would result from the balance of two antagonistic signals (Fig. 11A). One signal would act autonomously to promote the 1° fate. The second signal would act nonautonomously to stimulate the 2° fate. The two cells would then be linked in a competitive feedback circuit, such that only one cell can be of each type. If one cell is 1°, the other must be 2°. Stochastic processes (i.e., fluctuations in the concentration or activity of any component in the circuit) predispose one of the two cells to be more 1° or less 2°; this predisposition would be reinforced by the positive feedback loop acting in or on the 1° cell and a negative feedback loop acting in or on the 2° cell. This general concept of a competitive feedback circuit for lateral inhibition in *Anabena* has been suggested by Wilcox *et al.* (1973), who described mathematical models demonstrating the plausibility of such a hypothesis. The important distinction between these classes of hypothetical mechanisms is that the bistable mechanism requires no input from cells other than the members of the equivalence group.

Fig. 11 Lateral signaling and induction. (A) Bistable behavior and indeterminate fate specification. Positive regulatory interactions are indicated by arrows; negative interactions, by bars. The 1° and 2° cell types are mutually exclusive: A cell expresses either 1°-specific or 2°-specific functions. *lin-12* stimulates 2°, and thus indirectly negatively regulates 1° functions. Cells are coupled via a lateral signal acting between the cells. In one scenario a cell that is 1° expresses a lateral signal. The metastability of the initial state of such a system evolves to either to two stable states; both states have one cell 1° and one cell 2° (e.g., the AC/VU decision, and the 1°/2° VPC decision in an anchor cell-deficient *lin-15* hermaphrodite. [Adapted from Sternberg (1988b) and Greenwald and Seydoux (1990).] (B) Induction of the vulva in a *lin-12(0)* animal has an inductive signal from the anchor cell (AC) to the VPCs acting via the products of the *Vul* genes. The action of the *Vul* genes stimulates 1°, which inhibits 2°. There is no lateral signaling pathway, because *lin-12* activity is deficient. Both cells differentiate as 1°. [Based on the results and model by Sternberg and Horvitz (1989).] (C) Induction and lateral signaling combined. If the inductive signal is overlain on the lateral signaling shown in (A), then the final state is as shown here. The inductive signal acting via the *Vul* gene products stimulate 1° in both cells, but more strongly in the presumed 1° VPC. (The thick arrows indicate a stronger regulatory interaction than the thin arrows.) This biases the underlying competition for 1° via the lateral signaling pathway. The competition is unfair: P6.p always wins.

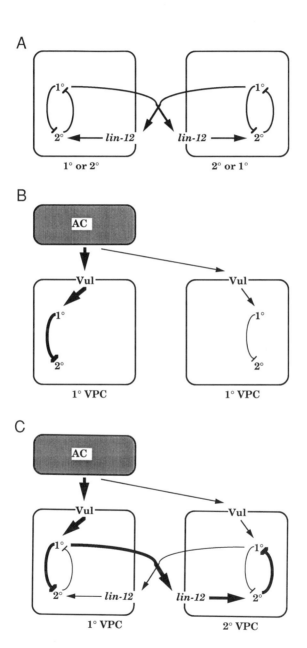

For the AC/VU decision, the experiments by Seydoux and Greenwald (1989) support the second class of mechanism and argue against the first. Seydoux and Greenwald constructed genetic mosaic animals in which Z1 and Z4 were of distinct genotypes, one being *lin-12*(+), the other, *lin-12*(0). The action of *lin-12* for the AC/VU decision is cell autonomous, suggesting that *lin-12* acts at the receiving end of a cell–cell interaction (Seydoux and Greenwald, 1989). In particular the cell with *lin-12* activity always becomes secondary (VU).

B. Changes in the Flexibility of Cell Fate Specification during Evolution

While the AC/VU group is the most intensively studied one, other equivalence groups have similar, but nonidentical, fate specification. If a common mechanism operates in each group, the same gene products might be involved in each two-celled equivalence group. If so, one can ask what causes the differences between groups. Since analogous equivalence groups are present in different species, one can ask whether a change in cell type specification occurs during evolution.

In contrast to the AC/VU and Bα/Bβ groups (see Section II,A), there are other equivalence groups which comprise two cells, one of which is known to be bipotent, but the other (primary) cell is only suspected to be bipotent. The G2/W equivalence group consists of the two cells G2/W-L and G2/W-R. These two cells are bilaterally symmetric homologs that migrate to the ventral midline and assume relative anteroposterior positions with G2/W-L (the left homolog) anterior to G2/W-R (the right homolog). G2/W-L always becomes the G2 ectoblast, the G2/W-R always becomes the W neuroblast. Nonetheless, after destruction of G2/W-L, G2/W-R becomes the G2 ectoblast (Sulston *et al.*, 1983). These observations indicate that G2 is the primary fate and that G2/W-R is bipotent. G2/W-L is *assumed* to be bipotent. Similarly, the P11/P12 equivalence group consists of the pair of homologous cells P11/12-L and P11/12-R that migrate to the ventral midline and assume new positions, with P11/12-L anterior to P11/12-R. P11/12-L becomes P11, and P11/12-R becomes P12. P11 and P12 are ectoblasts that differ in the types of neurons and hypodermal cells they generate (Sulston and Horvitz, 1977). After ablation of P11/12-R, P11/12-L becomes P12 (Fig. 12).

In other equivalence groups there is a partial bias in fate specifications. During gonadogenesis of the *C. elegans* male, two cells have the potential to become either the LC or a VD cell (Kimble and Hirsh, 1979). Like the AC/VU equivalence group, in the LC/VD group the LC fate is primary and the VD fate is secondary (Kimble, 1981) (see Fig. 6B). The more anterior cell, Z1.paa, is more likely to become the LC (Kimble and Hirsh, 1979). In the *P. redivivus* male two cells have the potential to become either the LC or an ED cell (Sternberg and Horvitz, 1981). The more anterior LC/ED cell, Z1.aaa, usually (i.e., all seven observed) becomes the LC; however, after ablation of Z1 and hence Z1.aaa, another cell (presumably Z4.aaa) becomes the LC (Sternberg and Horvitz, 1981).

Specification of the fates in the G2/W, P11/P12, and LC/VD (or LC/ED) groups differs from that in the AC/VU group because the fates of these apparently equivalent cells are strongly biased. Either the migration of the G2/W,

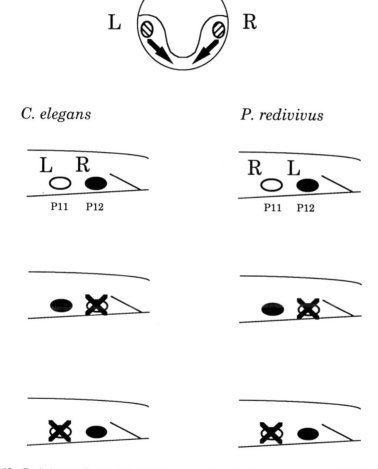

Fig. 12 Evolutionary changes in P11/P12 determination. The bilateral homologs P11/P12-L and P11/P12-R migrate from their sublateral positions to the ventral midline. In *C. elegans* the left (L) monolog ends up more anterior and becomes P11. In *P. redivivus* the right (R) homolog ends up more anterior and becomes P11. The P12 fate (see Fig. 2 for details) is 1°. Ablation of P12 results in presumed P11 becoming P12. Ablation of P11 does not affect the fate of P12. Data are from Sulston and Horvitz (1977), Sulston and White (1980), and Sternberg and Horvitz (1982).

P11/P12, and LC/VD cells is invariant or one cell inherits a predisposition to become primary. In the case of the LC/ED cells in *P. redivivus*, it is clear that Z1.aaa is formed more anterior than Z4.aaa; thus, if the more anterior of the two cells becomes the LC, the outcome is strongly biased in favor of Z1.aaa.

A comparison of gonadal development in *C. elegans* and *P. redivivus* suggests that the flexibility of fate specification in equivalence groups can change during evolution. In *C. elegans*, as described in Section V,A, two cells have the potential to become the AC. In wild type one of these cells becomes the AC, while the remaining cell becomes a VU cell. In *P. redivivus* only Z4.aaa can become the AC. Ablation of Z4, but not Z1, prevents formation of an AC (Sternberg and Horvitz, 1981).

Another example of evolutionary divergence in cell fate decisions within an equivalence group is the decision between the P11 and P12 fates (Fig. 13). These decisions are nonrandom in both *C. elegans* and *P. redivivus*, but the biases are opposite in the two species. The left homolog, P11/P12-L, becomes P11 in *C. elegans*, but P12 in *P. redivivus*. This difference between the two species might have arisen if, in the common ancestor of these two species, the fates of the left and right homologs, P11/P12-L and P11/P12-R, respectively, were chosen at random, but subsequently evolved independently to become strongly biased. One could imagine that overall bilateral asymmetry is reversed in the two species, but this is not the case: Both species display an anterior–right posterior–left asymmetry, for example, in juvenile coelomocyte position, and anterior versus posterior migration of the Q neuroblast and its descendants (Sulston and Horvitz, 1977; Sternberg and Horvitz, 1982). This hypothesis predicts that one could easily find a nematode species with random P11/P12 fate specification.

All of these cases of two-cell equivalence groups appear to involve essentially equivalent cells that become determined to particular fates. In some groups this process occurs randomly by cell–cell interactions (AC/VU, Bα/β); in other cases the outcome of the cell–cell interactions is biased by cell lineage or additional positional cues (G2/W, P11/P12, and LC/VD in *C. elegans* and LC/ED in *P. redivivus*), and in another case the outcome might have become fixed by cell lineage (AC/"VU" in *P. redivivus*).

When a gene has analogous effects on developmental decisions in distinct tissues, its product is likely to be a general component of a mechanism, rather than being responsible for the particular features of the cell types involved [e.g., *lin-12*, *lin-14*, *lin-15*, *lin-17*, and *mab-5* (Greenwald *et al.*, 1983; Ambros and Horvitz, 1984; Fixsen *et al.*, 1985; Kenyon, 1986; Ferguson *et al.*, 1987; Sternberg and Horvitz, 1988)]. *lin-12* is one such gene that controls cell fates in a number of equivalence groups. The cell fates in the LC/VD and G2/W groups are controlled by the *lin-12* locus. The role of *lin-12* in binary decisions in several equivalence groups suggests that a common mechanism underlies these decisions, but there are clear differences among the decisions mediated by *lin-12*. As mentioned above, which LC/VD cell becomes the LC is random, but which

G2/W cell becomes G2 is strongly biased. Surprisingly, in the AC/VU equivalence group a high level of *lin-12* activity specifies the secondary fate, while in
the G2/W equivalence group *lin-12* specifies the primary fate. In addition *lin-12*
controls the fates of another pair of homologous cells, the neuroblast Y and the
neuron DA9, whose fates apparently are not specified by cell–cell interactions.
Y/DA9 might be another example of a "former" equivalence group, comprising
cells whose fates might once have been set by cell interactions but are now
specified by asymmetric cell division. One can imagine that the *lin-12* pathway is
regulated in a slightly different manner in each case, thereby altering the ability
of cells to regulate their fates.

   lin-12 also affects the fate of B.pa and B.pp, sister cells in the male tail. The
role of *lin-12* in the specification of sister cell fates might come about in two
ways. The fate of these sisters might be specified by intercellular signals acting
between them in a manner analogous to the G2/W fate. Another possibility is
that in this instance the activity state of *lin-12* might be set by an autonomous
process. It is also conceivable that *lin-12* could act in B.p as a receptor for a
signal that allows B.p to divide asymmetrically; in this view, as discussed above
(see Fig. 5), the precursor that undergoes asymmetric cell division must be
specified to do so.

   In contrast to the *C. elegans* AC/VU, LC/VD, and G2/W equivalence groups,
the decision in the P11/P12 group between the P11 and P12 fates is not controlled by *lin-12*, but by gene products that include *lin-15*, *let-23*, and *let-60*
(Fixsen *et al.*, 1985; Han *et al.*, 1990; Beitel *et al.*, 1990; Aroian and Sternberg,
1991). In *lin-15* mutants both cells in the group have the P12 fate, while in *let-23*
mutants both cells in the group have the P11 fate. Thus, the *lin-15* gene product
is inferred to be necessary for the P11 fate, and the *let-23* gene product is inferred
to be necessary for the P12 fate. These gene products appear to have antagonistic
effects on the decision between these alternative cell fates.

VI. The Combination of Intercellular Signals Specifies a Complex Pattern of Cell Fates during Vulval Induction

During induction of the *C. elegans* hermaphrodite vulva, six tripotent VPCs
become specified to form a pattern of three cell types. In the simplest view only
seven cells participate in vulval induction: the AC of the gonad and the VPCs of
the hypodermis (but see below). The three VPCs closest to the AC are induced to
become 1° and 2° cells and thus to generate vulval tissue (Fig. 13); the remaining
three cells remain as 3° cells and generate nonspecialized hypodermis. The
names of the three cell types (1°, 2°, and 3°) derive from the hierarchy of changes
in cell type after ablation: A primary cell type is the one that is replaced by either
a secondary or tertiary cell after it is destroyed; a secondary cell is one that
replaces a primary cell or is replaced by a tertiary cell (Kimble *et al.*, 1979).

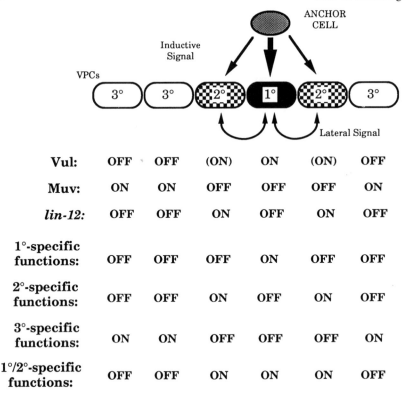

Vul:	OFF	OFF	(ON)	ON	(ON)	OFF
Muv:	ON	ON	OFF	OFF	OFF	ON
lin-12:	OFF	OFF	ON	OFF	ON	OFF
1°-specific functions:	OFF	OFF	OFF	ON	OFF	OFF
2°-specific functions:	OFF	OFF	ON	OFF	ON	OFF
3°-specific functions:	ON	ON	OFF	OFF	OFF	ON
1°/2°-specific functions:	OFF	OFF	ON	ON	ON	OFF

Fig. 13 Model for vulval induction. The fates of six multipotent vulval precursor cells (VPCs) depends on a somehow graded inductive signal from the anchor cell of the gonad. The lateral signal must act bilaterally among at least the presumed 1° and two presumed 2° VPCs. The progeny of the 1° and 2° VPCs generates vulval cells. The progeny of the three 3° VPCs generates nonspecialized hypodermis. [Adapted from Sternberg (1988a) and Sternberg and Horvitz (1989).] A simple view of the roles of the specification genes is as shown. The *Muv* genes are necessary to prevent VPCs from becoming 1° or 2° in the absence of inductive signal. Thus, the *Muv* genes can be thought of as being active in the presumed 3° VPCs or acting on these cells. The *Vul* genes are necessary for VPCs to become 1° or 2°. Thus, the *Vul* genes are active in or on the presumed 1° and 2° VPCs. In addition, since the presumed 2° cells must somehow be responding to a lower "level" of inductive signal, or receiving inductive signal at a later time than presumed 1° VPCs, the activity of some *Vul* genes might be lower in or on the presumed 2° VPCs (indicated by parentheses). *lin-12* is necessary only for the 2° VPC fate, and thus can be thought of as being active in or on presumed 2° VPCs. The actions of the specification genes result in the restricted activities of cell type specifications. For example, 1° VPCs might express 1°-specific function, etc. Other sets of functions might also be regulated (e.g., 1°/2° functions would be active in 1° and 2°, but not 3° VPCs).

Each of these cell types generates a characteristic sublineage (see Fig. 16). The typically invariant pattern of VPC types is established by the actions of the inductive signal from the anchor cell and a lateral signal among the VPCs (Kimble, 1981; Sternberg and Horvitz, 1986; Sternberg, 1988a).

Each vulval precursor cell has been shown, by perturbation of essentially wild-type development, to have the potential to adopt each of three fates (Sulston and White, 1980; Kimble, 1981; Sternberg and Horvitz, 1986; Thomas et al., 1990). Some equivalences (e.g., P6.p can be 2°) have been shown by alterations in body shape and other defects leading to mispositioning of the gonad [lon-1 and dig-1 (Sternberg and Horvitz, 1986; Thomas et al., 1990)]. The fates result in particular patterns of cell division: a 3° VPC generates nonvulval hypodermis, and 1° and 2° VPCs generate characteristic sets of vulval cells. Many mutants with defective vulval induction result in "hybrid" vulval lineages (Sulston and Horvitz, 1981; Ferguson et al., 1987; Sternberg and Horvitz, 1989; Aroian and Sternberg, 1991), and while such lineages are not inconsistent with the hypothesis that specification of the vulval sublineages occurs in the VPCs (see Sternberg and Horvitz, 1986)—the simplest hypothesis is that specification takes place primarily in the VPC—it is conceivable that additional cell interactions occur among some or all of the VPC progeny cells.

The reproducibility of wild-type vulval development allows determination of mutant phenotypes with a high degree of accuracy. Mutants with abnormal vulval cell lineages can be readily obtained because they can be recognized on a Petri plate under a dissecting microscope and are fertile (Horvitz and Sulston, 1980; Ferguson and Horvitz, 1985). In general mutants defective in vulval development have either of two phenotypes: *Vulvaless* (*Vul*) mutants lack a vulva and are egg-laying defective; *Multivulva* (*Muv*) mutants have extra vulval cells that form protrusions on the ventral surface of the animal. (Mutations causing Vul and Muv phenotypes are referred to as *Vul* and *Muv* mutations, respectively.) Mutations in over 30 genes have been assigned to individual steps in the genetic pathway for vulval development based on the phenotypes of the mutants, the phenotypes of double mutants, and the temperature-sensitive periods of several of these mutations (Ferguson et al., 1987; Sternberg and Horvitz, 1989; Kim and Horvitz, 1990). At least five of these genes have been cloned [let-23, let-60, lin-10, lin-11, and lin-12 (Greenwald, 1985; Kim and Horvitz, 1990; Freyd et al., 1990; Arioan et al., 1990; Han et al., 1990)], and additional molecular analysis of these and other genes is likely to be forthcoming in the near future. More than 20 genes control the specification of VPC type. As I describe in Section VI,A, these "specification" genes act in two pathways: The *Muv* and *Vul* genes mediate the inductive signal, and *lin-12* mediates the lateral signal. The two pathways interact to specify the precise pattern of cell types. Either pathway is sufficient to specify cell types, but the specification of the three VPC types requires the action of both pathways.

A. Inductive Signal and the Muv and Vul Genes

The "ground state" of each precursor cell is to generate the nonvulval 3° lineage. In the absence of the AC and neighboring VPCs, a VPC is a 3° cell. Therefore, the role of the AC is to elevate VPCs from the ground state, and thus generate vulval cells. Destruction of the AC blocks induction of the vulva, while destruction of all gonadal cells but the AC still allows a vulva to be formed (Kimble, 1981). The nature of the signal is not known, and the existence of multiple signals from the AC has not been ruled out (e.g., Sternberg and Horvitz, 1986; see also Greenwald, 1989).

The AC can signal each precursor cell independently. A single VPC (in the absence of its five neighbors) can be 1°, 2°, or 3°. The observation that an isolated VPC can be 2° tends to rule out the simple model that the AC signal specifies the 1° cell and the 1° cell specifies its neighbors to be 2° (Sternberg and Horvitz, 1986; P. W. Sternberg, unpublished observations). Moreover, the position of a precursor cell at the apparent time of fate specification is correlated with its fate, suggesting that distance from the AC determines its fate, and thus that the inductive signal is graded. An alternative possibility is that in these experiments the fate of the isolated VPC is set at random, and then it moves to the appropriate position with respect to the AC. In other words the fate of a VPC could determine its position.

Does the signal act at a distance? Thomas *et al.* (1990) and E. M. Hedgecock (personal communication) examined mutant animals in which the gonad was displaced dorsally, and found that if the AC was dorsal, some vulval induction could occur in the ventrally located VPCs. While it is possible that a long cellular process extends from the AC, or that the mutations used result in ectopic production of inductive signal, the simplest interpretation of these observations is that the inductive signal can act at a distance. (An alternative hypothesis is that the inductive signal acts via an intermediary, hyp7; see below).

The inductive signaling pathway is defined by two classes of mutations. Reduction-of-function mutations in any of several *Muv* genes (e.g., *lin-15*) result in the specification of 1° and 2° fates in the absence of an inductive signal (see Fig. 15D and E). Each VPC is 1° or 2°, and the additional vulval cells generated result in the presence of ectopic vulval structures, the Muv phenotype. The *Muv* genes include *lin-15* and at least eight other genes, *lin-1*, *lin-8*, *lin-9*, *lin-13*, *lin-35*, *lin-36*, *lin-37*, and *lin-38* (Horvitz and Sulston, 1980; Sulston and Horvitz, 1981; Ferguson and Horvitz, 1985, 1989; Ferguson *et al.*, 1987; Sternberg and Horvitz, 1989). Since extra 1° and 2° cells occur even if the AC has been destroyed, the *Muv* genes do not act solely in the AC. Thus, the function of the *Muv* gene products in a wild-type animal may be to negatively regulate the response to the inductive signal. At least one *Muv* gene, *lin-15*, acts in cells other than the VPCs (i.e., nonautonomously). Genetic mosaic data are consistent with the action of *lin-15* in the hypodermal syncytium, hyp7, suggesting that hyp7 might act to prevent VPCs from becoming 1° or 2° in the absence of inductive signal (Herman and Hedgecock, 1990) (Fig. 14).

At least six *Vul* genes (*let-23*, *let-60*, *lin-2*, *lin-3*, *lin-7*, and *lin-10*) are necessary for vulval induction (Horvitz and Sulston, 1980; Sulston and Horvitz, 1981; Ferguson and Horvitz, 1985; Ferguson *et al.*, 1987; Sternberg and Horvitz, 1989; Beitel *et al.*, 1990; Han *et al.*, 1990; Kim and Horvitz, 1990; Aroian and Sternberg, 1991; R. Hill and P. W. Sternberg, unpublished observations). Reduction or loss of function of any of the *Vul* genes causes VPCs to remain in the 3° ground state (Fig. 15C). Genetic analysis indicates that the Vul phenotype results from a decrease in the activity of *lin-2*, *lin-3*, *lin-7*, *lin-10*, *let-23*, or *let-60*. More extreme reduction in the activity of *let-23*, *let-60*, or *lin-3* causes larvae to die prior to vulval induction. Gain-of-function mutations in *let-60* result in a Muv phenotype (Beitel *et al.*, 1990; Han *et al.*, 1990).

It is not known whether these *Vul* gene products act in the AC (and thus in the production of the inductive signals) or in the VPCs (and thus in response to the inductive signal). An indirect genetic argument suggests that five of the *Vul* genes (*let-23*, *let-60*, *lin-2*, *lin-7*, and *lin-10*) act in the VPCs and hence in response to the signal: Mutations in each of these *Vul* genes are epistatic to at least one *Muv* mutation (Ferguson *et al.*, 1987; Han *et al.*, 1990). Since these *Muv* mutations act in cells other than the AC, presumably in the VPCs (see above), this observation suggests that these *Vul* genes do not act in the AC either. Or, at least in this mutant background, the *Vul* genes are not acting in the AC. The cells in which each *Vul* gene acts can, in principle, be determined by genetic mosaic analysis (Herman, 1989), but cannot be done until suitable genetic tools are available for these *Vul* genes. Since *lin-15* acts not only in the VPCs, *Vul* genes epistatic to *lin-15* mutations might act in cells other than the VPCs. However, the simplest interpretation of existing data is still that the *Vul* genes act

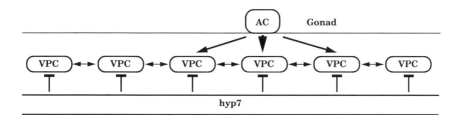

Fig. 14 Vulval induction from the perspective of the Herman–Hedgecock hypothesis. The nonautonomous action of a *lin-15* mutation suggests that hyp 7, the large hypodermal syncytium, prevents vulval precursor cells (VPCs) from proliferating and generating vulval cells. Inductive signal from the anchor cell (AC) overcomes this inhibition and allows three VPCs to compete via lateral signal for the 1° fate. The VPCs are in contact with one another and with hyp 7. A variation proposed by Herman and Hedgecock (1990) is that the AC signal acts on hyp 7; however, it is unlikely that this is the case, since VPCs respond to the AC in a *lin-15* mutant (Sternberg, 1988a; see also Han *et al.*, 1990). [Based on models by Herman and Hedgecock (1990) and Sternberg (1988a).]

in the VPCs. These *Vul* genes are therefore candidates for encoding components of the signal transduction apparatus that senses the inductive signal and specifies the 1° and 2° cell types by positively regulating "execution" genes specific for 1° and 2° cell types by positively regulating "execution" genes specific for 1° and 2° VPCs and negatively regulating execution genes specific for 3° VPCs. If *lin-15* *Muv* results from a failure of hyp7 to inhibit VPCs from becoming 1° or 2°,

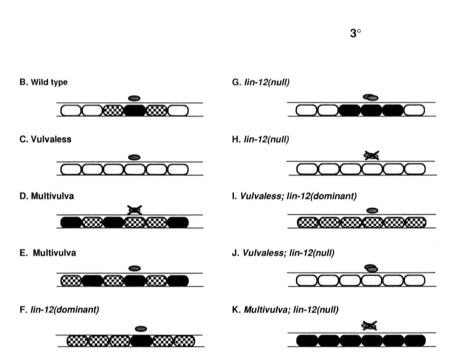

Fig. 15 A simple regulatory pathway for the control of vulval precursor cell (VPC) fates in *C. elegans*, and its derivation. (A) The pathway. (B–K) Schematics of the phenotypes of single and double mutants defective either in a *Vul* or *Muv* gene and in *lin-12*. Solid ovals indicate 1° VPCs; checkered ovals, 2° VPCs; open ovals, 3° VPCs. Stippled ovals indicate the anchor cell; X indicates an ablated cell. Data are from Sulston and Horvitz (1981), Greenwald *et al.* (1983), Ferguson *et al.* (1987), and Sternberg and Horvitz (1989).

suppression of *lin-15 Muv* by *let-23* and *let–60* (Aroian and Sternberg, 1991; Han *et al.*, 1990) implies that *lin-15* acts via these genes.

Some of the wild-type *Muv* gene products might encode components of the signal transduction apparatus that, in general, act antagonistically to those encoded by some or all of the *Vul* genes. *Vul* genes promote 1° and 2° cell fates, while *Muv* genes promote 3°. Moreover, in some cases *Muv* and *Vul* mutations partially suppress each other: The phenotype of a *Muv–Vul* double mutant can be wild type (Ferguson *et al.*, 1987; Sternberg and Horvitz, 1989; Han *et al.*, 1990). Furthermore, as described below, *Muv* mutations have been obtained as suppressors of *Vul* mutations, and *Vul* mutations have been obtained as suppressors of *Muv* mutations (e.g., Han *et al.*, 1990; Beitel *et al.*, 1990; Aroian and Sternberg, 1991). In summary the *Muv* and *Vul* gene products have antagonistic effects on the fates of the VPCs. In the wild type the *Vul* products promote 1° and 2° fates, while the *Muv* products promote 3° fates.

Genetic interactions between various *Muv* and *Vul* mutations suggest that these gene products normally act in a common pathway (Ferguson *et al.*, 1987; Han *et al.*, 1990). One cannot order the action of genes defined by the same mutant phenotypes. However, if one has available alleles of a single gene with opposite effects, then one can use the alleles in an epistasis test to define an apparent order of action. *lin-34 Muv* mutations result in an elevation of *let-60* activity (Han *et al.*, 1990; Beitel *et al.*, 1990; Han and Sternberg, 1990), and are now called *let-60(gf)* mutations, since they are gain-of-function mutations of *let-60*. Since *let-60(gf)* mutations confer a gonad-independent Muv phenotype, and *let-60(gf)* mutations are epistatic to *let-23* mutations, *let-60* is likely to act downstream of *let-23* (Han *et al.*, 1990). Note that the inferred order of action depends on certain assumptions; in particular, whether the pathway is biochemical or regulatory. A biochemical, or assembly, pathway is characterized by a series of discrete steps with recognizable differences between the steps; disruption of any step results in a unique intermediate phenotype (e.g., accumulation of a precursor). A regulatory, or signal-processing, pathway is characterized by discrete, usually binary, outcomes; disruption of any step forces the outcome to either of the two normal states. Many pathways are expected to be a combination of biochemical and information-processing pathways.

The products of *let-23* and *let-60* have been inferred from conceptual translation of their nucleotide sequences. *let-23* encodes a tyrosine kinase of the human EGF-receptor subfamily (Aroian *et al.*, 1990). This similarity in overall architecture and in known key amino acid residues suggests that *let-23* protein is likely to act in a similar manner to the EGF receptor: to bind an extracellular ligand, transduce the signal across the plasma membrane, and regulate the activities of other proteins by phosphorylating them on tyrosine residues (for reviews see Ullrich and Schlessinger, 1990; Carpenter and Wahl, 1990). Based on the structural similarity, Aroian *et al.* (1990) proposed that *let-23* might be the receptor for the AC inductive signal. *let-60* encodes a ras protein, strikingly similar to the oncogenic p21[ras] protein (Han and Sternberg, 1990). Genetic analyses indicate that *let-60* acts after *let-23* in a regulatory pathway (Han *et al.*, 1990; Han and Sternberg, 1990; G. Jongeward and P. W. Sternberg, unpublished observations). Thus, the chief effect of the *let-23* tyrosine kinase is exerted through *let-60* ras. Analysis of the sites of action and the expression of these genes will test these hypotheses.

B. Lateral Signal and *lin-12*

VPCs interact during the establishment of the pattern of cell fates. Destruction of the cell destined to be a 1° cell allows one presumed 2° cell to become 1° (Sulston and White, 1980; Sternberg and Horvitz, 1986). Similarly, destruction of a 2° cell allows a cell destined to be 3° to become, instead, a 2° cell. Therefore, the presence of an AC proximal cell may prevent a more distal cell from adopting a "higher" fate. This inhibition could come about in either of two ways: A proximal cell could passively prevent a more distal cell from receiving a sufficient level of inductive signal, or a higher-fated cell could actively signal its neighbor not to adopt so high a fate. In a wild-type animal it is not possible to distinguish between the active and passive inhibition of presumed 2° cells by the presumptive 1° cell, P6.p, because of the presence of a graded signal. However, the interactions among VPCs have been studied in the background of a mutation that renders the VPCs partially independent of the inductive signal (Sternberg, 1988a). In a *lin-15* mutant in which the gonad, and hence the AC, has been destroyed, all six VPCs adopt a 1° or 2° fate. Each VPC can be either 1° or 2° (Sternberg, 1988a; Sternberg and Horvitz, 1989). Although adjacent cells are only rarely 1°, they can often both be 2°. Therefore, a presumptive 1° VPC might prevent its immediate neighbors from also becoming 1°. Indeed, in the wild type, in the absence of neighbors, a VPC differentiates as 1°, while in the presence of neighbors, a VPC is 1° or 2°, depending on its neighbor. Thus, VPCs compete to become 1°. This competition occurs between pairs of VPCs, and is thus formally equivalent to the AC/VU decision. There must therefore be a lateral signal generated by the 1° cells that either inhibits neighboring cells from also becoming 1° or stimulates them to be 2° (and thus not 1°). The VPCs must be in close proximity for lateral signaling (Sternberg, 1988a): VPCs close to one another are susceptible to lateral inhibition; VPCs more distant are not susceptible.

The *lin-12* locus controls the specification of 2° cells (Greenwald *et al.*, 1983; Sternberg and Horvitz, 1989). Genetic studies suggest that a high level of *lin-12* activity is sufficient to specify a 2° cell, while a low level of *lin-12* activity renders a VPC incapable of becoming a 2° cell (Fig. 15F–H). Recessive mutations that eliminate *lin-12* activity [*lin-12(0)*] prevent VPCs from becoming 2° cells. Semidominant mutations that increase *lin-12* activity [*lin-12(d)*] allow

VPCs to become 2° cells in the absence of the inductive signal. In the absence of the AC, a high level of *lin-12* activity causes a VPC to become 2°, while a low level of *lin-12* activity causes it to become 3°. In the presence of the AC, the VPCs near the AC become 1° regardless of the level of *lin-12* activity; therefore, *lin-12* activity is irrelevant to whether a cell becomes 1°. While *lin-12* also controls the AC/VU decision discussed earlier, all available evidence indicates that the roles of *lin-12* in the specification of AC/VU and the VPC fates are independent (e.g., Greenwald *et al.*, 1983; Sternberg and Horvitz, 1989). As mentioned earlier, in the context of the AC/VU decision (Section V,A), the structure of the *lin-12* product suggests that it is likely to be a transmembrane receptor and thus plays a role in cell–cell signaling. *lin-12* is necessary for lateral inhibition during vulval induction: in a *lin-12(0)–lin-15* double mutant, all six VPCs become 1° (Sternberg and Horvitz, 1989). Mosaic analysis of the role of *lin-12* in the AC/VU lateral signaling indicates that it acts cell autonomously. It is thus likely that *lin-12* plays an analogous role in the VPC lateral signaling, and thus might be a receptor for lateral signal.

C. Interplay of Inductive and Lateral Signals—Combinatorial Control of VPC Fates

The fate of each VPC depends both on its position with respect to the AC and on the fates of its neighbors. In *lin-15* mutants the inductive signal is no longer necessary for cells to become 1° or 2°, but the inductive signal can bias the competition between cells to become 1°: The cell closest to the AC in a *lin-15* mutant (just as in wild type) becomes 1° (Sternberg, 1988a) (Fig. 15D and E). Therefore, a simple hypothesis for the role of the AC in wild-type development is that the inductive signal induces cells to compete for the 1° fate, and it also biases that competition such that P6.p always wins. Thus, there are two ways in which 2° fates might be specified in an intact wild-type animal: by an intermediate level of inductive signal or by a lateral signal from the 1° cell.

The lateral signal is likely to be controlled by the inductive signal. The inductive signal might induce VPCs to produce and respond to the lateral signal. The inductive signal might also bias the outcome of the lateral signaling process. This hypothesis suggests further a means by which the fate specification in two-cell equivalence groups can be altered: Two VPCs in a *lin-15* mutant act like the AC/VU, since their fates are random and depend on *lin-12* activity. In other equivalence groups a signal analogous to the AC signal could bias the probability of either outcome.

Neither the *Muv/Vul* pathway nor the *lin-12* pathway alone is sufficient to specify the fate of a VPC. The actions of the *Vul* and *Muv* genes can distinguish 3° from 1° or 2° cells. There is no evidence that this pathway can discriminate between 1° and 2° cell fates. The *lin-12* pathway does not appear to be involved in the specification of 1° cells. However, genetic evidence suggests that the combined action of these two pathways is sufficient to specify the three potential fates of the VPCs (Sternberg and Horvitz, 1989). Analysis of double-mutant phenotypes indicates that all six VPCs are of the same type in strains defective in both pathways (Fig. 15). All VPCs are 1° in a strain deficient in both *lin-12* and *Muv* activity, all VPCs are 2° in a strain deficient in *Vul* activity but having an abnormally high level of *lin-12* activity, and all VPCs are 3° in a strain deficient in both *lin-12* and *Vul* activity (Fig. 15I and J). These observations also suggest that the *Muv/Vul* and *lin-12* pathways can work independently. Specifically, if *lin-12* activity is severely reduced, the *Muv* and *Vul* genes control the decision between 1° and 3° cells; and if *Vul* activity is severely reduced, *lin-12* controls the decision between 2° and 3° cells. In *lin-12(0)* mutants VPCs can be 1° or 3°, depending on whether they receive inductive signal. In the absence of an inductive signal, the level of *lin-12* activity controls the decision between 2° and 3°: A high level of *lin-12* activity promotes the 2° cell type; a low level of *lin-12* activity promotes the 3° cell type.

These genetic interaction studies indicate that *lin-12* acts after the *Vul* and *Muv* genes in the pathway of response to the inductive signal. 2° VPC fates can be specified in the absence of *Vul* gene activity if *lin-12* is hyperactive (Fig. 15I). The inductive signal might override the action of *lin-12*. The presence of an AC in a *lin-12(d)* mutant results in a single 1° VPC, which would have become a 2° cell if there were no AC (Sternberg and Horvitz, 1989) (Fig. 15F). However, *Vul* activity is necessary for induction of a 1° fate in a *lin-12(d)* background (Fig. 15I). Therefore, *Vul* activity is necessary to specify 1° independent of *lin-12* and 2° via *lin-12*. In a *lin-12(d)–Muv* double mutant, some VPCs can be 1°; thus, a decrease in *Muv* activity overrides the effect of the *lin-12(d)* mutation, just as does inductive signal in a *lin-12(d)* mutant.

In the AC/VU group *lin-12(d)* acts in the affected cell (Greenwald and Seydoux, 1990). Similarly, in the vulval equivalence group an isolated *lin-12(d)* VPC is 2° (W. Katz and P. W. Sternberg, unpublished observations). In wild type a single VPC can become 2° in response to inductive signal, presumably some intermediate level (Sternberg and Horvitz, 1986). Since genetic data indicate that specification of 2° occurs if and only if *lin-12* is active, inductive signal must activate *lin-12* (or functions downstream). The simplest hypothesis is that *lin-12* acts autonomously in the VPCs. (It is also possible that *lin-12* is active initially in at least the presumed 1° and 2° VPCs, but gets inactivated in a presumed 1° cell.) If *lin-12* is a receptor for the lateral signal, then how is *lin-12* activated in a single 2° VPC? One possibility is that the lateral signal can act on the cell that produces it, as well as on a neighboring cell. Another possibility is that in a *lin-12(d)* mutant a signal comes from other cells, thereby specifying them to be 2°. Seydoux *et al.* (1990) proposed that the signal from the AC acting on the VU via *lin-12* can act on the germ line via *glp-1*. Similarly, an AC/VU signal could act on VPCs, in effect, constituting a second inductive signal. Further analysis of the *lin-12* product and other genes in the *lin-12* pathway might resolve these issues.

The interplay of inductive and lateral signals might reflect activation of the *lin-12* pathway by *Vul* activity, and inactivation of the *lin-12* pathway or the 2° fate by high *Vul* activity. The *Muv* and *Vul* gene products that most directly control the *lin-12* pathway and thus tip the balance between 1° and 2° are not yet defined. A VPC receiving lateral signal through its receptor is directed toward the 2° fate. Lateral inhibition might occur by a regulatory circuit of this form: The inductive signal promotes cells to become 1° and to produce lateral signal. Lateral signal stimulates neighbors to become 2°, rather than 1°. VPCs receiving a high level of inductive signal become 1°, because 1° functions might override 2° functions.

The *Muv* and *Vul* genes and *lin-12* pathway each act in a two-fate equivalence group to specify cell type. In the three-fate vulval equivalence group both pathways act. The action of these pathways in VPC specification can be shown to be separate under some experimental conditions, but normally they act in concert. Together, they constitute a three-way developmental switch.

D. Comparative Aspects of Vulval Development

A comparative study of vulval development in *C. elegans* and *P. redivivus* (Fig. 16) suggested that there must be several levels of genetic control (Sternberg and Horvitz, 1982). Additional studies by Fixsen *et al.* (1985) have extended these observations to additional species. Most of these levels of control have now been identified by the extensive genetic analysis of *C. elegans* vulval development (e.g., Ferguson *et al.*, 1987).

1. Establishment of the equivalence group boundaries. Mutations that shrink the vulval equivalence groups have been identified. Mutations in several genes result in VPCs that are transformed to other fates, as does *P. redivivus* (e.g., Ferguson *et al.*, 1987). These genes may define the boundaries of the equivalence group.

2. Specification of which cells of the equivalence group participate in vulval formation. A number of genes are known to be involved in determining which cells in the equivalence group actually participate in vulval development—for example, the *Vul* and *Muv* genes described in Section VI,A.

3. Specification of which vulval sublineage (1° or 2°) is executed by those cells participating in vulval formation. The choice between 1° and 2° is mediated in part by the action of *lin-12*, which is necessary for the specification of the 2° VPC.

4. Specification of the nature of each sublineage. The nature of each sublineage is less well defined, although a number of genes acting in the execution

have been identified. For example, *lin-11* is necessary for some of the cell types produced by the 2° lineage (Ferguson *et al.*, 1987; Freyd *et al.*, 1990). There are no mutations that alter the *C. elegans* lineages such that they resemble the *P. redivivus* 1° or 2° lineages.

E. Sequential Cell–Cell Interactions

The vulva is but one component in the egg-laying system, which also consists of the 16 uterine and vulval muscle cells and the HSN and VC motoneurons. Li and Chalfie (1990) have examined the organization of the egg-laying system and found that a sequence of cell interactions occur. As described in Section VI, the AC of the gonad induces the hypodermal VPCs to proliferate and generate the various

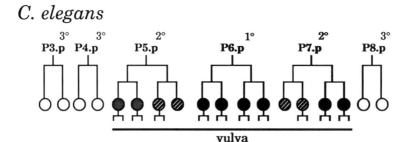

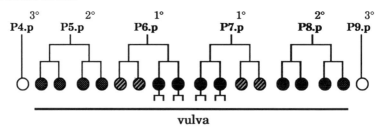

Fig. 16 Comparison of *C. elegans* and *P. redivivus* vulval development. The vulval cells are crudely split into three types for the purpose of this comparison. The progeny of the *C. elegans* 1° vulval precursor cells (VPCs) is shown as solid circles; these cells invaginate and at least two can attach to the anchor cell. The "inner" progeny of the 2° VPCs is shown as cross-hatched circles; these cells invaginate, but do not attach to the anchor cell. The "outer" progeny of the 2° VPCs are shown as hatched circles; these cells do not invaginate. The inner progeny of the *P. redivivus* 1° VPCs (P6.p and P7) is shown as solid circles; these cells are analogous to the 1° cells of *C. elegans*. The outer progeny of P6.p and P7 of *P. redivivus* is likely analogous to the inner progeny of P5.p and P7.p in *C. elegans*. Based on observations by Sulston and Horvitz (1977) and Sternberg and Horvitz 1982, 1986, 1989).

types of vulval cells. At the same time the two sex myoblasts (SML and SMR) each undergo three rounds of cell division to generate the total of 16 sex muscles. Two classes of motoneurons innervate the eight uterine and eight vulval muscles. The two HSN neurons are necessary to stimulate egg-laying (Desai *et al.*, 1988; White *et al.*, 1986). The six VC motoneurons of the ventral nerve cord innervate the vulval muscles, but have not yet been assigned a function in egg-laying. By immunocytochemical staining Li and Chalfie (1990) demonstrated that the VC neurons branch into the vulval region. Neither the vulval muscles, the HSNs, nor the gonad is necessary for this branching to occur. Rather, the vulval cells are necessary to induce branching: In *Vul* mutants branching occurs rarely, and in *Muv* mutants branching occurs ectopically. The position of the vulval muscles depends on the vulval and gonadal cells. The gonad is the major determinant of vulval muscle position: In the absence of the gonad vulval muscles attach near ectopic pseudovulva present in *Muv* mutant animals. Displacement of the gonad results in a concomitant displacement of the vulval and uterine muscles (Thomas *et al.*, 1990). Finally, vulval cells induce neuropeptide expression in the gonad. The complexity of this sequence of interactions begins to approach the type of complexity one would expect to find during the development of any animal.

VII. Concluding Remarks

The invariant development of nematodes such as *C. elegans* is due not only to a deterministic cell lineage, but also to highly reproducible cell interactions. A rigidly determined cell lineage ensures that cells are born in identical positions in each animal, thereby allowing a precise fate specification by cell interactions. One can imagine that additional cell interactions will be discovered by the presence and function of molecules typically involved in cell interactions present in cells whose fates were thought to be autonomously specified. The flexibility of fate specification can vary during evolution. Cell fates that are autonomously specified in one species can be nonautonomously specified in another species. A gene necessary for fate specification in response to cell interaction may also be involved in autonomous specification. The suggestion that a gene such as *lin-12* can be involved in cell interactions and autonomous specification implies that the differences between these modes of specification may be subtle. We may find, by carrying out comparative developmental studies and by elucidating molecular mechanisms, that the important differences may be at the level of mechanism, not phenomenology.

Acknowledgments

I thank Lynn Carta, Russell Hill, Paul Kayne, and Wendy Katz for sharing their unpublished observations; Ed Hedgecock, Einhard Schierenberg, John Sulston, and Bill Wood for communicating

220   Paul W. Sternberg

their results prior to publication; and Andy Golden, Paul Kayne, Linda Huang, Wendy Katz, and Lynn Carta for editorial suggestions. I am grateful to John Sulston, Bob Horvitz, Judith Kimble, John White, Victor Ambros, Marty Chalfie, and Bill Fixsen for encouragement and spirited discussion of the cell lineage problem, and to Eric Davidson for enlightening discussions on comparative embryology. Research from my laboratory reviewed here has been supported by a Presidential Young Investigator Award from the National Science Foundation, the Howard Hughes Medical Institute, the U.S. Public Health Service (grant HD23690), the Searle Scholars Program of the Chicago Community Trust, and the March of Dimes Birth Defects Foundation. The author is an Assistant Investigator of the Howard Hughes Medical Institute and a Searle Scholar.

References

Ambros, V. (1989). A hierarchy of regulatory genes controls a larval to adult developmental switch in *C. elegans. Cell* **57,** 49–57.
Ambros, V., and Fixsen, W. (1987). Cell lineage variation among nematodes. *In* (R. A. Raff and E. C. Raff, eds.). "Development as an Evolutionary Process" Liss, New York.
Ambros, V., and Horvitz, H. R. (1984). Heterochronic mutants of the nematode *Caenorhabditis elegans. Science* **226,** 409–416.
Ambros, V., and Horvitz, H. R. (1987). The *lin-14* locus of *C. elegans* controls the time of expression of specific postembryonic developmental events. *Genes Dev.* **1,** 398–414.
Anderson, R. V., and Darling, H. M. (1964). Embryology and reproduction of *Ditylenchus destructor* Thorne with emphasis on gonad development. *Proc. Helminthol. Soc. Wash.* **31,** 240–256.
Aroian, R. V., and Sternberg, P. W. (1991). Multiple functions of *let-23*, a *C. elegans* receptor tyrosine kinase gene required for vulval induction. *Genetics* **128,** 251–267.
Aroian, R. V., Koga, M., Mendel, J. E., Ohshima, Y., and Sternberg, P. W. (1990). The *let-23* gene necessary for *Caenorhabditis elegans* vulval induction encodes a tyrosine kinase of the EGF receptor subfamily. *Nature (London)* **348,** 693–699.
Austin, J., and Kimble, J. (1987). *glp-1* is required in the germ line for regulation of the decision between mitosis and meiosis in *C. elegans. Cell* **51,** 589–599.
Austin, J., and Kimble, J. (1989). Transcript analysis of *glp-1* and *lin-12*, homologous genes required for cell interactions during development of *C. elegans. Cell* **58,** 565–571.
Beitel, G., Clark, S., and Horvitz, H. R. (1990). The *Caenorhabditis elegans ras* gene *let-60* acts as a switch in the pathway of vulval induction. *Nature (London)* **348,** 503–509.
Boveri, T. (1892). Über die Entstehung des Gegansgtzes Zwischen den Geschlectszellen und der Somatischen Zellen bei *Ascaris megalocephala. Ges. Morph. Physiol. Sitzbev.* **8,** 114–125.
Brown, N. A., and Wolpert, L. (1990). The development of handedness in left/right asymmetry. *Development* **109,** 1–9.
Cameron, R. A., Hough-Evans, B. R., Britten, R. J., and Davidson, E. H. (1987). Lineage and fate of each blastomere of the eight-cell sea urchin embryo. *Genes Dev.* **1,** 75–84.
Campos-Ortega, J. A. (1990). Mechanisms of a cellular decision during embryonic development of *Drosophila melanogaster*: Epidermogenesis or neurogenesis. *Adv. Genet.* **27,** 403–453.
Carpenter, G., and Wahl, M. I. (1990). The epidermal growth factor family. *Handb. Exp. Pharmacol.* **95,** 69–171.
Chalfie, M., Sulston, J. E., and Horvitz, H. R. (1981). Mutations that lead to reiterations in the cell lineages of *Caenorhabditis elegans. Cell* **24,** 59–69.
Coffman, C., Harris, W., and Kintner, C. (1990). *Xotch*, the *Xenopus* homolog of *Drosophila Notch. Science* **249,** 1438–1441.

Costa, M., Weir, M., Coulson, A., Sulston, J., and Kenyon, C. (1988). Posterior pattern formation in *C. elegans* involves position-specific expression of a gene containing a homeobox. *Cell* **55**, 747–756.

Coulson, A. R., Sulston, J., Brenner, S., and Karn, J. (1986). Toward a physical map of the genome of the nematode *Caenorhabditis elegans*. *Proc. Natl. Acad. Sci. U.S.A.* **83**, 7821–7825.

Coulson, A., Waterston, R., Kiff, J., Sulston, J., and Kohara, Y. (1988). Genome linking with yeast artificial chromosomes. *Nature (London)* **335**, 184–186.

Cowan, A. E., and McIntosh, J. R. (1985). Mapping the distribution of differentiation potential for intestine, muscle, and hypodermis during early development in *Caenorhabditis elegans*. *Cell* **41**, 923–932.

Davidson, E. H. (1990). How embryos work: A comparative view of diverse modes of cell fate specification. *Development* **108**, 365–389.

de Coninck, L. (1965). Systematique des nematodes. *In* "Traité de Zoologie" (Grasse, P. P., ed.), Vol. 4, parts 2 and 3, pp. 586–1200. Masson et Cie, Paris.

Deppe, U., Schierenberg, E., Cole, T., Krieg, C., Schmitt, D., Yoder, B., and von Ehrenstein, G. (1978). Cell lineages of the embryo of the nematode *Caenorhabditis elegans*. *Proc. Natl. Acad. Sci. U.S.A.* **75**, 376–380.

Desai, C., Garriga, G., McIntire, S. L., and Horvitz, H. R. (1988). A genetic pathway for the development of the *Caenorhabditiis elegans* HSN motor neurons. *Nature (London)* **336**, 638–646.

Doe, C. Q., and Goodman, C. S. (1985). Early events in insect neurogenesis. II. The role of cell interactions and cell lineage in the determination of neuronal precursor cells. *Dev. Biol.* **111**, 206–219.

Edgar, L. G., and McGhee, J. D. (1986). Embryonic expression of a gut-specific esterase in *Caenorhabditis elegans*. *Dev. Biol.* **114**, 109–118.

Ferguson, E., and Horvitz, H. R. (1985). Identification and characterization of 22 genes that affect the vulval cell lineages of *Caenorhabditis elegans*. *Genetics* **110**, 17–72.

Ferguson E., and Horvitz, H. R. (1989). The multivulva phenotype of certain *C. elegans* mutants results from defects in two functionally-redundant pathways. *Genetics* **123**, 109–121.

Ferguson, E. L., Sternberg, P. W., and Horvitz, H. R. (1987). A genetic pathway for the specification of the vulval cell lineages of *Caenorhabditis elegans*. *Nature (London)* **326**, 259–267.

Finney, M., and Ruvkun, G. (1990). The *unc-86* gene product couples cell lineage and cell identity in *Caenorhabditis elegans*. *Cell* **63**, 895–905.

Finney, M., Ruvkun, G., and Horvitz, H. R. (1988). The *C. elegans* cell lineage and differentiation gene *unc-86* encodes a protein containing a homeo domain and extended sequence similarity to mammalian transcription factors. *Cell* **55**, 757–769.

Fixsen, W., Sternberg, P., Ellis, H., and Horvitz, R. (1985). Genes that affect cell fates during the development of *Caenorhabditis elegans*. *Cold Spring Harbor Symp. Quant. Biol.* **50**, 99–104.

Freyd, G., Kim, S. K., and Horvitz, H. R. (1990). Novel cysteine-rich motif and homeodomain in the product of the *Caenorhabditis elegans* cell lineage gene *lin-11*. *Nature (London)* **344**, 876–879.

Greenwald, I. S. (1985). *lin-12*, a nematode homeotic gene, is homologous to a set of mammalian proteins that includes epidermal growth factor. *Cell* **43**, 583–590.

Greenwald, I. (1989). Cell–cell interactions that specify certain cell fates in *C. elegans* development. *Trends Genet.* **5**, 237–241.

Greenwald, I., and Seydoux, G. (1990). Analysis of gain-of-function mutations of the *lin-12* gene of *Caenorhabditis elegans*. *Nature (London)* **346**, 197–199.

Greenwald, I. S., Sternberg, P. W., and Horvitz, H. R. (1983). The *lin-12* locus specifies cell fates in *C. elegans. Cell* **34**, 435–444.

Gubanov, N. M. (1951). A giant nematode from the placenta of cetaceans: Placentonema gigantissima n.g.n. sp. *Dokl. Akad. Nauk. SSSR* **77**, 1123–1125.

Han, M., and Sternberg, P. W. (1990). *let-60*, a gene that specifies cell fates during *C. elegans* vulval induction, encodes a ras protein. *Cell* **63**, 921–931.

Han, M., Aroian, R., and Sternberg, P. W. (1990). The *let-60* locus controls the switch between vulval and non-vulval cell types in *C. elegans. Genetics* **126**, 899–913.

Hartley, D. A., Xu, T., and Artavanis-Taskonas, S. (1987). The embryonic expression of the *Notch* locus of *Drosophila melanogaster* and the implications of point mutations in the extracellular EGF-like domain of the predicted protein. *EMBO J.* **6**, 3407–3417.

Hartwell, L. H., and Unger, M. W. (1977). Unequal division in *Saccharomyces cerevisiae* and its implications for the control of cell division. *J. Cell Biol.* **75**, 422–435.

Hechler, H. C. (1970). Reproduction, chromosome number, and postembryonic development of Panagrellus redivivus (*Nematoda:* Cephalobidae). *J. Nematol.* **2**, 355–361.

Hedgecock, E. (1985). Cell lineage mutants in the nematode. *Caenorhabditis elegans. Trends Neurosci. (Pers. Ed.)* **8**, 288–293.

Hedgecock, E. M., and White, J. G. (1985). Polyploid tissues in the nematode *Caenorhabditis elegans. Dev. Biol.* **107**, 128–133.

Hedgecock, E. M., Culotti, J. G., and Hall, D. H. (1990). The *unc-5*, *unc-6*, and *unc-40* genes guide circumferential migrations of pioneer axons and mesodermal cells on the epidermis in *C. elegans. Neuron* **2**, 61–85.

Herman, R. K. (1989). Mosaic analysis in the nematode *Caenorhabditis elegans. J. Neurogenet.* **5**, 1–24.

Herman, R. K., and Hedgecock, E. M. (1990). Limitation of the size of the vulval primordium of *Caenorhabditis elegans* by *lin-15* expression in surrounding hypodermis. *Nature (London)* **348**, 169–171.

Hill, D. P., and Strome, S. (1990). Brief cytochalasin-induced disruption of microfilaments during a critical interval in 1-cell *C. elegans* embryos alters the partitioning of developmental instructions to the 2-cell embryo. *Development* **108**, 159–172.

Hill, D. P., Shakes, D. C., Ward, S., and Strome, S. (1989). A sperm-supplied product essential for initiation of normal embryogenesis in *Caenorhabditis elegans* is encoded by the paternal-effect embryonic-lethal gene, *spe-11. Dev. Biol.* **136**, 154–166.

Hirsh, D., Oppenheim, D., and Klass, M. (1976). Development of the reproductive system of *Caenorhabditis elegans. Dev. Biol.* **49**, 200–219.

Hoppe, P. E., and Greenspan, R. J. (1990). The *Notch* locus of *Drosophila* is required in epidermal cells for epidermal development. *Development* **109**, 875–885.

Horvitz, H. R., and Sulston, J. E. (1980). Isolation and genetic characterization of cell-lineage mutants of the nematode *Caenorhabditis elegans. Genetics* **96**, 435–454.

Horvitz, H. R., Ellis, H. M., and Sternberg, P. W. (1983). Programmed cell death in nematode development. *Neurosci. Commun.* **1**, 56–65.

Kemphues, K. (1989). *Caenorhabditis. In* "Genes and Embryos" (D. M. Glover and E. D. Hanes, ed.). IRL Press, London.

Kemphues, K. J., Priess, J. R., Morton, D. G., and Cheng, N. (1988). Identification of genes required for cytoplasmic localization in early *C. elegans* embryos. *Cell* **52**, 311–320.

Kenyon, C. (1986). A gene involved in the development of the posterior body region of *C. elegans. Cell* **46**, 477–487.

Kidd, S., Kelley, M. R., and Young, M. W. (1986). Sequence of the *Notch* locus of *Drosophila:* Relationship of the encoded protein to mammalian clotting and growth factors. *Mol. Cell Biol.* **6**, 3094–3108.

Kim, S. K., and Horvitz, H. R. (1990). The *Caenorhabditis elegans* gene *lin-10* is broadly expressed while required specifically for the determination of vulval cell fates. *Genes Dev.* **4**, 357–371.

Kimble, J. (1978). The postembryonic cell lineages of the hermaphrodite and male gonads in *Caenorhabditis elegans*. Ph.D. thesis, University of Colorado, Boulder, Colorado.

Kimble, J. (1981). Lineage alterations after ablation of cells in the somatic gonad of *Caenorhabditis elegans*. *Dev. Biol.* **87**, 286–300.

Kimble, J., and Hirsh, D. (1979). Postembryonic cell lineages of the hermaphrodite and male gonads in *Caenorhabditis elegans*. *Dev. Biol.* **70**, 396–417.

Kimble, J., Sulston, J., and White, J. (1979). Regulative development in the postembryonic lineages of *Caenorhabditis elegans*. *INSERM Symp.* **10**, 59–68.

Laufer, J. S., Bazzicalupo, P., and Wood, W. B. (1980). Segregation of developmental potential in early embryos of *Caenorhabditis elegans*. *Cell* **19**, 569–577.

Li, C., and Chalfie, M. (1990). Organogenesis in *C. elegans*: Positioning of neurons and muscles in the egg-laying system. *Neuron* **4**, 681–695.

Liu, Z., and Ambros, V. (1989). Heterochronic genes control the stage-specific initiation and expression of the dauer larva developmental program in *Caenorhabditis elegans*. *Genes Dev.* **3**, 2039–2049.

Maine, E., and Kimble, J. E. (1989). Identification of genes that interact with *glp-1*, a gene required for inductive cell interactions in *Caenorhabditis elegans*. *Development* Cambridge UK **103**, 133–143.

Mains, P. E., Sulston, I. A., and Wood, W. B. (1990). Dominant maternal-effect mutations causing embryonic lethality in *Caenorhabditis elegans*. *Genetics* **125**, 351–369.

McGhee, J. D., and Cottrell, D. A. (1986). The major gut esterase locus in the nematode *Caenorhabditis elegans*. *Mol. Gen. Genet.* **202**, 30–34.

Nishida, H., and Satoh, N. (1989). Determination and regulation in the pigment cell lineage of the ascidian embryo. *Dev. Biol.* **132**, 355–367.

Pai, S. (1928). Die Phasen des Lebenscyclus der Anguillula aceti Ehrbg. und ihre experimentell-morphologische Beeinflussung. *Z. Wiss. Zool.* **131**, 293–344.

Priess, J. R., and Hirsh, D. I. (1986). *Caenorhabditis elegans* morphogenesis: The role of the cytoskeleton in elongation of the embryo. *Dev. Biol.* **117**, 156–173.

Priess, J. R., and Thomson, J. N. (1987). Cellular interactions in early *C. elegans* embryos. *Cell* **48**, 241–250.

Priess, J. R., Schnabel, H., and Schnabel, R. (1987). The *glp-1* locus and cellular interactions in early *C. elegans* embryos. *Cell* **51**, 610–611.

Robertson, L. (1990). The worm project. *Science* **248**, 1310–1313.

Robertson, A. M. G., and Thomson, J. N. (1982). Morphology of programmed cell death in the ventral nerve cord of *Caenorhabditis elegans* larvae. *J. Embryol. Exp. Morphol.* **67**, 89–100.

Roman, J., and Hirschmann, H. (1969). Embryogenesis and postembryogenesis in species of *Pratylenchus* (Nematoda: Tylenchidae). *Proc. Helminthol. Soc. Wash.* **36**, 164–174.

Ruvkun, G., and Giusto, J. (1989). The *Caenorhabditis elegans* heterochronic gene *lin-14* encodes a nuclear protein that forms a temporal developmental switch. *Nature (London)* **338**, 313–319.

Ruvkun, G., Ambros, V., Coulson, A., Waterston, R., Sulston, J., and Horvitz, H. R. (1989). Molecular genetics of the *Caenorhabditis elegans* heterochronic gene *lin-14*. *Genetics* **121**, 501–516.

Schierenberg, E. (1984). Altered cell division rates after laser induced cell fusion in nematode embryos. *Dev. Biol.* **101**, 240–245.

Schierenberg, E. (1987). Reversal of cellular polarity and early cell–cell interaction in the embryo of *Caenorhabditis elegans*. *Dev. Biol.* **122**, 452–463.

Schierenberg, E., and Wood, W. B. (1985). Control of cell-cycle timing in early embryos of *Caenorhabditis elegans*. *Dev. Biol.* **107**, 337–354.

Schnabel, R., and Schnabel, H. (1989). Early determination in the *C. elegans* embryo: A gene, *cib-1*, required to specify a set of stem-cell like blastomeres. *Development* **108**, 107–119.

Seydoux, G., and Greenwald, I. (1989). Cell autonomy of *lin-12* function in a cell fate decision in *C. elegans*. *Cell* **57**, 1237–1245.

Seydoux, G., Schedl, T., and Greenwald, I. (1990). Cell–cell interactions prevent a potential inductive interaction between soma and germline in *C. elegans*. *Cell* **61**, 939–951.

Shankland, M. (1987). Cell lineage in leech embryogenesis. *Trends Genet.* **3**, 314–319.

Simpson, P. (1990). Lateral inhibition and the development of the sensory bristles of the adult peripheral nervous system of *Drosophila*. *Development* **109**, 509–519.

Sternberg, P. W. (1988a). Lateral inhibition during vulval induction in *Caenorhabditis elegans*. *Nature (London)* **335**, 551–554.

Sternberg, P. W. (1988b). Control of cell fates in equivalence groups in *C. elegans*. *Trends NeuroSci. (Pers. Ed.)* **11**, 259–264.

Sternberg, P. W., and Horvitz, H. R. (1981). Gonadal cell lineages of the nematode *Panagrellus redivivus* and implications for evolution by the modification of cell lineage. *Dev. Biol.* **88**, 147–166.

Sternberg, P. W., and Horvitz, H. R. (1982). Postembryonic cell lineages of the nematode *Panagrellus redivivus*: Description and comparison with those of *Caenorhabditis elegans*. *Dev. Biol.* **93**, 181–205.

Sternberg, P. W., and Horvitz, H. R. (1986). Pattern formation during vulval development in *Caenorhabditis elegans*. *Cell* **44**, 761–772.

Sternberg, P. W., and Horvitz, H. R. (1988). *lin-17* mutations of *C. elegans* disrupt asymmetric cell divisions. *Dev. Biol.* **130**, 67–73.

Sternberg, P. W., and Horvitz, H. R. (1989). The combined action of two intercellular signalling pathways specifies three cell fates during vulval induction in *C. elegans*. *Cell* **58**, 679–693.

Strome, S. (1989). Generation of cell diversity during early embryogenesis in the nematode *Caenorhabditis elegans*. *Int. Rev. Cytol.* **114**, 81–123.

Sulston, J. E. (1988). The nematode *Caenorhabditis elegans*. *In* "Cell Lineage" (Wood, W. B., ed.), pp. 123–155. Cold Spring Harbor Laboratory, New York.

Sulston, J., and Horvitz, H. R. (1977). Postembryonic cell lineages of the nematode *Caenorhabditis elegans*. *Dev. Biol.* **56**, 110–156.

Sulston, J., and Horvitz, H. R. (1981). Abnormal cell lineages in mutants of the nematode *Caenorhabditis elegans*. *Dev. Biol.* **82**, 41–55.

Sulston, J. E., and White, J. G. (1980). Regulation and cell autonomy during postembryonic development of *Caenorhabditis elegans*. *Dev. Biol.* **78**, 577–597.

Sulston, J. E., Albertson, D. G., and Thomson, J. N. (1980). The *Caenorhabditis elegans* male: Postembryonic development of nongonadal structures. *Dev. Biol.* **78**, 542–576.

Sulston, J. E., Schierenberg, E., White, J. G., and Thomson, J. N. (1983). The embryonic cell lineage of the nematode *Caenorhabditis elegans*. *Dev. Biol.* **100**, 64–119.

Thomas, J. H., Stern, M. J., and Horvitz, H. R. (1990). Cell interactions coordinate the development of the *C. elegans* egg-laying system. *Cell* **62**, 1041–1052.

Ullrich, A., and Schlessinger, J. (1990). Signal transduction by receptors with tyrosine kinase activity. *Cell* **61**, 203–212.

Waring, D., and Kenyon, C. (1990). Selective silencing of cell communication influences anteroposterior pattern formation in *C. elegans*. *Cell* **60**, 123–131.

Way, J. C., and Chalfie, M. (1988). *mec-3*, a homeobox-containing gene that specifies differentiation of the touch receptor neurons in *C. elegans*. *Cell* **54**, 5–16.

Way, J. C., and Chalfie, M. (1989). The *mec-3* gene of *Caenorhabditis elegans* requires its own product for maintained expression and is expressed in three neuronal cell types. *Genes Dev.* **3**, 1823–1833.

Weisblat, D. A., Kim, S. Y., and Stent, G. S. (1984). Embryonic origins of cells in the leech *Helobdella triserialis*. *Dev. Biol.* **104**, 65–85.

Wharton, K. A., Johansen, K. M., Xu, T., and Artavanis-Tsakonas, S. (1985). Nucleotide sequence from the neurogenic locus *Notch* implies a gene product that shares homology with proteins containing EGF-like repeats. *Cell* 43, 567–581.

White, J. G., Southgate, E., Thomson, J. N., and Brenner, S. (1986). The structure of the nervous system of the nematode *Caenorhabditis elegans*. *Philos. Trans. R. Soc. London, B* **314**, 1–340.

Whittaker, J. R. (1973). Segregation during ascidian embryogenesis of egg cytoplasmic information for tissue-specific enzyme development. *Proc. Natl. Acad. Sci. U.S.A.* **70**, 2096–2100.

Wilcox, M., Mitchison, G. J., and Smith, R. J. (1973). Pattern formation in the blue–green alga, Anabaena. *J. Cell Sci.* **12**, 702–723.

Wood, W. B., ed. (1988). "The Nematode *Caenorhabditis elegans*." Cold Spring Harbor Lab., Cold Spring Harbor, New York.

Wood, W. B. (1991). Evidence from reversal of handedness in *C. elegans* for early cell interactions determining cell fates. *Nature (London)* **349**, 536–539.

Yochem, J., and Greenwald, I. (1989). *glp-1* and *lin-12*, genes implicated in distinct cell–cell interactions in *C. elegans*, encode similar transmembrane proteins. *Cell* **58**, 553–563.

Yochem, J., Weston, K., and Greenwald, I. (1988). *C. elegans lin-12* encodes a transmembrane protein similar to *Drosophila Notch* and yeast cell cycle gene products. *Nature (London)* **335**, 547–550.

zur Strassen, O. (1892). *Bradynema rigidum* u. Siebold. *Z. Wiss. Zool.* **54**,

zur Strassen, O. (1959). Neue Beiträge zur Entwicklungsmechanik der Nematoden. *Zoologica (N.Y.)* **107**, 1–142.

Index